PEARSON EDEXCEL INTERNATIONAL A LEVEL
FURTHER PURE MATHEMATICS 2
Student Book

Series Editors: Joe Skrakowski and Harry Smith

Authors: Greg Attwood, Jack Barraclough, Tom Begley, Dave Berry, Ian Bettison, Linnet Bruce, Lee Cope, Charles Garnet Cox, Keith Gallick, Tim Garry, Alistair Macpherson, Bronwen Moran, Johnny Nicholson, Laurence Pateman, Joe Petran, Keith Pledger, Joe Skrakowski, Harry Smith, Geoff Staley, Ibrahim Wazir, Dave Wilkins

Published by Pearson Education Limited, 80 Strand, London, WC2R 0RL.

www.pearsonglobalschools.com

Copies of official specifications for all Pearson qualifications may be found on the website: https://qualifications.pearson.com

Text © Pearson Education Limited 2019
Edited by Richard Hutchinson
Typeset by Tech-Set Ltd, Gateshead, UK
Original illustrations © Pearson Education Limited 2019
Illustrated by © Tech-Set Ltd, Gateshead, UK
Cover design by © Pearson Education Limited 2019

Cover images: *Front*: **Getty Images:** Werner Van Steen
Inside front cover: **Shutterstock.com:** Dmitry Lobanov

The rights of Greg Attwood, Jack Barraclough, Tom Begley, Dave Berry, Ian Bettison, Linnet Bruce, Lee Cope, Charles Garnet Cox, Keith Gallick, Tim Garry, Alistair Macpherson, Bronwen Moran, Johnny Nicholson, Laurence Pateman, Joe Petran, Keith Pledger, Joe Skrakowski, Harry Smith, Geoff Staley, Ibrahim Wazir and Dave Wilkins to be identified as the authors of this work have been asserted by them in accordance with the Copyright, Designs and Patents Act 1988.

First published 2019

22 21
10 9 8 7 6 5

British Library Cataloguing in Publication Data
A catalogue record for this book is available from the British Library

ISBN 978 1 292244 65 5

Printed in Slovakia by Neografia

Acknowledgments

Images:
Shutterstock.com: Tatiana Shepeleva 90, Jag_cz 125; **Getty Images:** Steve DF 22, Digital Vision. 105, mbbirdy 149; **Alamy Stock Photo:** Kevin Britland 1, Science Photo Library 46; **Science Photo Library:** Andrew Brookes, National Physical Laboratory 14

All other images © Pearson Education Limited 2019
All artwork © Pearson Education Limited 2019

COURSE STRUCTURE iv

ABOUT THIS BOOK vi

QUALIFICATION AND ASSESSMENT OVERVIEW viii

EXTRA ONLINE CONTENT x

1 INEQUALITIES 1

2 SERIES 14

3 COMPLEX NUMBERS 22

4 FURTHER ARGAND DIAGRAMS 46

REVIEW EXERCISE 1 83

5 FIRST-ORDER DIFFERENTIAL EQUATIONS 90

6 SECOND-ORDER DIFFERENTIAL EQUATIONS 105

7 MACLAURIN AND TAYLOR SERIES 125

8 POLAR COORDINATES 149

REVIEW EXERCISE 2 168

EXAM PRACTICE 178

GLOSSARY 180

ANSWERS 183

INDEX 230

CHAPTER 1 INEQUALITIES   1
1.1 ALGEBRAIC METHODS   2
1.2 USING GRAPHS TO SOLVE
    INEQUALITIES   5
1.3 MODULUS INEQUALITIES   8
CHAPTER REVIEW 1   11

CHAPTER 2 SERIES   14
2.1 THE METHOD OF DIFFERENCES   15
CHAPTER REVIEW 2   20

CHAPTER 3 COMPLEX
NUMBERS   22
3.1 EXPONENTIAL FORM OF
    COMPLEX NUMBERS   23
3.2 MULTIPLYING AND DIVIDING
    COMPLEX NUMBERS   26
3.3 DE MOIVRE'S THEOREM   29
3.4 TRIGONOMETRIC IDENTITIES   32
3.5 nTH ROOTS OF A COMPLEX
    NUMBER   37
CHAPTER REVIEW 3   42

CHAPTER 4 FURTHER ARGAND
DIAGRAMS   46
4.1 LOCI IN AN ARGAND DIAGRAM   47
4.2 FURTHER LOCI IN AN ARGAND
    DIAGRAM   55
4.3 REGIONS IN AN ARGAND DIAGRAM   63
4.4 FURTHER REGIONS IN AN
    ARGAND DIAGRAM   65
4.5 TRANSFORMATIONS OF THE
    COMPLEX PLANE   70
CHAPTER REVIEW 4   78

REVIEW EXERCISE 1   83

CHAPTER 5 FIRST-ORDER
DIFFERENTIAL EQUATIONS   90
5.1 SOLVING FIRST-ORDER
    DIFFERENTIAL EQUATIONS
    WITH SEPARABLE VARIABLES   91
5.2 FIRST-ORDER LINEAR DIFFERENTIAL
    EQUATIONS OF THE FORM
    $\frac{dy}{dx} + Py = Q$ WHERE P AND Q
    ARE FUNCTIONS OF x 95
5.3 REDUCIBLE FIRST-ORDER
    DIFFERENTIAL EQUATIONS   98
CHAPTER REVIEW 5   102

CHAPTER 6 SECOND-ORDER DIFFERENTIAL EQUATIONS 105

6.1 SECOND-ORDER HOMOGENEOUS
DIFFERENTIAL EQUATIONS 106
6.2 SECOND-ORDER
NON-HOMOGENEOUS
DIFFERENTIAL EQUATIONS 110
6.3 USING BOUNDARY CONDITIONS 115
6.4 REDUCIBLE SECOND-ORDER
DIFFERENTIAL EQUATIONS 118
CHAPTER REVIEW 6 121

CHAPTER 7 MACLAURIN AND TAYLOR SERIES 125

7.1 HIGHER DERIVATIVES 126
7.2 MACLAURIN SERIES 128
7.3 SERIES EXPANSIONS OF
COMPOUND FUNCTIONS 132
7.4 TAYLOR SERIES 136
7.5 SERIES SOLUTIONS OF
DIFFERENTIAL EQUATIONS 140
CHAPTER REVIEW 7 144

CHAPTER 8 POLAR COORDINATES 149

8.1 POLAR COORDINATES AND
EQUATIONS 150
8.2 SKETCHING CURVES 153
8.3 AREA ENCLOSED BY A
POLAR CURVE 158
8.4 TANGENTS TO POLAR CURVES 162
CHAPTER REVIEW 8 165

REVIEW EXERCISE 2 168

EXAM PRACTICE 178

GLOSSARY 180

ANSWERS 183

INDEX 230

ABOUT THIS BOOK

The following three themes have been fully integrated throughout the Pearson Edexcel International Advanced Level in Mathematics series, so they can be applied alongside your learning.

1. Mathematical argument, language and proof

- Rigorous and consistent approach throughout
- Notation boxes explain key mathematical language and symbols

2. Mathematical problem-solving

- Hundreds of problem-solving questions, fully integrated into the main exercises
- Problem-solving boxes provide tips and strategies
- Challenge questions provide extra stretch

The Mathematical Problem-Solving Cycle

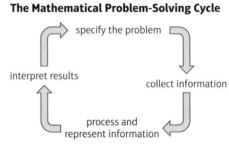

specify the problem

collect information

process and represent information

interpret results

3. Transferable skills

- Transferable skills are embedded throughout this book, in the exercises and in some examples
- These skills are signposted to show students which skills they are using and developing

Finding your way around the book

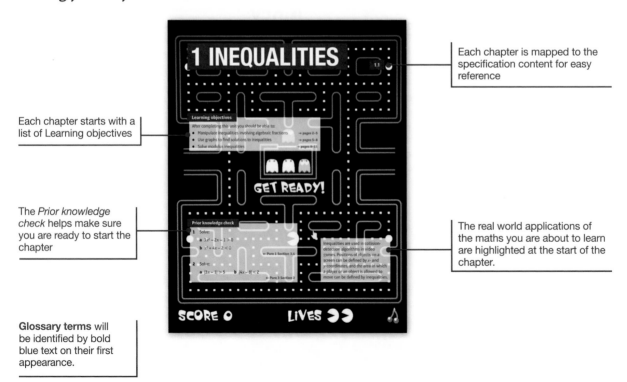

Each chapter is mapped to the specification content for easy reference

Each chapter starts with a list of Learning objectives

The *Prior knowledge check* helps make sure you are ready to start the chapter

The real world applications of the maths you are about to learn are highlighted at the start of the chapter.

Glossary terms will be identified by bold blue text on their first appearance.

Each section begins with explanation and key learning points

Exercise questions are carefully graded so they increase in difficulty and gradually bring you up to exam standard

Exercises are packed with exam-style questions to ensure you are ready for the exams

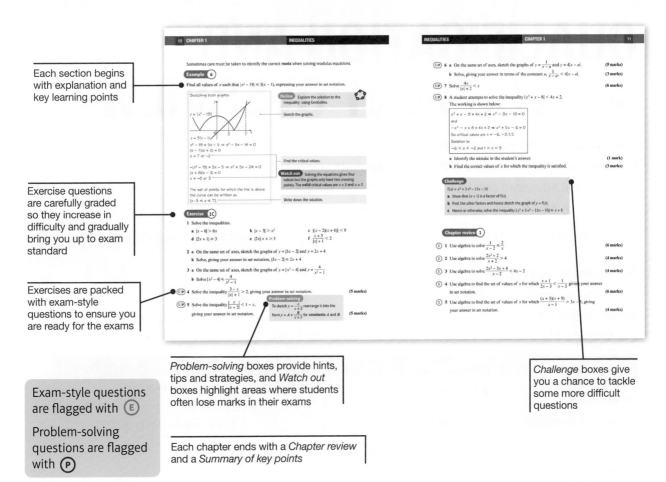

Exam-style questions are flagged with Ⓔ

Problem-solving questions are flagged with ⓟ

Problem-solving boxes provide hints, tips and strategies, and *Watch out* boxes highlight areas where students often lose marks in their exams

Each chapter ends with a *Chapter review* and a *Summary of key points*

Challenge boxes give you a chance to tackle some more difficult questions

After every few chapters, a *Review exercise* helps you consolidate your learning with lots of exam-style questions

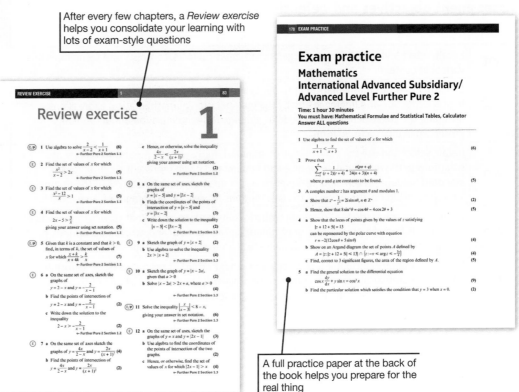

A full practice paper at the back of the book helps you prepare for the real thing

QUALIFICATION AND ASSESSMENT OVERVIEW

Qualification and content overview

Further Pure Mathematics 2 (FP2) is an **optional*** unit in the following qualifications:

International Advanced Subsidiary in Further Mathematics

International Advanced Level in Further Mathematics

*It is compulsory to study **either** FP2 **or** FP3 for the International Advanced Level in Further Mathematics.

Assessment overview

The following table gives an overview of the assessment for this unit.

We recommend that you study this information closely to help ensure that you are fully prepared for this course and know exactly what to expect in the assessment.

Unit	Percentage	Mark	Time	Availability
FP2: Further Pure Mathematics 2	$33\frac{1}{3}$ % of IAS	75	1 hour 30 mins	January and June
Paper code WFM02/01	$16\frac{2}{3}$ % of IAL			First assessment June 2020

IAS: International Advanced Subsidiary, IAL: International Advanced A Level.

Assessment objectives and weightings

		Minimum weighting in IAS and IAL
AO1	Recall, select and use their knowledge of mathematical facts, concepts and techniques in a variety of contexts.	30%
AO2	Construct rigorous mathematical arguments and proofs through use of precise statements, logical deduction and inference and by the manipulation of mathematical expressions, including the construction of extended arguments for handling substantial problems presented in unstructured form.	30%
AO3	Recall, select and use their knowledge of standard mathematical models to represent situations in the real world; recognise and understand given representations involving standard models; present and interpret results from such models in terms of the original situation, including discussion of the assumptions made and refinement of such models.	10%
AO4	Comprehend translations of common realistic contexts into mathematics; use the results of calculations to make predictions, or comment on the context; and, where appropriate, read critically and comprehend longer mathematical arguments or examples of applications.	5%
AO5	Use contemporary calculator technology and other permitted resources (such as formulae booklets or statistical tables) accurately and efficiently; understand when not to use such technology, and its limitations. Give answers to appropriate accuracy.	5%

Relationship of assessment objectives to units

FP2	Assessment objective				
	AO1	AO2	AO3	AO4	AO5
Marks out of 75	25–30	25–30	0–5	7–12	5–10
%	$33\frac{1}{3}$–40	$33\frac{1}{3}$–40	0–$6\frac{2}{3}$	$9\frac{1}{3}$–16	$6\frac{2}{3}$–$13\frac{1}{3}$

Calculators

Students may use a calculator in assessments for these qualifications. Centres are responsible for making sure that calculators used by their students meet the requirements given in the table below.

Students are expected to have available a calculator with at least the following keys: $+$, $-$, $\times$, $\div$, π, x^2, $\sqrt{x}$, $\frac{1}{x}$, x^y, $\ln x$, e^x, $x!$, sine, cosine and tangent and their inverses in degrees and decimals of a degree, and in radians; memory.

Prohibitions

Calculators with any of the following facilities are prohibited in all examinations:

- databanks
- retrieval of text or formulae
- built-in symbolic algebra manipulations
- symbolic differentiation and/or integration
- language translators
- communication with other machines or the internet

Extra online content

Whenever you see an *Online* box, it means that there is extra online content available to support you.

SolutionBank

SolutionBank provides worked solutions for questions in the book. Download the solutions as a PDF or quickly find the solution you need online.

Use of technology

Explore topics in more detail, visualise problems and consolidate your understanding. Use pre-made GeoGebra activities or Casio resources for a graphic calculator.

Online Find the point of intersection graphically using technology.

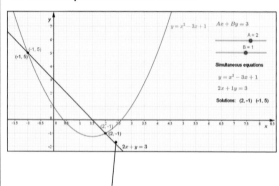

GeoGebra-powered interactives

Interact with the maths you are learning using GeoGebra's easy-to-use tools

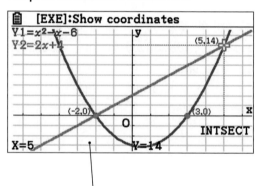

Graphic calculator interactives

Explore the maths you are learning and gain confidence in using a graphic calculator

Calculator tutorials

Our helpful video tutorials will guide you through how to use your calculator in the exams. They cover both Casio's scientific and colour graphic calculators.

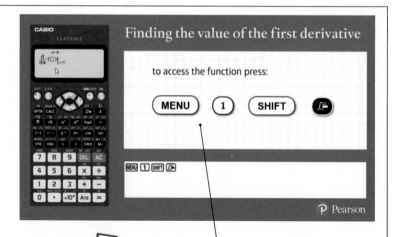

Online Work out each coefficient quickly using the $^{n}C_{r}$ and power functions on your calculator.

Step-by-step guide with audio instructions on exactly which buttons to press and what should appear on your calculator's screen

1 INEQUALITIES

Learning objectives

After completing this unit you should be able to:

* Manipulate inequalities involving algebraic fractions → pages 2–5
* Use graphs to find solutions to inequalities → pages 5–8
* Solve modulus inequalities → pages 8–11

GET READY!

Prior knowledge check

1 Solve:

  a $3x^2 - 2x - 1 > 0$

  b $x^2 + 4x - 2 < 0$

                ← Pure 1 Section 3.4

2 Solve:

  a $|3x - 1| > 5$ **b** $|4x - 8| < 2$

                ← Pure 3 Section 2

Inequalities are used in collision-detection algorithms in video games. Positions of objects on a screen can be defined by x- and y-coordinates, and the area in which a player or an object is allowed to move can be defined by inequalities.

SCORE 0   LIVES

1.1 Algebraic methods

If you multiply both sides of an inequality by a negative number you reverse the direction of the inequality sign.

You need to be more careful if you multiply or divide both sides of an inequality by a **variable** or **expression**. If the variable or expression could take either a positive or a negative value then you don't know which direction is correct for the inequality sign. You can overcome this problem by multiplying by an expression squared.

Suppose you want to solve the inequality $\frac{1}{x} > x, \ x \neq 0$.

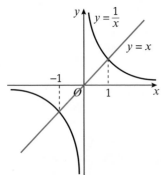 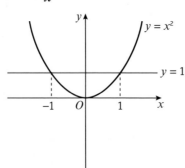 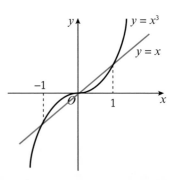

The values of x where the graph of $y = \frac{1}{x}$ is above the graph of $y = x$ give you the solution: $x < -1$ or $0 < x < 1$.

If you multiply both sides of the inequality by x you get $1 > x^2$. The solution to this inequality is $-1 < x < 1$, which is not the required solution.

If you multiply both sides of the inequality by x^2 you get $x > x^3$. The graph of $y = x$ is above the graph of $y = x^3$ for $x < -1$ and $0 < x < 1$, which is the solution to the original inequality.

In the third example above, you can solve the inequality $x > x^3$ by **algebraically** rearranging and factorising.

$$x^3 - x < 0 \quad \longleftarrow \quad \text{You can add or subtract any term from both sides of an inequality.}$$
$$x(x^2 - 1) < 0$$
$$x(x - 1)(x + 1) < 0$$

The **critical values** are $x = 0$, $x = 1$ and $x = -1$. You can consider a sketch of the graph of $y = x(x - 1)(x + 1)$ to work out which **intervals** satisfy (i.e. meet the requirements of) the inequality.

- To solve an inequality involving algebraic fractions:
  - Step 1: multiply by an expression squared to remove fractions
  - Step 2: rearrange the inequality to get 0 on one side
  - Step 3: find critical values
  - Step 4: use a sketch to identify the correct intervals

Example 1

Use algebra to solve the inequality $\dfrac{x^2}{x-2} < x + 1$, $x \neq 2$

Multiply both sides by $(x - 2)^2$

$(x - 2)^2 \times \dfrac{x^2}{x - 2} < (x - 2)^2 \times (x + 1)$

$(x - 2)^{\cancel{2}} \times \dfrac{x^2}{\cancel{(x - 2)}} < (x - 2)^2 \times (x + 1)$

$(x - 2)x^2 - (x + 1)(x - 2)^2 < 0$

$(x - 2)(x^2 - (x + 1)(x - 2)) < 0$

$(x - 2)(x^2 - x^2 + x + 2) < 0$

or $(x - 2)(x + 2) < 0$

Critical values are $x = \pm 2$

The sketch of $y = (x - 2)(x + 2)$ is

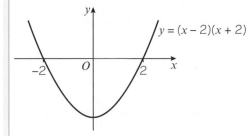

The solution to $(x - 2)(x + 2) < 0$
is $-2 < x < 2$.

Problem-solving

A natural first step would be to multiply both sides by $(x - 2)$ but we cannot be sure that this is positive. A simple solution is to multiply both sides of the inequality by $(x - 2)^2$ as this will always be positive.

Do **not** aim to multiply out but cancel, collect terms on one side and **factorise**.

This is a **quadratic** inequality so you can solve it in the usual way. ← Pure 1 Section 3.5

Watch out When a question says 'Use algebra...' you can still use a sketch to identify which intervals to include in your solution set. However, you should make sure you show algebraic working to find the critical values.

When the inequality is not strict you have to be a bit more careful. In the above example, the left-hand side of the inequality is undefined when $x = 2$, so you cannot include $x = 2$ in your solution set.

Hint Values for which one side of the inequality is undefined will usually be explicitly excluded. In the above example you are given $x \neq 2$.

■ **When solving an inequality involving ⩽ or ⩾, check whether or not each of your critical values should be included in the solution set.**

Example 2

Find all values of x such that $\dfrac{x}{x+1} \leq \dfrac{2}{x+3}$ where $x \neq -1$ and $x \neq -3$, and express your answer using set notation.

Multiply both sides by
$(x + 1)^2(x + 3)^2$

In order to remove the fractions and guarantee that you are not multiplying by a negative quantity, use $(x + 1)^2(x + 3)^2$.

So

$$\frac{x(x + 1)^2(x + 3)^2}{x + 1} \leqslant \frac{2(x + 1)^2(x + 3)^2}{x + 3}$$

Cancel terms on each side.

$x(x + 1)(x + 3)^2 - 2(x + 1)^2(x + 3) \leqslant 0$

$(x + 1)(x + 3)(x(x + 3) - 2(x + 1)) \leqslant 0$

Collect terms on LHS.

$(x + 1)(x + 3)(x^2 + x - 2) \leqslant 0$

$(x + 1)(x + 3)(x + 2)(x - 1) \leqslant 0$

Factorise as much as possible.

So the critical values are:

$x = -1, -3, -2$ or 1

A sketch of $y = (x + 1)(x + 3)(x + 2)(x - 1)$ is

To find the critical values you need to solve $(x + 1)(x + 3)(x + 2)(x - 1) = 0$.

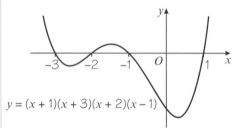

$y = (x + 1)(x + 3)(x + 2)(x - 1)$

The curve $y = (x + 1)(x + 3)(x + 2)(x - 1)$ is a quartic graph with positive x^4 **coefficient**, so it starts in top left and ends in top right and passes through $(-3, 0)$, $(-2, 0)$, $(-1, 0)$ and $(1, 0)$.

The solution to
$(x + 1)(x + 3)(x + 2)(x - 1) \leqslant 0$ corresponds to the sections of this graph that are on or below the x-axis.

So the solution is

$\{x : -3 < x \leqslant -2\} \cup \{x : -1 < x \leqslant 1\}$

The inequality is non-strict so you need to check whether the critical values should be included in the solution. The conditions $x \neq -1$ and $x \neq -3$ are given in the question, so use strict inequalities to exclude these values.

Exercise 1A

1 Solve the inequalities.

a $x^2 < 5x + 6$

b $x(x + 1) \geqslant 6$

c $\dfrac{2}{x^2 + 1} > 1$

d $\dfrac{2}{x^2 - 1} > 1$

e $\dfrac{x}{x - 1} \leqslant 2x$ $\quad x \neq 1$

f $\dfrac{3}{x + 1} < \dfrac{2}{x}$

g $\dfrac{3}{(x + 1)(x - 1)} < 1$

h $\dfrac{2}{x^2} \geqslant \dfrac{3}{(x + 1)(x - 2)}$

i $\dfrac{2}{x - 4} < 3$

j $\dfrac{3}{x + 2} > \dfrac{1}{x - 5}$

2 Solve the inequalities, giving your answers using set notation.

a $\dfrac{3x^2 + 5}{x + 5} > 1$

b $\dfrac{3x}{x - 2} > x$

c $\dfrac{1 + x}{1 - x} > \dfrac{2 - x}{2 + x}$

d $\dfrac{x^2 + 7x + 10}{x + 1} > 2x + 7$

e $\dfrac{x + 1}{x^2} > 6$

f $\dfrac{x^2}{x + 1} > \dfrac{1}{6}$

(E) **3 a** Use algebra to find the set of values for which $\dfrac{2x+1}{x+5} < \dfrac{x+2}{x+4}$ **(6 marks)**

(E) **4 a** Use algebra to find the set of values for which $\dfrac{x}{2x+1} < \dfrac{1}{x-3}$ giving your answer

     in set notation.   **(6 marks)**

(E/P) **5** A teacher asks a student to solve the inequality $\dfrac{x}{3x+4} < \dfrac{1}{x}$

     The student's attempt was as follows:

> $\dfrac{x}{3x+4} < \dfrac{1}{x}$
>
> $x^2 < 3x + 4$
>
> $x^2 - 3x - 4 < 0$
>
> $(x-4)(x+1) < 0$
>
> $-1 < x < 4$

     a Identify the mistake made by the student and explain why it will produce an incorrect

       answer.   **(2 marks)**

     b Solve the inequality correctly.   **(6 marks)**

(E/P) **6** Use algebra to solve $\dfrac{4}{x} < x < \dfrac{1}{2x+1}$ giving your answer using set notation.   **(6 marks)**

Challenge

Solve $\dfrac{1}{1-e^x} < \dfrac{1}{e^x}$

Hint You probably won't be able to sketch the graph in this question. Find the critical values, then test values within each interval to determine the solution set.

1.2   **Using graphs to solve inequalities**

- If you can sketch the graphs of $y = f(x)$ and $y = g(x)$ then you can solve an inequality such as $f(x) < g(x)$ by observing when one curve is above the other. The critical values will be the solutions to the **equation** $f(x) = g(x)$.

Watch out If you are asked to solve an inequality **algebraically** you should not start by sketching graphs.

Example **3**

     a On the same set of axes, sketch the graphs of the curves with equations $y = \dfrac{7x}{3x+1}$ and $y = 4 - x$

     b Find the points of **intersection** of $y = \dfrac{7x}{3x+1}$ and $y = 4 - x$

     c Solve $\dfrac{7x}{3x+1} < 4 - x$

a Sketch $y = 4 - x$ and $y = \dfrac{7x}{3x + 1}$:

$y = 4 - x$ is a straight line crossing the axes at
$(4, 0)$ and $(0, 4)$.

$y = \dfrac{7x}{3x + 1}$ crosses the coordinate axes at $(0, 0)$.

There is a vertical asymptote at $x = -\dfrac{1}{3}$

There is a horizontal asymptote at $y = \dfrac{7}{3}$

So the sketch looks like this

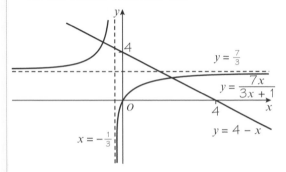

b Using algebra to find critical values:

$\dfrac{7x}{3x + 1} = 4 - x$

$7x = 12x + 4 - 3x^2 - x$

$3x^2 - 4x - 4 = 0$

$(3x + 2)(x - 2) = 0$

So $x = -\dfrac{2}{3}$ or 2

c Marking these points on the graph:

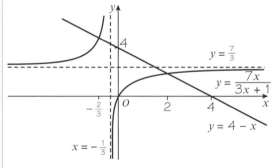

So the solution is

$x < -\dfrac{2}{3}$ or $-\dfrac{1}{3} < x < 2$

Problem-solving

To sketch unfamiliar curves, look for:
- points where the curve meets or crosses the axes
- vertical **asymptotes** (where the **denominators** of fractions equal 0)
- behaviour on either side of vertical asymptotes
- behaviour as x gets very large or very small.

You can find horizontal asymptotes by rearranging the fraction to see how it behaves as $x \to \infty$.

$$\dfrac{7x}{3x + 1} = \dfrac{7}{3}\left(\dfrac{3x}{3x + 1}\right) = \dfrac{7}{3}\left(1 - \dfrac{1}{3x + 1}\right)$$

As $x \to \infty$, $\dfrac{1}{3x + 1} \to 0$ so the curve has a horizontal asymptote at $y = \dfrac{7}{3}$

Multiply both sides by $3x + 1$. This is an equation, not an inequality, so you don't need to multiply by an expression squared.

Multiply out and collect terms to form a quadratic equation.

Solve the equation in the usual way: this one factorises.

Look on the sketch for the places where the line is above the curve.
These places will give the solution.

Watch out   Any vertical asymptotes will also be critical values when you are finding your solution set.

Online   Explore the solution to the inequality using GeoGebra.

Exercise (1B)   **SKILLS**   PROBLEM-SOLVING

1 Sketch the graphs of the **functions**.

   a $y = x^2 - 5x + 6$

   b $y = x^3 + 2x^2 - 3x$

   c $y = \dfrac{1}{x + 1}$

   d $y = \dfrac{4x}{1 - 2x}$

2 Sketch each pair of functions on the same sets of axes.

   a $y = x^2 - 2x + 1$ and $y = 4 - 4x^2$

   b $y = x$ and $y = \dfrac{1}{x}$

   c $y = 2x - 1$ and $y = \dfrac{3}{x - 2}$

   d $y = 4 - 3x$ and $y = \dfrac{x}{4x - 2}$

3 Find the points of intersection of the pairs of functions.

   a $y = \dfrac{2}{x + 1}$ and $y = \dfrac{1}{x - 3}$

   b $y = x - 2$ and $y = \dfrac{3x}{x + 2}$

   c $y = x^2 - 4$ and $y = \dfrac{4(x + 2)}{x - 2}$

(E) 4 **a** On the same set of axes, sketch the graphs of $y = x - 1$ and $y = \dfrac{4}{x - 1}$ **(3 marks)**

       b Find the points of intersection of $y = x - 1$ and $y = \dfrac{4}{x - 1}$ **(2 marks)**

       c Write down the solution to the inequality $x - 1 > \dfrac{4}{x - 1}$ **(2 marks)**

(E/P) 5 $f(x) = \dfrac{3}{x^2}$ $x \neq 0$ and $g(x) = \dfrac{2}{3 - x}$ $x \neq 3$

       a Sketch $y = f(x)$ and $y = g(x)$ on the same set of axes.   **(3 marks)**

       b Solve $f(x) = g(x)$ **(2 marks)**

       c Hence write down the solution to the inequality $f(x) > g(x)$. Give your answer
             using set notation.   **(3 marks)**

(E/P) 6 **a** On the same set of axes, sketch the graphs of $y = \dfrac{3x}{2 - x}$ and $y = \dfrac{4x}{(x - 1)^2}$ **(4 marks)**

       b Find the points of intersection of $y = \dfrac{3x}{2 - x}$ and $y = \dfrac{4x}{(x - 1)^2}$ **(2 marks)**

       c Hence, or otherwise, solve the inequality $\dfrac{3x}{2 - x} \leqslant \dfrac{4x}{(x - 1)^2}$ **(2 marks)**

(E/P) 7 **a** On the same set of axes, sketch the graphs of $y = x - 2$ and $y = \dfrac{6(2 - x)}{(x + 2)(x - 3)}$ **(4 marks)**

       b Find the points of intersection of $y = x - 2$ and $y = \dfrac{6(2 - x)}{(x + 2)(x - 3)}$ **(3 marks)**

       c Write down the solution to the inequality $x - 2 \leqslant \dfrac{6(2 - x)}{(x + 2)(x - 3)}$ **(2 marks)**

(E) 8 **a** On the same set of axes, sketch the graphs of $y = \dfrac{1}{x}$ and $y = \dfrac{x}{x + 2}$ **(3 marks)**

       b Find the points of intersection of $y = \dfrac{1}{x}$ and $y = \dfrac{x}{x + 2}$ **(2 marks)**

       c Solve $\dfrac{1}{x} > \dfrac{x}{x + 2}$ **(2 marks)**

Challenge

a Sketch the circle with equation $(x - 2)^2 + (y - 4)^2 = 10$

b Determine the **coordinates** of all points of intersection between this circle and the curve with equation $y = \dfrac{4x - 5}{x - 2}$

c Sketch this curve on the same set of axes as your answer to part **a**.

d Hence, or otherwise, find the solutions to the inequality

$$(x - 2)^2 + \left(\dfrac{4x - 5}{x - 2} - 4\right)^2 < 10$$

1.3 Modulus inequalities

You need to be able to solve inequalities that include **modulus** signs. It is often useful to sketch the relevant modulus graph when solving inequalities like this.

Example 4

Solve $|x^2 - 4x| < 3$

Sketch $y = |x^2 - 4x|$ and $y = 3$:

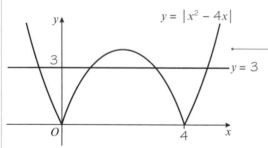

To find the critical values, solve $|x^2 - 4x| = 3$

$x^2 - 4x = 3 \Rightarrow x^2 - 4x - 3 = 0$

$(x - 2)^2 - 4 - 3 = 0$

$\qquad (x - 2)^2 = 7$

$\qquad\qquad x = 2 \pm \sqrt{7}$

$-(x^2 - 4x) = 3 \Rightarrow x^2 - 4x + 3 = 0$

$(x - 3)(x - 1) = 0$

$x = 1$ or 3

Sketch $y = |x^2 - 4x|$ and $y = 3$ on the same set of axes. To sketch $y = |x^2 - 4x|$ consider the graph of $y = x^2 - 4x$, and reflect any sections of the graph that are below the x-**axis** in the x-axis.

← **Pure 3 Section 2.1**

Watch out Solve $|x^2 - 4x| = 3$ to find the critical values. You need to consider the two separate cases: when the **argument** of $|x^2 - 4x|$ is positive and when it is negative. Use your sketch to determine whether these critical values all correspond to points of intersection.

Complete the square or use the quadratic formula.

The line $y = 3$ **intersects** the graph of $y = |x^2 - 4x|$ at four places, so all of these values of x correspond to points of intersection. Look at example 6 for a situation where this is not the case.

Marking these values on the sketch:

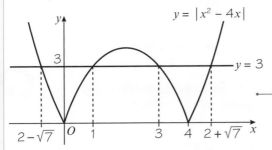

$$y = |x^2 - 4x|$$

$$y = 3$$

You need to identify where the points of intersection are on the sketch.

So the solution is:

$$2 - \sqrt{7} < x < 1 \text{ or } 3 < x < 2 + \sqrt{7}$$

Finally write down the solution to the inequality: the points where the line $y = 3$ is above the curve.

Example 5

Solve $|3x| + x \leqslant 2$

Rearranging gives:
$$|3x| \leqslant 2 - x$$
Sketching $y = |3x|$ and $y = 2 - x$ gives

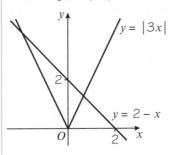

Problem-solving

Sketching $y = |3x| + x$ is quite difficult so it is usually simpler to rearrange and isolate the modulus function.

Critical values are given by:
$$3x = 2 - x$$
$$4x = 2$$
$$x = \frac{1}{2}$$
or
$$-3x = 2 - x$$
$$-2 = 2x$$
$$x = -1$$

Find the critical values in the usual way. Remember the two cases.

So the line is above $|3x|$ for
$$-1 \leqslant x \leqslant \frac{1}{2}$$

By considering (i.e. taking into account) the positions of the critical values, identify the places where the line is above the V-shaped graph.

Sometimes care must be taken to identify the correct **roots** when solving modulus equations.

Example 6

Find all values of x such that $|x^2 - 19| \leqslant 5(x - 1)$, expressing your answer in set notation.

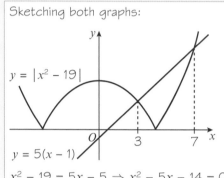

Sketching both graphs:

$y = |x^2 - 19|$

$y = 5(x - 1)$

$x^2 - 19 = 5x - 5 \Rightarrow x^2 - 5x - 14 = 0$

$(x - 7)(x + 2) = 0$

$x = 7$ or -2

$-(x^2 - 19) = 5x - 5 \Rightarrow x^2 + 5x - 24 = 0$

$(x + 8)(x - 3) = 0$

$x = -8$ or 3

The set of points for which the line is above the curve can be written as

$\{x : 3 \leqslant x \leqslant 7\}$.

Online Explore the solution to the inequality using GeoGebra.

Sketch the graphs.

Find the critical values.

Watch out Solving the equations gives four values but the graphs only have two crossing points. The **valid** critical values are $x = 3$ and $x = 7$.

Write down the solution.

Exercise 1C

1 Solve the inequalities.

   a $|x - 6| > 6x$

   b $|x - 3| > x^2$

   c $|(x - 2)(x + 6)| < 9$

   d $|2x + 1| \geqslant 3$

   e $|2x| + x > 3$

   f $\dfrac{x + 3}{|x| + 1} < 2$

2 a On the same set of axes, sketch the graphs of $y = |3x - 2|$ and $y = 2x + 4$

   b Solve, giving your answer in set notation, $|3x - 2| \leqslant 2x + 4$

3 a On the same set of axes, sketch the graphs of $y = |x^2 - 4|$ and $y = \dfrac{4}{x^2 - 1}$

   b Solve $|x^2 - 4| \leqslant \dfrac{4}{x^2 - 1}$

(E/P) **4** Solve the inequality $\dfrac{3 - x}{|x| + 1} > 2$, giving your answer in set notation.   **(5 marks)**

(E/P) **5** Solve the inequality $\left|\dfrac{x}{x + 2}\right| < 1 - x$,

   giving your answer in set notation.

Problem-solving

To sketch $y = \dfrac{x}{x + 2}$ rearrange it into the

form $y = A + \dfrac{B}{x + 2}$ for **constants** A and B.   **(5 marks)**

(E/P) **6 a** On the same set of axes, sketch the graphs of $y = \dfrac{1}{x-a}$ and $y = 4|x - a|$. **(5 marks)**

    b Solve, giving your answer in terms of the constant a, $\dfrac{1}{x-a} < 4|x - a|$. **(3 marks)**

(E/P) **7** Solve $\dfrac{4x}{|x| + 2} < x$ **(6 marks)**

(E/P) **8** A student attempts to solve the inequality $|x^2 + x - 8| < 4x + 2$.
The working is shown below:

> $x^2 + x - 8 = 4x + 2 \Rightarrow x^2 - 3x - 10 = 0$
>
> and
>
> $-x^2 - x + 8 = 4x + 2 \Rightarrow x^2 + 5x - 6 = 0$
>
> So critical values are $x = -6, -2, 1, 5$.
>
> Solution is:
>
> $-6 < x < -2$ and $1 < x < 5$

    a Identify the mistake in the student's answer. **(1 mark)**

    b Find the correct values of x for which the inequality is satisfied. **(3 marks)**

Challenge

$f(x) = x^3 + 3x^2 - 13x - 15$

a Show that $(x + 1)$ is a factor of $f(x)$.

b Find the other factors and hence sketch the graph of $y = f(x)$.

c Hence or otherwise, solve the inequality $|x^3 + 3x^2 - 13x - 15| \leqslant x + 5$

Chapter review (**1**)

(E) **1** Use algebra to solve $\dfrac{1}{x-2} \leqslant \dfrac{2}{x}$ **(6 marks)**

(E) **2** Use algebra to solve $\dfrac{2x^2 - 2}{x + 2} > 4$ **(4 marks)**

(E) **3** Use algebra to solve $\dfrac{2x^2 - 3x + 4}{x - 2} < 4x - 2$ **(4 marks)**

(E) **4** Use algebra to find the set of values of x for which $\dfrac{x+1}{2x-3} < \dfrac{1}{x-3}$ giving your answer in set notation. **(6 marks)**

(E) **5** Use algebra to find the set of values of x for which $\dfrac{(x+3)(x+9)}{x-1} > 3x - 5$, giving your answer in set notation. **(4 marks)**

(P) **6 a** Sketch, on the same axes, the line with equation $y = 2x + 2$ and the graph with equation $y = \dfrac{2x + 4}{x - 2}$

    b Solve the inequality $2x + 2 > \dfrac{2x + 4}{x - 2}$

(P) **7 a** Sketch, on the same set of axes, the graph with equation $y = \dfrac{2x - 4}{x^2 - 2}$ and the line with equation $y = 2 - 4x$

    b Solve the inequality $2 - 4x < \dfrac{2x - 4}{x^2 - 2}$

(E/P) **8 a** Sketch, on the same set of axes, the graphs with equations $y = \dfrac{x - 2}{3x - 1}$ and $y = \dfrac{2}{x + 2}$ **(4 marks)**

    b Solve the inequality $\dfrac{x - 2}{3x - 1} < \dfrac{2}{x + 2}$ **(3 marks)**

(E/P) **9 a** Sketch, on the same set of axes, the graphs with equations $y = \dfrac{x + 1}{x - 2}$ and $y = \dfrac{2x - 1}{x + 4}$ **(4 marks)**

    b Solve the inequality $\dfrac{x + 1}{x - 2} < \dfrac{2x - 1}{x + 4}$ **(3 marks)**

10 Solve the inequality $|x^2 - 7| < 3(x + 1)$

11 Solve the inequality $\dfrac{x^2}{|x| + 6} < 1$

(E) **12** Find the set of values of x for which $|x - 1| > 6x - 1$ **(3 marks)**

(E) **13** Find the complete set of values of x for which $|x^2 - 2| > 2x$ **(3 marks)**

(E) **14 a** Sketch, on the same set of axes, the graph with equation $y = |2x - 3|$, and the line with equation $y = 5x - 1$ **(3 marks)**

    b Solve the inequality $|2x - 3| < 5x - 1$ **(3 marks)**

(E) **15 a** Use algebra to find the exact solution of $|2x^2 + x - 6| = 6 - 3x$ **(4 marks)**

    b On the same diagram, sketch the curve with equation $y = |2x^2 + x - 6|$ and the line with equation $y = 6 - 3x$ **(3 marks)**

    c Find the set of values of x for which $|2x^2 + x - 6| > 6 - 3x$ **(1 mark)**

(E/P) **16 a** On the same diagram, sketch the graphs of $y = |x^2 - 4|$ and $y = |2x - 1|$, showing the coordinates of the points where the graphs meet the x-axis. **(4 marks)**

    b Solve $|x^2 - 4| = |2x - 1|$, giving your answers in **surd** form where appropriate. **(4 marks)**

    c Hence, or otherwise, find the set of values of x for which $|x^2 - 4| > |2x - 1|$ **(1 mark)**

Challenge

Solve the inequality $|x^2 - 5x + 2| > |x - 3|$

Give your answer in set notation, expressing any critical values as surds where appropriate.

Summary of key points

1 To solve an inequality involving algebraic fractions:
   - Step 1: multiply by an expression squared to remove fractions
   - Step 2: rearrange the inequality to get 0 on one side
   - Step 3: find critical values
   - Step 4: use a sketch to identify the correct intervals.

2 When solving an inequality involving $\leqslant$ or $\geqslant$, check whether or not each of your critical values should be included in the solution set.

3 If you can sketch the graphs of $y = f(x)$ and $y = g(x)$ then you can solve an inequality such as $f(x) < g(x)$ by observing when one curve is above the other. The critical values will be the solutions to the equation $f(x) = g(x)$.

4 When solving inequalities that include modulus signs, it is often useful to sketch a graph.

2 SERIES

Learning objectives

After completing this unit you should be able to:

● Understand and use the method of differences to sum finite series
→ pages 15–19

Prior knowledge check

1 Find the sums of the following series.

a $\displaystyle\sum_{n=1}^{18}(99 - 4n)$ **b** $\displaystyle\sum_{n=6}^{16}\frac{1}{2}(3)^{n-1}$

← Pure 2 Section 5.6

2 **a** Show that

$$\sum_{r=1}^{n}(r^2 + 2r + 3) = \frac{1}{6}n(2n^2 + 9n + 25)$$

b Hence find $\displaystyle\sum_{10}^{30}(r^2 + 2r + 3)$

← Further Pure 1 Section 8.1

Series are widely used in the mathematics of disciplines such as physics, computer science, statistics and finance. The method of differences allows the sums of many finite series to be calculated quickly and easily.

2.1 The method of differences

You can use the **method of differences** to find the **sum** of a **finite series**.

■ If the general term, u_n of a **series** can be expressed in the form

$$f(r) - f(r + 1)$$

then $\displaystyle\sum_{r=1}^{n} u_r = \sum_{r=1}^{n} (f(r) - f(r + 1))$

> You can also start with u_r written in the form $f(r + 1) - f(r)$. After adding and cancelling, you get $\displaystyle\sum_{r=1}^{n} u_r = f(n + 1) - f(1)$

so $u_1 = f(1) - f(2)$

$u_2 = f(2) - f(3)$

$u_3 = f(3) - f(4)$

$\vdots$

$u_n = f(n) - f(n + 1)$

Then adding $\displaystyle\sum_{r=1}^{n} u_r = f(1) - f(n + 1)$

> $u_1 + u_2 = f(1) - f(2) + f(2) - f(3)$
> $\qquad\quad = f(1) - f(3)$
>
> The f(2) terms cancel.
>
> By summing $u_1 + u_2 + \ldots + u_n$ all terms cancel except the very first term, f(1), and the very last term, f(n + 1).

Example 1

a Show that $4r^3 \equiv r^2(r + 1)^2 - (r - 1)^2 r^2$

b Hence prove, by the method of differences, that

$$\sum_{r=1}^{n} r^3 = \tfrac{1}{4}n^2(n + 1)^2$$

a $r^2(r + 1)^2 - (r - 1)^2 r^2$

$\equiv r^2(r^2 + 2r + 1) - (r^2 - 2r + 1)r^2$

$\equiv r^4 + 2r^3 + r^2 - r^4 + 2r^3 - r^2$

$\equiv 4r^3$

> Start with the RHS.
>
> Expand and simplify the brackets.

b Consider $\displaystyle\sum_{r=1}^{n} (r^2(r + 1)^2 - (r - 1)^2 r^2)$

Let $r = 1$: $1^2(2)^2 - (0)^2 1^2$

$r = 2$: $2^2(3)^2 - (1)^2 2^2$

$r = 3$: $3^3(4)^2 - (2)^2 2^3$

$\vdots$

$r = n$: $n^2(n + 1)^2 - (n - 1)^2 n^2$

Sum of terms $= n^2(n + 1)^2$

Then $4\displaystyle\sum_{r=1}^{n} r^3 = n^2(n + 1)^2$

So $\displaystyle\sum_{r=1}^{n} r^3 = \tfrac{1}{4}n^2(n + 1)^2$

> All the terms cancel except the first and last.

> **Watch out** When using the method of differences, be sure to write out enough terms to make it clear which terms cancel. When you cancel terms, make sure that they can still be clearly read. You could cross them out in pencil.

> The same result could be proved by mathematical induction.   ← **Further Pure 1 Section 8.1**

Example 2

Verify that $\dfrac{1}{r(r+1)} \equiv \dfrac{1}{r} - \dfrac{1}{r+1}$ and hence find $\displaystyle\sum_{r=1}^{n} \dfrac{1}{r(r+1)}$ using the method of differences.

$\dfrac{1}{r} - \dfrac{1}{r+1} \equiv \dfrac{r+1-r}{r(r+1)}$ ────── Write as a single fraction.

$\equiv \dfrac{1}{r(r+1)}$ ────── Simplify.

$\displaystyle\sum_{r=1}^{n} \dfrac{1}{r(r+1)} \equiv \sum_{r=1}^{n}\left(\dfrac{1}{r} - \dfrac{1}{r+1}\right)$

$\begin{aligned}
\text{Let } r = 1: \quad & \tfrac{1}{1} - \tfrac{1}{\cancel{2}}\\
r = 2: \quad & \tfrac{1}{\cancel{2}} - \tfrac{1}{\cancel{3}}\\
r = 3: \quad & \tfrac{1}{\cancel{3}} - \tfrac{1}{\cancel{4}}\\
& \vdots\\
r = n: \quad & \tfrac{1}{\cancel{n}} - \tfrac{1}{n+1}
\end{aligned}$ ────── All terms cancel except the first and last.

$\text{So } \displaystyle\sum_{r=1}^{n} \dfrac{1}{r(r+1)} = 1 - \dfrac{1}{n+1}$

$= \dfrac{n+1-1}{n+1}$ ────── Put over a common denominator.

$= \dfrac{n}{n+1}$

Example 3

Find $\displaystyle\sum_{r=1}^{n} \dfrac{1}{4r^2 - 1}$ using the method of differences.

$\dfrac{1}{4r^2 - 1} \equiv \dfrac{1}{(2r+1)(2r-1)}$ ────── Use the difference of two squares to factorise the denominator.

$\dfrac{1}{(2r+1)(2r-1)} \equiv \dfrac{A}{2r+1} + \dfrac{B}{2r-1}$ ────── Split the fraction into partial fractions.

← **Pure 4 Section 2.1**

$\equiv \dfrac{A(2r-1) + B(2r+1)}{(2r+1)(2r-1)}$ ────── Add the fractions.

so $\qquad 1 \equiv A(2r-1) + B(2r+1)$ ────── Set **numerators** of both sides equal to each other.

Let $r = \frac{1}{2}$: $1 = 0 + B \times 2$
$$B = \frac{1}{2}$$

Let $r = -\frac{1}{2}$: $1 = A \times -2$
$$A = -\frac{1}{2}$$

Put values of r in to find A and B.

So $\dfrac{1}{4r^2 - 1} \equiv \dfrac{-\frac{1}{2}}{2r + 1} + \dfrac{\frac{1}{2}}{2r - 1}$

$\equiv \frac{1}{2}\left(\dfrac{1}{2r - 1} - \dfrac{1}{2r + 1}\right)$

$\Rightarrow \displaystyle\sum_{r=1}^{n} \dfrac{1}{4r^2 - 1} = \frac{1}{2}\sum_{r=1}^{n}\left(\dfrac{1}{2r - 1} - \dfrac{1}{2r + 1}\right)$

Let $r = 1$: $\frac{1}{1} - \cancel{\frac{1}{3}}$

$r = 2$: $\cancel{\frac{1}{3}} - \cancel{\frac{1}{5}}$

$r = 3$: $\cancel{\frac{1}{5}} - \cancel{\frac{1}{7}}$

$\vdots$

$r = n$: $\cancel{\dfrac{1}{2n - 1}} - \dfrac{1}{2n + 1}$

All terms cancel except the first and last. Substitute the values of r into $\dfrac{1}{2r - 1} - \dfrac{1}{2r + 1}$ only. The $\frac{1}{2}$ is only required later.

So $\displaystyle\sum_{r=1}^{n} \dfrac{1}{4r^2 - 1} = \frac{1}{2}\left(1 - \dfrac{1}{2n + 1}\right)$

$= \frac{1}{2}\left(\dfrac{2n + 1 - 1}{2n + 1}\right)$

$= \dfrac{n}{2n + 1}$

If the general term of the series is given in the form $f(r) - f(r + 2)$, you need to adapt the method of differences to consider the terms $f(1)$, $f(2)$, $f(n + 1)$ and $f(n + 2)$.

Example 4

a Express $\dfrac{2}{(r + 1)(r + 3)}$ in partial fractions.

b Hence prove by the method of differences that

$$\sum_{r=1}^{n} \dfrac{2}{(r + 1)(r + 3)} = \dfrac{n(an + b)}{6(n + 2)(n + 3)}$$

where a and b are constants to be found.

c Find the value of $\displaystyle\sum_{r=21}^{30} \dfrac{2}{(r + 1)(r + 3)}$ to 5 decimal places.

a $\dfrac{2}{(r+1)(r+3)} \equiv \dfrac{A}{r+1} + \dfrac{B}{r+3}$

| Split into partial fractions. |

$\equiv \dfrac{A(r+3) + B(r+1)}{(r+1)(r+3)}$

| Add the fractions. |

$\Rightarrow \quad 2 \equiv A(r+3) + B(r+1)$

| Compare numerators. |

Let $r = -3$: $2 = -2B \Rightarrow B = -1$

Let $r = -1$: $2 = 2A \Rightarrow A = 1$

Therefore $\dfrac{2}{(r+1)(r+3)} \equiv \dfrac{1}{r+1} - \dfrac{1}{r+3}$

b Using the method of differences,

when $r = 1$: $\dfrac{1}{2} - \dfrac{1}{\cancel{4}}$

$r = 2$: $\dfrac{1}{3} - \dfrac{1}{\cancel{5}}$

$r = 3$: $\dfrac{1}{\cancel{4}} - \dfrac{1}{\cancel{6}}$

$\vdots$

$r = n - 1$: $\dfrac{1}{\cancel{n}} - \dfrac{1}{n+2}$

$r = n$: $\dfrac{1}{\cancel{n+1}} - \dfrac{1}{n+3}$

| Cancel terms. |

Problem-solving

$\displaystyle\sum_{r=1}^{n}(f(r) - f(r+2)) =$

$f(1) + f(2) - f(n+1) - f(n+2)$

So $\displaystyle\sum_{r=1}^{n} \dfrac{2}{(r+1)(r+3)} = \dfrac{5}{6} - \dfrac{1}{n+2} - \dfrac{1}{n+3}$

| Put these four terms over a common denominator. |

$= \dfrac{5(n+2)(n+3) - 6(n+3) - 6(n+2)}{6(n+2)(n+3)}$

$= \dfrac{5n^2 + 25n + 30 - 6n - 18 - 6n - 12}{6(n+2)(n+3)}$

$= \dfrac{5n^2 + 13n}{6(n+2)(n+3)}$

$= \dfrac{n(5n + 13)}{6(n+2)(n+3)}$

| Factorise. |

So $a = 5$ and $b = 13$.

c $\displaystyle\sum_{r=21}^{30} \dfrac{2}{(r+1)(r+3)} = \sum_{r=1}^{30} \dfrac{2}{(r+1)(r+3)} - \sum_{r=1}^{20} \dfrac{2}{(r+1)(r+3)}$

| Subtract $\displaystyle\sum_{r=1}^{20}$ from $\displaystyle\sum_{r=1}^{30}$ |

$= \dfrac{30(5 \times 30 + 13)}{6(30+2)(30+3)} - \dfrac{20(5 \times 20 + 13)}{6(20+2)(20+3)}$

$= \dfrac{815}{1056} - \dfrac{565}{759}$

| Evaluate. |

$= \dfrac{665}{24\,288} = 0.02738$ to 5 d.p.

| Give answer to 5 d.p. |

Exercise **2A**

1 a Show that $r \equiv \frac{1}{2}(r(r+1) - r(r-1))$.

  b Hence show that $\sum_{r=1}^{n} r = \frac{n}{2}(n+1)$ using the method of differences.

Ⓔ **2** Given $\dfrac{1}{r(r+1)(r+2)} \equiv \dfrac{1}{2r(r+1)} - \dfrac{1}{2(r+1)(r+2)}$

  find $\sum_{r=1}^{n} \dfrac{1}{r(r+1)(r+2)}$ using the method of differences.   **(5 marks)**

Ⓔ/Ⓟ **3 a** Express $\dfrac{1}{r(r+2)}$ in partial fractions.   **(1 mark)**

  b Hence find the sum of the series $\sum_{r=1}^{n} \dfrac{1}{r(r+2)}$ using the method of differences.   **(5 marks)**

Ⓔ **4 a** Express $\dfrac{1}{(r+2)(r+3)}$ in partial fractions.   **(1 mark)**

  b Hence find the sum of the series $\sum_{r=1}^{n} \dfrac{1}{(r+2)(r+3)}$ using the method of differences.   **(5 marks)**

Ⓔ/Ⓟ **5 a** Show that $\dfrac{r}{(r+1)!} \equiv \dfrac{1}{r!} - \dfrac{1}{(r+1)!}$ **(2 marks)**

  b Hence find $\sum_{r=1}^{n} \dfrac{r}{(r+1)!}$ **(5 marks)**

Ⓔ **6** Given that $\dfrac{2r+1}{r^2(r+1)^2} \equiv \dfrac{1}{r^2} - \dfrac{1}{(r+1)^2}$, find $\sum_{r=1}^{n} \dfrac{2r+1}{r^2(r+1)^2}$ **(6 marks)**

Ⓟ **7 a** Use the method of differences to prove that $\sum_{r=1}^{n} \dfrac{1}{(2r+3)(2r+5)} = \dfrac{n}{an+b}$, where a and b are
   constants to be found.

  b Prove your result from part **a** using mathematical induction.

Ⓔ/Ⓟ **8** Prove that $\sum_{r=1}^{n} \dfrac{8}{(3r-2)(3r+4)} = \dfrac{n(an+b)}{(3n+1)(3n+4)}$ where a and b are constants to be found.
                                                                                                          (6 marks)

> **Hint** This question can be answered using either the method
> of differences or **proof by mathematical induction**. In the
> exam, either method would be acceptable. If you use proof by
> induction, you will need to substitute values of n to find the
> values of a and b.

Ⓔ/Ⓟ **9** Prove that $\sum_{r=1}^{n} (r+1)^2 - (r-1)^2 = an(n+1)$, where a is a constant to be found.   **(4 marks)**

Chapter review 2

(E/P) **1 a** Express $\dfrac{2}{(r+2)(r+4)}$ in partial fractions. **(1 mark)**

    b Hence show that $\displaystyle\sum_{r=1}^{n} \dfrac{2}{(r+2)(r+4)} = \dfrac{7n^2 + 25n}{12(n+3)(n+4)}$ **(5 marks)**

(E/P) **2 a** Express $\dfrac{4}{(4r-1)(4r+3)}$ in partial fractions. **(2 marks)**

    b Using your answer to part **a** and the method of differences, show that

$$\sum_{r=1}^{n} \dfrac{4}{(4r-1)(4r+3)} = \dfrac{4n}{3(4n+3)}$$ **(3 marks)**

    c Evaluate $\displaystyle\sum_{r=100}^{200} \dfrac{4}{(4r-1)(4r+3)}$ giving your answer to 3 significant figures. **(2 marks)**

(E) **3 a** Show that $(r+1)^3 - (r-1)^3 = 6r^2 + 2$ **(2 marks)**

    b Using the result from part **a** and the method of differences, show that

$$\sum_{r=1}^{n} r^2 = \tfrac{1}{6}n(n+1)(2n+1)$$ **(5 marks)**

(E/P) **4** Prove that $\displaystyle\sum_{r=1}^{n} \dfrac{4}{(r+1)(r+3)} = \dfrac{n(an+b)}{3(n+2)(n+3)}$ where a and b are constants

    to be found. **(5 marks)**

(E/P) **5** Prove that $\displaystyle\sum_{r=n}^{2n} \left((r+1)^3 - (r-1)^3\right) = an^3 + bn^2 + cn + d$, where a, b, c and d are

    constants to be found. **(5 marks)**

(E/P) **6 a** Prove that $\displaystyle\sum_{r=1}^{n} \dfrac{3}{(3r+1)(3r+4)} = \dfrac{an}{bn+c}$ where a, b, and c are constants

    to be found. **(5 marks)**

    b Hence, or otherwise, show that $\displaystyle\sum_{r=n}^{2n} \dfrac{3}{(3r+1)(3r+4)} = \dfrac{3(n+1)}{2(3n+1)(3n+2)}$ **(4 marks)**

7 Robin claims that $\displaystyle\sum_{r=1}^{n} \dfrac{2r+1}{r(r+1)} = 1 - \dfrac{1}{n+1}$

His workings are shown below. Explain the error that he has made.

Using partial fractions:

$$\dfrac{2r+1}{r(r+1)} \equiv \dfrac{A}{r} + \dfrac{B}{r+1}$$

Therefore $2r + 1 \equiv A(r+1) + Br$

So $A = 1$ and $B = 1$.

Using the method of differences,

$$f(1) = 1 + \frac{1}{2}$$

$$f(2) = \frac{1}{2} + \frac{1}{3}$$

$$f(3) = \frac{1}{3} + \frac{1}{4}$$

$$\vdots$$

$$f(n - 1) = \frac{1}{n - 1} + \frac{1}{n}$$

$$f(n) = \frac{1}{n} + \frac{1}{n + 1}$$

Summing the differences: $\displaystyle\sum_{r=1}^{n} \frac{2r + 1}{r(r + 1)} = 1 - \frac{1}{n + 1}$

(2 marks)

(E/P) **8** Show that $\dfrac{1}{1 \times 3} + \dfrac{1}{2 \times 4} + \dfrac{1}{3 \times 5} + \ldots + \dfrac{1}{n(n + 2)} = \dfrac{3}{4} - \dfrac{an + b}{2(n + 1)(n + 2)}$ where a and b are

constants to be found. **(6 marks)**

(E/P) **9 a** Express $\dfrac{4}{(2r + 1)(2r + 5)}$ in partial fractions. **(3 marks)**

b Find the value of $\displaystyle\sum_{r=16}^{25} \frac{4}{(2r + 1)(2r + 5)}$ to 4 decimal places. **(5 marks)**

Challenge

a Given that $\displaystyle\sum_{r=1}^{30} \ln\left(1 + \frac{1}{r + 2}\right) = \ln k$, where k is an **integer**, find k.

b Given that $\displaystyle\sum_{r=1}^{n} \frac{18}{r(r + 3)} = \frac{n(an^2 + bn + c)}{(n + 1)(n + 3)(n + 3)}$ find a, b, and c.

Summary of key points

If the general term, u_r, of a series can be expressed in the form $f(r) - f(r + 1)$

then $\displaystyle\sum_{r=1}^{n} u_r = \sum_{r=1}^{n} (f(r) - f(r + 1))$

so $u_1 = f(1) - f(2)$

$u_2 = f(2) - f(3)$

$u_3 = f(3) - f(4)$

$\vdots$

$u_n = f(n) - f(n + 1)$

Then adding $\displaystyle\sum_{r=1}^{n} u_r = f(1) - f(n + 1)$

3 COMPLEX NUMBERS

Learning objectives

After completing this unit you should be able to:

* Express a complex number in exponential form → pages 23–26
* Multiply and divide complex numbers in exponential form → pages 26–29
* Understand de Moivre's theorem → pages 29–32
* Use de Moivre's theorem to derive trigonometric identities → pages 32–36
* Know how to solve completely equations of the form $z^n - a - ib = 0$, giving special attention to cases where $a = 1$ and $b = 0$ → pages 37–42

Prior knowledge check

1 $z = 4 + 4i\sqrt{3}$ and $w = 2\left(\cos\dfrac{\pi}{6} + i\sin\dfrac{\pi}{6}\right)$.
   Find:

   a $|z|$ **b** $\arg(z)$ **c** $|zw|$ **d** $\arg(zw)$

   e $\left|\dfrac{z}{w}\right|$ **f** $\arg\left(\dfrac{z}{w}\right)$ ← **Further Pure 1 Sections 1.5, 1.6**

2 $f(z) = z^4 + 4z^3 + 9z^2 + 4z + 8$

   Given that $z = i$ is a root of $f(z) = 0$, show all the roots of $f(z) = 0$ on an Argand diagram.   ← **Further Pure 1 Section 1.4**

3 Use the binomial expansion to find the n^4 term in the expansion of $(2 + n)^9$.   ← **Pure 2 Section 4.3**

The relationships between complex numbers and trigonometric functions allow electrical engineers to analyse oscillations of voltage and current in electrical circuits more easily.

3.1 Exponential form of complex numbers

You can use the **modulus–argument form** of a **complex number** to express it in the **exponential form**: $z = re^{i\theta}$.

Links The **modulus–argument** form of a complex number is $z = r(\cos\theta + i\sin\theta)$, where $r = |z|$ and $\theta = \arg z$.
← **Further Pure 1 Section 1.6**

You can write $\cos\theta$ and $\sin\theta$ as infinite series of powers of θ:

$$\cos\theta = 1 - \frac{\theta^2}{2!} + \frac{\theta^4}{4!} - \frac{\theta^6}{6!} + \dots + \frac{(-1)^r \theta^{2r}}{(2r)!} + \dots \quad \textbf{(1)}$$

$$\sin\theta = \theta - \frac{\theta^3}{3!} + \frac{\theta^5}{5!} - \frac{\theta^7}{7!} + \dots + \frac{(-1)^r \theta^{2r+1}}{(2r+1)!} + \dots \quad \textbf{(2)}$$

You can also write e^x, $x \in \mathbb{R}$, as a series expansion in powers of x.

Links These are the Maclaurin series expansions of $\sin\theta$, $\cos\theta$ and e^x.
→ **Further Pure 2 Section 7.2**

$$e^x = 1 + x + \frac{x^2}{2!} + \frac{x^3}{3!} + \frac{x^4}{4!} + \frac{x^5}{5!} + \dots + \frac{x^r}{r!} + \dots$$

You can use this expansion to define the exponential function for complex powers, by replacing x with a complex number. In particular, if you replace x with the **imaginary number** $i\theta$, you get

$$e^{i\theta} = 1 + i\theta + \frac{(i\theta)^2}{2!} + \frac{(i\theta)^3}{3!} + \frac{(i\theta)^4}{4!} + \frac{(i\theta)^5}{5!} + \frac{(i\theta)^6}{6!} + \dots$$

$$= 1 + i\theta + \frac{i^2\theta^2}{2!} + \frac{i^3\theta^3}{3!} + \frac{i^4\theta^4}{4!} + \frac{i^5\theta^5}{5!} + \frac{i^6\theta^6}{6!} + \dots$$

$$= 1 + i\theta - \frac{\theta^2}{2!} - \frac{i\theta^3}{3!} + \frac{\theta^4}{4!} + \frac{i\theta^5}{5!} - \frac{\theta^6}{6!} + \dots$$

$$= \left(1 - \frac{\theta^2}{2!} + \frac{\theta^4}{4!} - \frac{\theta^6}{6!} + \dots\right) + i\left(\theta - \frac{\theta^3}{3!} + \frac{\theta^5}{5!} - \dots\right)$$

By comparing this series expansion with **(1)** and **(2)**, you can write $e^{i\theta}$ as

$$e^{i\theta} = \cos\theta + i\sin\theta$$

This formula is known as **Euler's relation**. It is important for you to remember this result.

- You can use Euler's relation, $e^{i\theta} = \cos\theta + i\sin\theta$, to write a complex number z in exponential form:

$$z = re^{i\theta}$$

where $r = |z|$ and $\theta = \arg z$

Notation Substituting $\theta = \pi$ into Euler's relation yields **Euler's identity**:
$$e^{i\pi} + 1 = 0$$
This equation links the five fundamental constants 0, 1, π, e and i, and is considered an example of mathematical beauty.

Example 1

Express in the form $re^{i\theta}$, where $-\pi < \theta \leqslant \pi$.

a $z = \sqrt{2}\left(\cos\dfrac{\pi}{10} + i\sin\dfrac{\pi}{10}\right)$ **b** $z = 5\left(\cos\dfrac{\pi}{8} - i\sin\dfrac{\pi}{8}\right)$

---

a $z = \sqrt{2}\left(\cos\dfrac{\pi}{10} + i\sin\dfrac{\pi}{10}\right)$ •————— Compare with $r(\cos\theta + i\sin\theta)$.

So $r = \sqrt{2}$ and $\theta = \dfrac{\pi}{10}$

Therefore, $z = \sqrt{2}e^{\frac{\pi i}{10}}$ •————— $z = re^{i\theta}$

b $z = 5\left(\cos\dfrac{\pi}{8} - i\sin\dfrac{\pi}{8}\right)$

$z = 5\left(\cos\left(-\dfrac{\pi}{8}\right) + i\sin\left(-\dfrac{\pi}{8}\right)\right)$

Problem-solving

Use $\cos(-\theta) = \cos\theta$ and $\sin(-\theta) = -\sin\theta$.

So $r = 5$ and $\theta = -\dfrac{\pi}{8}$ •————— Compare with $r(\cos\theta + i\sin\theta)$.

Therefore, $z = 5e^{-\frac{\pi i}{8}}$ •————— $z = re^{i\theta}$

Example 2

Express $z = 2 - 3i$ in the form $re^{i\theta}$, where $-\pi < \theta \leqslant \pi$.

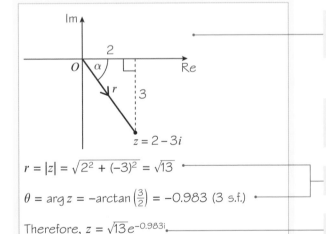

Sketch the **Argand diagram**, showing the position of the complex number.

Here z is in the fourth **quadrant** so the required argument is $-\alpha$.

$r = |z| = \sqrt{2^2 + (-3)^2} = \sqrt{13}$ •

$\theta = \arg z = -\arctan\left(\dfrac{3}{2}\right) = -0.983$ (3 s.f.)   •

Find r and θ.

Therefore, $z = \sqrt{13}\,e^{-0.983i}$ •————— $z = re^{i\theta}$

Example 3

Express $z = \sqrt{2}e^{\frac{3\pi i}{4}}$ in the form $x + iy$, where $x, y \in \mathbb{R}$.

$z = \sqrt{2}e^{\frac{3\pi i}{4}}$, so $r = \sqrt{2}$ and $\theta = \dfrac{3\pi}{4}$. —————— Compare with $re^{i\theta}$.

$z = \sqrt{2}\left(\cos\dfrac{3\pi}{4} + i\sin\dfrac{3\pi}{4}\right)$ —————— Write z in modulus–argument form.

$\quad = \sqrt{2}\left(-\dfrac{1}{\sqrt{2}} + i\dfrac{1}{\sqrt{2}}\right)$

Therefore, $z = -1 + i$ —————— Simplify.

Example 4

Express $z = 2e^{\frac{23\pi i}{5}}$ in the form $r(\cos\theta + i\sin\theta)$, where $-\pi < \theta \leqslant \pi$.

$z = 2e^{\frac{23\pi i}{5}}$, so $r = 2$ and $\theta = \dfrac{23\pi}{5}$. —————— Compare with $re^{i\theta}$.

$\dfrac{23\pi}{5} - 2\pi = \dfrac{13\pi}{5}, \dfrac{13\pi}{5} - 2\pi = \dfrac{3\pi}{5}$

$\dfrac{3\pi}{5}$ is in the range $-\pi < \theta \leqslant \pi$

So $z = 2\left(\cos\dfrac{3\pi}{5} + i\sin\dfrac{3\pi}{5}\right)$

Problem-solving

$\cos\theta = \cos(\theta + 2\pi)$ and $\sin\theta = \sin(\theta + 2\pi)$.

Subtract multiples of 2π from $\dfrac{23\pi}{5}$ until you find a value in the range $-\pi < \theta \leqslant \pi$.

—————— Write z in the form $r(\cos\theta + i\sin\theta)$.

Example 5

Use $e^{i\theta} = \cos\theta + i\sin\theta$ to show that $\cos\theta = \frac{1}{2}(e^{i\theta} + e^{-i\theta})$.

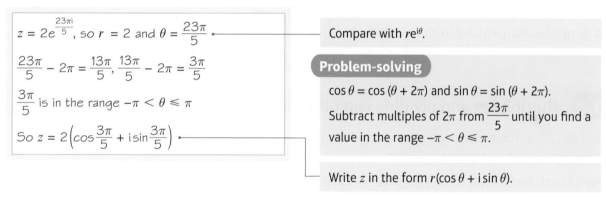

$e^{i\theta} = \cos\theta + i\sin\theta \qquad\qquad (1)$

$e^{-i\theta} = e^{i(-\theta)} = \cos(-\theta) + i\sin(-\theta)$

So $e^{-i\theta} = \cos\theta - i\sin\theta \qquad (2)$ —————— Use $\cos(-\theta) = \cos\theta$ and $\sin(-\theta) = -\sin\theta$.

$e^{i\theta} + e^{-i\theta} = 2\cos\theta$ —————— Add (1) and (2).

$\Rightarrow \dfrac{e^{i\theta} + e^{-i\theta}}{2} = \cos\theta$ —————— Divide both sides by 2.

Hence, $\cos\theta = \frac{1}{2}(e^{i\theta} + e^{-i\theta})$, as required.

Exercise (3A)

1 Express in the form $re^{i\theta}$, where $-\pi < \theta \leqslant \pi$. Use exact values of r and θ where possible, or values to 3 significant figures otherwise.

    a -3 **b** $6i$ **c** $-2\sqrt{3} - 2i$

    d $-8 + i$ **e** $2 - 5i$ **f** $-2\sqrt{3} + 2i\sqrt{3}$

    g $\sqrt{8}\left(\cos\dfrac{\pi}{4} + i\sin\dfrac{\pi}{4}\right)$ **h** $8\left(\cos\dfrac{\pi}{6} - i\sin\dfrac{\pi}{6}\right)$ **i** $2\left(\cos\dfrac{\pi}{5} - i\sin\dfrac{\pi}{5}\right)$

2 Express in the form $x + iy$ where $x, y \in \mathbb{R}$.

    a $e^{\frac{\pi i}{3}}$ **b** $4e^{\pi i}$ **c** $3\sqrt{2}\,e^{\frac{\pi i}{4}}$

    d $8e^{\frac{\pi i}{6}}$ **e** $3e^{-\frac{\pi i}{2}}$ **f** $e^{\frac{5\pi i}{6}}$

    g $e^{-\pi i}$ **h** $3\sqrt{2}e^{-\frac{3\pi i}{4}}$ **i** $8e^{-\frac{4\pi i}{3}}$

3 Express in the form $r(\cos\theta + i\sin\theta)$, where $-\pi < \theta \leqslant \pi$.

    a $e^{\frac{16\pi i}{13}}$ **b** $4e^{\frac{17\pi i}{5}}$ **c** $5e^{-\frac{9\pi i}{8}}$

(P) **4** Use $e^{i\theta} = \cos\theta + i\sin\theta$ to show that $\sin\theta = \dfrac{1}{2i}\left(e^{i\theta} - e^{-i\theta}\right)$

3.2 **Multiplying and dividing complex numbers**

You can apply the modulus–argument rules for multiplying and dividing complex numbers to numbers written in exponential form.

Recall that, for any two complex numbers z_1 and z_2,

- $|z_1 z_2| = |z_1||z_2|$
- $\arg(z_1 z_2) = \arg(z_1) + \arg(z_2)$
- $\left|\dfrac{z_1}{z_2}\right| = \dfrac{|z_1|}{|z_2|}$

> **Links** These results can be proved by considering the numbers z_1 and z_2 in the form $r(\cos\theta + i\sin\theta)$ and using the addition formulae for cos and sin. **← Further Pure 1 Section 1.6**

- $\arg\left(\dfrac{z_1}{z_2}\right) = \arg(z_1) - \arg(z_2)$

Applying these results to numbers in exponential form gives the following result:

- If $z_1 = r_1 e^{i\theta_1}$ and $z_2 = r_2 e^{i\theta_2}$, then:

    - $z_1 z_2 = r_1 r_2 e^{i(\theta_1 + \theta_2)}$

    - $\dfrac{z_1}{z_2} = \dfrac{r_1}{r_2} e^{i(\theta_1 - \theta_2)}$

> **Watch out** You cannot automatically assume the laws of indices work the same way with complex numbers as with **real numbers**. This result only shows that they can be applied in these specific cases.

Example 6

a Express $2e^{\frac{\pi i}{6}} \times \sqrt{3}e^{\frac{\pi i}{3}}$ in the form $x + iy$.

b $z = 2 + 2i$, $\text{Im}(zw) = 0$ and $|zw| = 3|z|$

Use geometrical reasoning to find the two possibilities for w, giving your answers in exponential form.

a $2e^{\frac{\pi i}{6}} \times \sqrt{3}e^{\frac{\pi i}{3}} = (2 \times \sqrt{3})e^{i\left(\frac{\pi}{6} + \frac{\pi}{3}\right)}$ ———→ $z_1 z_2 = r_1 r_2 e^{i(\theta_1 + \theta_2)}$

$\qquad\qquad\qquad = 2\sqrt{3}\, e^{\frac{\pi i}{2}}$

$\qquad\qquad\qquad = 2\sqrt{3}\left(\cos\frac{\pi}{2} + i\sin\frac{\pi}{2}\right)$ ———→ **Convert** the complex number to modulus–argument form.

$\qquad\qquad\qquad = 2\sqrt{3}(0 + i)$

$\qquad\qquad\qquad = 2i\sqrt{3}$

b $|zw| = 3|z| \Rightarrow |w| = 3$ ———→ $|zw| = |z||w| = 3|z|$.

$\arg z = \arctan\left(\frac{2}{2}\right) = \frac{\pi}{4}$

$\text{Im}(zw) = 0$ so $\arg(zw) = 0$ or π

So $\arg w = \frac{3\pi}{4}$ or $-\frac{\pi}{4}$ ———→ wz lies on the real axis, so z is rotated $\frac{3\pi}{4}$ clockwise or $\frac{\pi}{4}$ anticlockwise when multiplied by w.

$w_1 = 3e^{-\frac{\pi i}{4}}$ and $w_2 = 3e^{\frac{3\pi i}{4}}$

Example 7

Express $\dfrac{2\left(\cos\dfrac{\pi}{12} + i\sin\dfrac{\pi}{12}\right)}{\sqrt{2}\left(\cos\dfrac{5\pi}{6} + i\sin\dfrac{5\pi}{6}\right)}$ in the form $re^{i\theta}$.

$\dfrac{2\left(\cos\dfrac{\pi}{12} + i\sin\dfrac{\pi}{12}\right)}{\sqrt{2}\left(\cos\dfrac{5\pi}{6} + i\sin\dfrac{5\pi}{6}\right)} = \dfrac{2e^{\frac{\pi i}{12}}}{\sqrt{2}e^{\frac{5\pi i}{6}}}$ ———→ Convert the numerator and denominator to exponential form.

$\qquad\qquad\qquad\qquad = \dfrac{2}{\sqrt{2}}e^{i\left(\frac{\pi}{12} - \frac{5\pi}{6}\right)}$ ———→ $\dfrac{z_1}{z_2} = \dfrac{r_1}{r_2}e^{i(\theta_1 - \theta_2)}$

$\qquad\qquad\qquad\qquad = \sqrt{2}\, e^{-\frac{3\pi i}{4}}$ ———→ Simplify.

Exercise 3B

1 Express in the form $x + iy$, where $x, y \in \mathbb{R}$.

a $e^{\frac{\pi i}{3}} \times e^{\frac{\pi i}{4}}$ **b** $\sqrt{5}e^{i\theta} \times 3e^{3i\theta}$ **c** $\sqrt{2}e^{\frac{2\pi i}{3}} \times e^{-\frac{7\pi i}{3}} \times 3e^{\frac{\pi i}{6}}$

2 Express in the form $x + iy$ where $x, y \in \mathbb{R}$.

a $\dfrac{2e^{\frac{7\pi i}{2}}}{8e^{\frac{9\pi i}{2}}}$ **b** $\dfrac{\sqrt{3}e^{\frac{3\pi i}{7}}}{4e^{-\frac{2\pi i}{7}}}$ **c** $\dfrac{\sqrt{2}e^{-\frac{15\pi i}{6}}}{2e^{\frac{\pi i}{3}}} \times \sqrt{2}\,e^{\frac{19\pi i}{3}}$

3 Express in the form $re^{i\theta}$

a $(\cos 2\theta + i\sin 2\theta)(\cos 3\theta + i\sin 3\theta)$ **b** $\left(\cos\dfrac{3\pi}{11} + i\sin\dfrac{3\pi}{11}\right)\left(\cos\dfrac{8\pi}{11} + i\sin\dfrac{8\pi}{11}\right)$

c $3\left(\cos\dfrac{\pi}{4} + i\sin\dfrac{\pi}{4}\right) \times 2\left(\cos\dfrac{\pi}{12} + i\sin\dfrac{\pi}{12}\right)$

d $\sqrt{6}\left(\cos\left(-\dfrac{\pi}{12}\right) + i\sin\left(-\dfrac{\pi}{12}\right)\right) \times \sqrt{3}\left(\cos\dfrac{\pi}{3} + i\sin\dfrac{\pi}{3}\right)$

4 Express in the form $re^{i\theta}$

a $\dfrac{\cos 5\theta + i\sin 5\theta}{\cos 2\theta + i\sin 2\theta}$ **b** $\dfrac{\sqrt{2}\left(\cos\dfrac{\pi}{2} + i\sin\dfrac{\pi}{2}\right)}{\dfrac{1}{2}\left(\cos\dfrac{\pi}{4} + i\sin\dfrac{\pi}{4}\right)}$ **c** $\dfrac{3\left(\cos\dfrac{\pi}{3} + i\sin\dfrac{\pi}{3}\right)}{4\left(\cos\dfrac{5\pi}{6} + i\sin\dfrac{5\pi}{6}\right)}$

5 z and w are two complex numbers where $z = -9 + 3i\sqrt{3}$, $|w| = \sqrt{3}$ and $\arg w = \dfrac{7\pi}{12}$

Express in the form $re^{i\theta}$, where $-\pi < \theta \leqslant \pi$.

a z **b** w **c** zw **d** $\dfrac{z}{w}$

(P) **6** Use the exponential form for a complex number to show that

$$\frac{(\cos 9\theta + i\sin 9\theta)(\cos 4\theta + i\sin 4\theta)}{\cos 7\theta + i\sin 7\theta} \equiv \cos 6\theta + i\sin 6\theta$$

(E/P) **7** $z = 1 + i\sqrt{3}$, $\operatorname{Re}\left(\dfrac{z^2}{w}\right) = 0$ and $\left|\dfrac{z^2}{w}\right| = |z|$

Use geometrical reasoning to find the two possibilities for w, giving your answers in exponential form. **(4 marks)**

(E/P) **8 a** Evaluate $(1 + i)^2$, giving your answer in exponential form. **(2 marks)**

b Use mathematical induction to prove that $(1 + i)^n = 2^{\frac{n}{2}} e^{\frac{n\pi i}{4}}$ for $n \in \mathbb{Z}^+$. **(4 marks)**

c Hence find $(1 + i)^{16}$. **(1 mark)**

(P) **9** Use Euler's relation for $e^{i\theta}$ and $e^{-i\theta}$ to verify that $\cos^2\theta + \sin^2\theta \equiv 1$.

Challenge

a Given that n is a positive integer, prove by induction that
$$(re^{i\theta})^n = r^n e^{in\theta}$$

b Given further that $z^{-n} = \dfrac{1}{z^n}$ for all $z \in \mathbb{C}$, show that
$$(re^{i\theta})^{-n} = r^{-n} e^{-in\theta}$$

Watch out You cannot assume that the laws of indices will apply to complex numbers. Prove these results using only the properties
$$z_1 z_2 = r_1 r_2 e^{i(\theta_1 + \theta_2)}$$
$$\frac{z_1}{z_2} = \frac{r_1}{r_2} e^{i(\theta_1 - \theta_2)}$$

3.3   De Moivre's theorem

You can use Euler's relation to find powers of complex numbers given in modulus–argument form.
$$(r(\cos\theta + i\sin\theta))^2 = (re^{i\theta})^2$$
$$= re^{i\theta} \times re^{i\theta}$$
$$= r^2 e^{i2\theta}$$
$$= r^2(\cos 2\theta + i\sin 2\theta)$$

Similarly, $(r(\cos\theta + i\sin\theta))^3 = r^3(\cos 3\theta + i\sin 3\theta)$, and so on.

The generalisation of this result is known as **de Moivre's theorem**:

- **For any integer n,**

$$(r(\cos\theta + i\sin\theta))^n = r^n(\cos n\theta + i\sin n\theta)$$

You can prove de Moivre's theorem quickly using Euler's relation.
$$(r(\cos\theta + i\sin\theta))^n = (re^{i\theta})^n$$
$$= r^n e^{in\theta}$$
$$= r^n(\cos n\theta + i\sin n\theta)$$

This step is valid for any integer exponent n.   ← **Exercise 3B Challenge**

You can also prove de Moivre's theorem for **positive integer exponents** directly from the modulus–argument form of a complex number using the addition formulae for sin and cos.

Links This proof uses the method of proof by induction.
        ← **Further Pure 1 Section 8.1**

1. Basis step

$n = 1$; LHS $= (r(\cos\theta + i\sin\theta))^1 = r(\cos\theta + i\sin\theta)$
      RHS $= r^1(\cos 1\theta + i\sin 1\theta) = r(\cos\theta + i\sin\theta)$

As LHS = RHS, de Moivre's theorem is true for $n = 1$.

2. Assumption step

Assume that de Moivre's theorem is true for $n = k$, $k \in \mathbb{Z}^+$:
$$(r(\cos\theta + i\sin\theta))^k = r^k(\cos k\theta + i\sin k\theta)$$

3. Inductive step

When $n = k + 1$,

$$(r(\cos\theta + i\sin\theta))^{k+1} = (r(\cos\theta + i\sin\theta))^k \times r(\cos\theta + i\sin\theta)$$

$$= r^k(\cos k\theta + i\sin k\theta) \times r(\cos\theta + i\sin\theta) \quad\text{------ By assumption step}$$

$$= r^{k+1}(\cos k\theta + i\sin k\theta)(\cos\theta + i\sin\theta)$$

$$= r^{k+1}((\cos k\theta\cos\theta - \sin k\theta\sin\theta) + i(\sin k\theta\cos\theta + \cos k\theta\sin\theta))$$

$$= r^{k+1}(\cos(k\theta + \theta) + i\sin(k\theta + \theta)) \quad\text{------ By addition formulae}$$

$$= r^{k+1}(\cos((k+1)\theta) + i\sin((k+1)\theta))$$

Therefore, de Moivre's theorem is true when $n = k + 1$.

4. Conclusion step

If de Moivre's theorem is true for $n = k$, then it has been shown to be true for $n = k + 1$.

As de Moivre's theorem is true for $n = 1$, it is now proven to be true for all $n \in \mathbb{Z}^+$ by mathematical induction.

Links The **corresponding** proof for negative integer exponents is left as an exercise.

→ **Exercise 3C Challenge**

Example 8

Simplify $\dfrac{\left(\cos\dfrac{9\pi}{17} + i\sin\dfrac{9\pi}{17}\right)^5}{\left(\cos\dfrac{2\pi}{17} - i\sin\dfrac{2\pi}{17}\right)^3}$

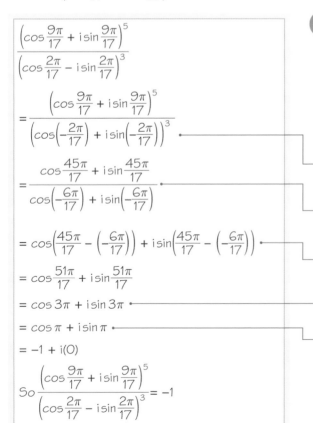

$$\frac{\left(\cos\dfrac{9\pi}{17} + i\sin\dfrac{9\pi}{17}\right)^5}{\left(\cos\dfrac{2\pi}{17} - i\sin\dfrac{2\pi}{17}\right)^3}$$

$$= \frac{\left(\cos\dfrac{9\pi}{17} + i\sin\dfrac{9\pi}{17}\right)^5}{\left(\cos\left(-\dfrac{2\pi}{17}\right) + i\sin\left(-\dfrac{2\pi}{17}\right)\right)^3}$$

$$= \frac{\cos\dfrac{45\pi}{17} + i\sin\dfrac{45\pi}{17}}{\cos\left(-\dfrac{6\pi}{17}\right) + i\sin\left(-\dfrac{6\pi}{17}\right)}$$

$$= \cos\left(\dfrac{45\pi}{17} - \left(-\dfrac{6\pi}{17}\right)\right) + i\sin\left(\dfrac{45\pi}{17} - \left(-\dfrac{6\pi}{17}\right)\right)$$

$$= \cos\dfrac{51\pi}{17} + i\sin\dfrac{51\pi}{17}$$

$$= \cos 3\pi + i\sin 3\pi$$

$$= \cos\pi + i\sin\pi$$

$$= -1 + i(0)$$

So $\dfrac{\left(\cos\dfrac{9\pi}{17} + i\sin\dfrac{9\pi}{17}\right)^5}{\left(\cos\dfrac{2\pi}{17} - i\sin\dfrac{2\pi}{17}\right)^3} = -1$

Problem-solving

You could also show this result by writing both numbers in exponential form:

$$\frac{\left(e^{\frac{9\pi i}{17}}\right)^5}{\left(e^{-\frac{2\pi i}{17}}\right)^3} = \frac{e^{\frac{45\pi i}{17}}}{e^{-\frac{6\pi i}{17}}} = e^{i\left(\frac{45\pi}{17} - \left(-\frac{6\pi}{17}\right)\right)} = e^{3\pi i} = e^{\pi i} = -1$$

$\cos(-\theta) = \cos\theta$ and $\sin(-\theta) = -\sin\theta$

Apply de Moivre's theorem to both the numerator and the denominator.

$\dfrac{z_1}{z_2} = \cos(\theta_1 - \theta_2) + i\sin(\theta_1 - \theta_2)$

Simplify.

Subtract 2π from the argument.

Example   9

Express $(1 + i\sqrt{3})^7$ in the form $x + iy$ where $x, y \in \mathbb{R}$.

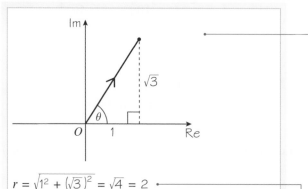

First, you need to find the modulus and argument of $1 + i\sqrt{3}$. You may want to draw an Argand diagram to help you.

$r = \sqrt{1^2 + (\sqrt{3})^2} = \sqrt{4} = 2$

$\theta = \arctan\left(\dfrac{\sqrt{3}}{1}\right) = \dfrac{\pi}{3}$

Find r and θ.

So $1 + i\sqrt{3} = 2\left(\cos\dfrac{\pi}{3} + i\sin\dfrac{\pi}{3}\right)$

Write $1 + i\sqrt{3}$ in modulus–argument form.

$(1 + i\sqrt{3})^7 = \left(2\left(\cos\dfrac{\pi}{3} + i\sin\dfrac{\pi}{3}\right)\right)^7$

$= 2^7\left(\cos\dfrac{7\pi}{3} + i\sin\dfrac{7\pi}{3}\right)$

Apply de Moivre's theorem.

$= 128\left(\cos\dfrac{\pi}{3} + i\sin\dfrac{\pi}{3}\right)$

Subtract 2π from the argument.

$= 128\left(\dfrac{1}{2} + i\left(\dfrac{\sqrt{3}}{2}\right)\right)$

Therefore, $(1 + i\sqrt{3})^7 = 64 + 64i\sqrt{3}$

Exercise   **3C**

1 Use de Moivre's theorem to express in the form $x + iy$, where $x, y \in \mathbb{R}$.

  a $(\cos\theta + i\sin\theta)^6$

  b $(\cos 3\theta + i\sin 3\theta)^4$

  c $\left(\cos\dfrac{\pi}{6} + i\sin\dfrac{\pi}{6}\right)^5$

  d $\left(\cos\dfrac{\pi}{3} + i\sin\dfrac{\pi}{3}\right)^8$

  e $\left(\cos\dfrac{2\pi}{5} + i\sin\dfrac{2\pi}{5}\right)^5$

  f $\left(\cos\dfrac{\pi}{10} - i\sin\dfrac{\pi}{10}\right)^{15}$

2 Express in the form $e^{in\theta}$

  a $\dfrac{\cos 5\theta + i\sin 5\theta}{(\cos 2\theta + i\sin 2\theta)^2}$

  b $\dfrac{(\cos 2\theta + i\sin 2\theta)^7}{(\cos 4\theta + i\sin 4\theta)^3}$

  c $\dfrac{1}{(\cos 2\theta + i\sin 2\theta)^3}$

  d $\dfrac{(\cos 2\theta + i\sin 2\theta)^4}{(\cos 3\theta + i\sin 3\theta)^3}$

  e $\dfrac{\cos 5\theta + i\sin 5\theta}{(\cos 3\theta - i\sin 3\theta)^2}$

  f $\dfrac{\cos\theta - i\sin\theta}{(\cos 2\theta - i\sin 2\theta)^3}$

3 Evaluate, giving your answers in the form $x + iy$, where $x, y \in \mathbb{R}$.

a $\dfrac{\left(\cos\dfrac{7\pi}{13} - i\sin\dfrac{7\pi}{13}\right)^4}{\left(\cos\dfrac{4\pi}{13} + i\sin\dfrac{4\pi}{13}\right)^6}$

b $\dfrac{\left(\cos\dfrac{3\pi}{7} - i\sin\dfrac{11\pi}{7}\right)^3}{\left(\cos\dfrac{15\pi}{7} + i\sin\dfrac{\pi}{7}\right)^2}$

c $\dfrac{\left(\cos\dfrac{4\pi}{3} - i\sin\dfrac{2\pi}{3}\right)^7}{\left(\cos\dfrac{10\pi}{3} + i\sin\dfrac{4\pi}{3}\right)^4}$

4 Express in the form $x + iy$ where $x, y \in \mathbb{R}$.

  a $(1 + i)^5$ **b** $(-2 + 2i)^8$ **c** $(1 - i)^6$

  d $(1 - i\sqrt{3})^6$ **e** $\left(\frac{3}{2} - \frac{1}{2}i\sqrt{3}\right)^9$ **f** $\left(-2\sqrt{3} - 2i\right)^5$

(E) **5** Express $(3 + i\sqrt{3})^5$ in the form $a + bi\sqrt{3}$ where a and b are integers.   **(2 marks)**

(E) **6** $w = 2\left(\cos\dfrac{\pi}{6} + i\sin\dfrac{\pi}{6}\right)$

    Find the exact value of w^4, giving your answer in the form $a + ib$ where $a, b \in \mathbb{R}$.   **(2 marks)**

(E) **7** $z = \sqrt{3}\left(\cos\dfrac{3\pi}{4} - i\sin\dfrac{3\pi}{4}\right)$

    Find the exact value of z^6, giving your answer in the form $a + ib$ where $a, b \in \mathbb{R}$.   **(3 marks)**

(E/P) **8 a** Express $\dfrac{1 + i\sqrt{3}}{1 - i\sqrt{3}}$ in the form $re^{i\theta}$ where $r > 0$ and $-\pi < \theta \leqslant \pi$.   **(3 marks)**

    b Hence find the smallest positive integer value of n for which $\left(\dfrac{1 + i\sqrt{3}}{1 - i\sqrt{3}}\right)^n$ is real and positive.   **(2 marks)**

(E/P) **9** Use de Moivre's theorem to show that $(a + bi)^n + (a - bi)^n$ is real for all integers n.   **(5 marks)**

Challenge

Without using Euler's relation, prove that if n is a positive integer,

$(r(\cos\theta + i\sin\theta))^{-n} = r^{-n}(\cos(-n\theta) + i\sin(-n\theta))$

Problem-solving

You may assume de Moivre's theorem for positive integer exponents, but do not write any complex numbers in exponential form.

3.4 Trigonometric identities

You can use de Moivre's theorem to derive trigonometric identities.

Applying the binomial expansion to $(\cos\theta + i\sin\theta)^n$ allows you to express $\cos n\theta$ in terms of powers of $\cos\theta$, and $\sin n\theta$ in terms of powers of $\sin\theta$.

Links $(a + b)^n = a^n + {}^nC_1 a^{n-1}b + {}^nC_2 a^{n-2}b^2 + \ldots + {}^nC_r a^{n-r}b^r + \ldots + b^n, n \in \mathbb{N}$

where ${}^nC_r = \binom{n}{r} = \dfrac{n!}{r!(n-r)!}$ ← **Pure 2 Section 4.3**

Example 10

Use de Moivre's theorem to show that

$$\cos 6\theta = 32\cos^6\theta - 48\cos^4\theta + 18\cos^2\theta - 1$$

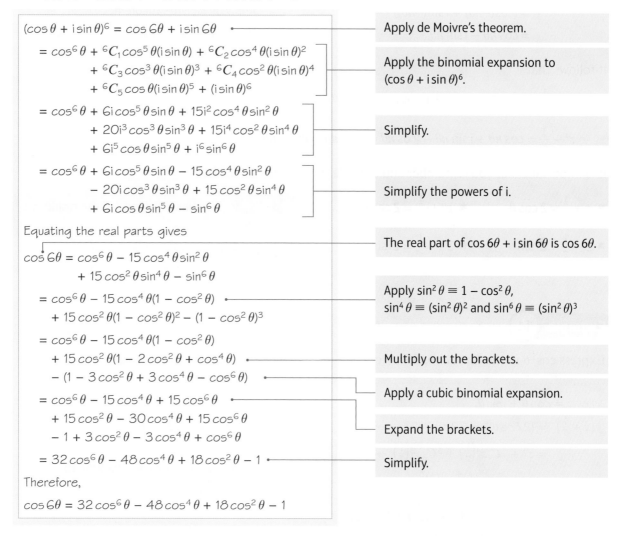

$(\cos\theta + i\sin\theta)^6 = \cos 6\theta + i\sin 6\theta$ —— Apply de Moivre's theorem.

$\begin{aligned}= \cos^6\theta &+ {}^6C_1\cos^5\theta(i\sin\theta) + {}^6C_2\cos^4\theta(i\sin\theta)^2 \\ &+ {}^6C_3\cos^3\theta(i\sin\theta)^3 + {}^6C_4\cos^2\theta(i\sin\theta)^4 \\ &+ {}^6C_5\cos\theta(i\sin\theta)^5 + (i\sin\theta)^6\end{aligned}$ —— Apply the binomial expansion to $(\cos\theta + i\sin\theta)^6$.

$\begin{aligned}= \cos^6\theta &+ 6i\cos^5\theta\sin\theta + 15i^2\cos^4\theta\sin^2\theta \\ &+ 20i^3\cos^3\theta\sin^3\theta + 15i^4\cos^2\theta\sin^4\theta \\ &+ 6i^5\cos\theta\sin^5\theta + i^6\sin^6\theta\end{aligned}$ —— Simplify.

$\begin{aligned}= \cos^6\theta &+ 6i\cos^5\theta\sin\theta - 15\cos^4\theta\sin^2\theta \\ &- 20i\cos^3\theta\sin^3\theta + 15\cos^2\theta\sin^4\theta \\ &+ 6i\cos\theta\sin^5\theta - \sin^6\theta\end{aligned}$ —— Simplify the powers of i.

Equating the real parts gives

—— The real part of $\cos 6\theta + i\sin 6\theta$ is $\cos 6\theta$.

$\begin{aligned}\cos 6\theta = \cos^6\theta &- 15\cos^4\theta\sin^2\theta \\ &+ 15\cos^2\theta\sin^4\theta - \sin^6\theta\end{aligned}$

$\begin{aligned}= \cos^6\theta &- 15\cos^4\theta(1 - \cos^2\theta) \\ &+ 15\cos^2\theta(1 - \cos^2\theta)^2 - (1 - \cos^2\theta)^3\end{aligned}$ —— Apply $\sin^2\theta \equiv 1 - \cos^2\theta$, $\sin^4\theta \equiv (\sin^2\theta)^2$ and $\sin^6\theta \equiv (\sin^2\theta)^3$

$\begin{aligned}= \cos^6\theta &- 15\cos^4\theta(1 - \cos^2\theta) \\ &+ 15\cos^2\theta(1 - 2\cos^2\theta + \cos^4\theta) \\ &- (1 - 3\cos^2\theta + 3\cos^4\theta - \cos^6\theta)\end{aligned}$ —— Multiply out the brackets.

—— Apply a cubic binomial expansion.

$\begin{aligned}= \cos^6\theta &- 15\cos^4\theta + 15\cos^6\theta \\ &+ 15\cos^2\theta - 30\cos^4\theta + 15\cos^6\theta \\ &- 1 + 3\cos^2\theta - 3\cos^4\theta + \cos^6\theta\end{aligned}$ —— Expand the brackets.

$= 32\cos^6\theta - 48\cos^4\theta + 18\cos^2\theta - 1$ —— Simplify.

Therefore,

$$\cos 6\theta = 32\cos^6\theta - 48\cos^4\theta + 18\cos^2\theta - 1$$

You can also find trigonometric identities for $\sin^n\theta$ and $\cos^n\theta$ where n is a positive integer.
If $z = \cos\theta + i\sin\theta$, then

$$\begin{aligned}\frac{1}{z} = z^{-1} &= (\cos\theta + i\sin\theta)^{-1} \\ &= (\cos(-\theta) + i\sin(-\theta)) \qquad\text{—— Apply de Moivre's theorem.} \\ &= \cos\theta - i\sin\theta \qquad\qquad\text{—— Use } \cos\theta = \cos(-\theta) \text{ and } -\sin\theta = \sin(-\theta).\end{aligned}$$

It follows that

$$z + \frac{1}{z} = \cos\theta + i\sin\theta + \cos\theta - i\sin\theta = 2\cos\theta$$

$$z - \frac{1}{z} = \cos\theta + i\sin\theta - (\cos\theta - i\sin\theta) = 2i\sin\theta$$

Also,

$$z^n = (\cos\theta + i\sin\theta)^n = \cos n\theta + i\sin n\theta \quad\text{—————— By de Moivre's theorem.}$$

$$\frac{1}{z^n} = z^{-n} = (\cos\theta + i\sin\theta)^{-n}$$

$$= (\cos(-n\theta) + i\sin(-n\theta)) \quad\text{—————— Apply de Moivre's theorem.}$$

$$= \cos n\theta - i\sin n\theta \quad\text{—————— Use } \cos\theta = \cos(-\theta) \text{ and } \sin(-\theta) = -\sin\theta.$$

It follows that

$$z^n + \frac{1}{z^n} = \cos n\theta + i\sin n\theta + \cos n\theta - i\sin n\theta = 2\cos n\theta$$

$$z^n - \frac{1}{z^n} = \cos n\theta + i\sin n\theta - (\cos n\theta - i\sin n\theta) = 2i\sin n\theta$$

It is important that you remember and are able to apply these results:

- $z + \dfrac{1}{z} = 2\cos\theta$ - $z^n + \dfrac{1}{z^n} = 2\cos n\theta$

- $z - \dfrac{1}{z} = 2i\sin\theta$ - $z^n - \dfrac{1}{z^n} = 2i\sin n\theta$

Notation In exponential form, these results are equivalent to:

$$\cos n\theta = \frac{1}{2}(e^{in\theta} + e^{-in\theta}) \qquad \sin n\theta = \frac{1}{2i}(e^{in\theta} - e^{-in\theta})$$

Example 11

Express $\cos^5\theta$ in the form $a\cos 5\theta + b\cos 3\theta + c\cos\theta$, where a, b and c are constants.

Let $z = \cos\theta + i\sin\theta$

$$\left(z + \frac{1}{z}\right)^5 = (2\cos\theta)^5 = 32\cos^5\theta \quad\text{—————— Use } z + \frac{1}{z} = 2\cos\theta.$$

$$= z^5 + {}^5C_1 z^4\left(\frac{1}{z}\right) + {}^5C_2 z^3\left(\frac{1}{z}\right)^2 + {}^5C_3 z^2\left(\frac{1}{z}\right)^3$$

$$+ {}^5C_4 z\left(\frac{1}{z}\right)^4 + \left(\frac{1}{z}\right)^5 \quad\text{—————— Apply the binomial expansion to } \left(z + \frac{1}{z}\right)^5.$$

$$= z^5 + 5z^4\left(\frac{1}{z}\right) + 10z^3\left(\frac{1}{z^2}\right) + 10z^2\left(\frac{1}{z^3}\right)$$

$$+ 5z\left(\frac{1}{z^4}\right) + \left(\frac{1}{z^5}\right)$$

$$= z^5 + 5z^3 + 10z + \frac{10}{z} + \frac{5}{z^3} + \frac{1}{z^5} \quad\text{—————— Simplify.}$$

$$= \left(z^5 + \frac{1}{z^5}\right) + 5\left(z^3 + \frac{1}{z^3}\right) + 10\left(z + \frac{1}{z}\right) \quad\text{—————— Group } z^n \text{ and } \frac{1}{z^n} \text{ terms.}$$

$$= 2\cos 5\theta + 5(2\cos 3\theta) + 10(2\cos\theta) \quad\text{—————— Use } z^n + \frac{1}{z^n} = 2\cos n\theta$$

So, $32\cos^5\theta = 2\cos 5\theta + 10\cos 3\theta + 20\cos\theta$

$$\Rightarrow \quad \cos^5\theta = \frac{1}{16}\cos 5\theta + \frac{5}{16}\cos 3\theta + \frac{5}{8}\cos\theta \quad\text{—————— This is in the required form with } a = \frac{1}{16}, b = \frac{5}{16} \text{ and } c = \frac{5}{8}$$

Example 12

a Express $\sin^4 \theta$ in the form $d\cos 4\theta + e\cos 2\theta + f$, where d, e and f are constants.

b Hence find the exact value of $\displaystyle\int_0^{\frac{\pi}{2}} \sin^4 \theta \, d\theta$.

a Let $z = \cos\theta + i\sin\theta$

$$\left(z - \frac{1}{z}\right)^4 = (2i\sin\theta)^4 = 16i^4\sin^4\theta = 16\sin^4\theta$$

Use $z - \dfrac{1}{z} = 2i\sin\theta$, noting that $i^4 = 1$

$$= z^4 + {}^4C_1 z^3\left(-\frac{1}{z}\right) + {}^4C_2 z^2\left(-\frac{1}{z}\right)^2$$
$$+ {}^4C_3 z^1\left(-\frac{1}{z}\right)^3 + \left(-\frac{1}{z}\right)^4$$

Apply the binomial expansion to $\left(z - \dfrac{1}{z}\right)^4$

$$= z^4 + 4z^3\left(-\frac{1}{z}\right) + 6z^2\left(\frac{1}{z^2}\right)$$
$$+ 4z\left(-\frac{1}{z^3}\right) + \left(\frac{1}{z^4}\right)$$

$$= z^4 - 4z^2 + 6 - \frac{4}{z^2} + \frac{1}{z^4}$$

Simplify.

$$= \left(z^4 + \frac{1}{z^4}\right) - 4\left(z^2 + \frac{1}{z^2}\right) + 6$$

Group z^n and $\dfrac{1}{z^n}$ terms.

$$= 2\cos 4\theta - 4(2\cos 2\theta) + 6$$

Use $z^n + \dfrac{1}{z^n} = 2\cos n\theta$

So, $16\sin^4\theta = 2\cos 4\theta - 8\cos 2\theta + 6$

$$\Rightarrow \quad \sin^4\theta = \frac{1}{8}\cos 4\theta - \frac{1}{2}\cos 2\theta + \frac{3}{8}$$

This is in the required form with $d = \dfrac{1}{8}$, $e = -\dfrac{1}{2}$ and $f = \dfrac{3}{8}$

b $\displaystyle\int_0^{\frac{\pi}{2}} \sin^4\theta \, d\theta = \int_0^{\frac{\pi}{2}}\left(\frac{1}{8}\cos 4\theta - \frac{1}{2}\cos 2\theta + \frac{3}{8}\right)d\theta$

Use the answer from part **a**.

$$= \left[\frac{1}{32}\sin 4\theta - \frac{1}{4}\sin 2\theta + \frac{3}{8}\theta\right]_0^{\frac{\pi}{2}}$$

$\cos k\theta$ integrates to $\dfrac{1}{k}\sin k\theta$.

$$= \left(\frac{1}{32}\sin 2\pi - \frac{1}{4}\sin \pi + \frac{3}{8}\left(\frac{\pi}{2}\right)\right) - 0$$

$$= 0 - 0 + \frac{3\pi}{16}$$

$$= \frac{3\pi}{16}$$

Exercise 3D

Use de Moivre's theorem to prove the trigonometric identities:

(P) **1 a** $\sin 3\theta \equiv 3\sin\theta - 4\sin^3\theta$

    b $\sin 5\theta \equiv 16\sin^5\theta - 20\sin^3\theta + 5\sin\theta$

    c $\cos 7\theta \equiv 64\cos^7\theta - 112\cos^5\theta + 56\cos^3\theta - 7\cos\theta$

    d $\cos^4\theta \equiv \frac{1}{8}(\cos 4\theta + 4\cos 2\theta + 3)$

    e $\sin^5\theta \equiv \frac{1}{16}(\sin 5\theta - 5\sin 3\theta + 10\sin\theta)$

(E/P) **2 a** Use de Moivre's theorem to show that
$$\cos 5\theta \equiv 16\cos^5\theta - 20\cos^3\theta + 5\cos\theta$$ **(5 marks)**

  b Hence, given also that $\cos 3\theta = 4\cos^3\theta - 3\cos\theta$, find all the solutions of $\cos 5\theta + 5\cos 3\theta = 0$ in the interval $0 \leqslant \theta < \pi$. Give your answers to 3 decimal places. **(6 marks)**

(E/P) **3 a** Show that $32\cos^6\theta \equiv \cos 6\theta + 6\cos 4\theta + 15\cos 2\theta + 10$. **(6 marks)**

  b Hence find $\displaystyle\int_0^{\frac{\pi}{6}} \cos^6\theta \, d\theta$ in the form $a\pi + b\sqrt{3}$ where a and b are rational constants to be found. **(3 marks)**

(E/P) **4 a** Show that $32\cos^2\theta\sin^4\theta \equiv \cos 6\theta - 2\cos 4\theta - \cos 2\theta + 2$. **(6 marks)**

  b Hence find the exact value of $\displaystyle\int_0^{\frac{\pi}{3}} \cos^2\theta\sin^4\theta \, d\theta$. **(3 marks)**

(P) **5** By using de Moivre's theorem, or otherwise, compute the integrals.

  a $\displaystyle\int_0^{\frac{\pi}{2}} \sin^6\theta \, d\theta$ **b** $\displaystyle\int_0^{\frac{\pi}{4}} \sin^2\theta\cos^4\theta \, d\theta$ **c** $\displaystyle\int_0^{\frac{\pi}{6}} \sin^3\theta\cos^5\theta \, d\theta$

(E/P) **6 a** Use de Moivre's theorem to show that
$$\cos 6\theta \equiv 32\cos^6\theta - 48\cos^4\theta + 18\cos^2\theta - 1$$ **(5 marks)**

  b Hence find the six **distinct** solutions of the equation
$$32x^6 - 48x^4 + 18x^2 - \frac{3}{2} = 0$$
giving your answers to 3 decimal places where necessary. **(5 marks)**

> **Problem-solving**
>
> Use the substitution $x = \cos\theta$ to reduce the equation to the form $\cos 6\theta = k$. Find as many values of θ as you need to find six distinct values of x.

(E/P) **7 a** Use de Moivre's theorem to show that $\sin 4\theta \equiv 4\cos^3\theta\sin\theta - 4\cos\theta\sin^3\theta$ **(4 marks)**

  b Hence, or otherwise, show that $\tan 4\theta \equiv \dfrac{4\tan\theta - 4\tan^3\theta}{1 - 6\tan^2\theta + \tan^4\theta}$ **(4 marks)**

  c Use your answer to part **b** to find, to 2 decimal places, the four solutions of the equation
$$x^4 + 4x^3 - 6x^2 - 4x + 1 = 0$$ **(5 marks)**

3.5 nth roots of a complex number

You can use de Moivre's theorem to solve an equation of the form $z^n = w$, where $z, w \in \mathbb{C}$.
This is equivalent to finding the nth roots of w.

Just as a real number, x, has two square roots, $\sqrt{x}$ and $-\sqrt{x}$, any complex number has n distinct nth roots.

- If z and w are non-zero complex numbers and n is a positive integer, then the equation $z^n = w$ has n distinct solutions.

You can find the solutions to $z^n = w$ using
de Moivre's theorem, and by considering the fact
that the **argument of a complex number** is not unique.

Notation $\cos(\theta + 2k\pi) = \cos\theta$ and
$\sin(\theta + 2k\pi) = \sin\theta$ for integer values of k.

- For any complex number $z = r(\cos\theta + i\sin\theta)$, you can write $z = r(\cos(\theta + 2k\pi) + i\sin(\theta + 2k\pi))$, where k is any integer.

Example 13

a Solve the equation $z^3 = 1$

b Represent your solutions to part **a** on an Argand diagram.

c Show that the three cube roots of 1 can be written as 1, ω and ω^2 where $1 + \omega + \omega^2 = 0$

---

a $z^3 = 1$

$z^3 = \cos 0 + i\sin 0$ •————————— Start by writing 1 in modulus–argument form.

$(r(\cos\theta + i\sin\theta))^3 =$
$\quad \cos(0 + 2k\pi) + i\sin(0 + 2k\pi), \ k \in \mathbb{Z}$ •——— Write z in modulus–argument form, and write the general form of the argument on the right-hand side by adding integer multiples of 2π.

$r^3(\cos 3\theta + i\sin 3\theta) =$
$\quad \cos(0 + 2k\pi) + i\sin(0 + 2k\pi), \ k \in \mathbb{Z}$ •——— Apply de Moivre's theorem to the left-hand side of the equation.

So $r = 1$ •————————— Compare the modulus on both sides to get $r = 1$.

$3\theta = 2k\pi$ •—————————

$k = 0 \Rightarrow \theta = 0$, so $z_1 = \cos 0 + i\sin 0 = 1$ •——— Compare the arguments on both sides.

$k = 1 \Rightarrow \theta = \dfrac{2\pi}{3}$

so $z_2 = \cos\left(\dfrac{2\pi}{3}\right) + i\sin\left(\dfrac{2\pi}{3}\right) = -\dfrac{1}{2} + i\dfrac{\sqrt{3}}{2}$

$k = -1 \Rightarrow \theta = -\dfrac{2\pi}{3}$

so $z_3 = \cos\left(-\dfrac{2\pi}{3}\right) + i\sin\left(-\dfrac{2\pi}{3}\right) = -\dfrac{1}{2} - i\dfrac{\sqrt{3}}{2}$

Therefore,

$z = 1, \ z = -\dfrac{1}{2} + i\dfrac{\sqrt{3}}{2}$ or $z = -\dfrac{1}{2} - i\dfrac{\sqrt{3}}{2}$ •——— These are the cube roots of unity.

Problem-solving

Choose values of k to find the three distinct roots. By choosing values on either side of $k = 0$ you can find three different arguments in the interval $[-\pi, \pi]$.

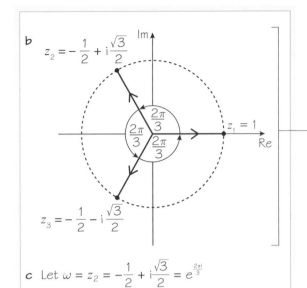

b $z_2 = -\dfrac{1}{2} + i\dfrac{\sqrt{3}}{2}$

$z_3 = -\dfrac{1}{2} - i\dfrac{\sqrt{3}}{2}$

Plot the points $z_1 = 1$, $z_2 = -\frac{1}{2} + i\frac{\sqrt{3}}{2}$ and $z_3 = -\frac{1}{2} - i\frac{\sqrt{3}}{2}$ on an Argand diagram:

The points z_1, z_2 and z_3 lie on a circle of radius 1 unit.

The angles between each of the **vectors** z_1, z_2 and z_3 are $\frac{2\pi}{3}$, as shown on the Argand diagram.

c Let $\omega = z_2 = -\dfrac{1}{2} + i\dfrac{\sqrt{3}}{2} = e^{\frac{2\pi i}{3}}$

Then, $\omega^2 = \left(e^{\frac{2\pi i}{3}}\right)^2 = e^{\frac{4\pi i}{3}}$

$= e^{-\frac{2\pi i}{3}} = -\dfrac{1}{2} - i\dfrac{\sqrt{3}}{2} = z_3$ ← Notice that $\omega^* = \omega^2$.

$1 + \omega + \omega^2 =$

$1 + \left(-\dfrac{1}{2} + i\dfrac{\sqrt{3}}{2}\right) + \left(-\dfrac{1}{2} - i\dfrac{\sqrt{3}}{2}\right) = 0$

Notation It can be proved that the sum of the nth roots of unity is zero, for any positive integer $n \geqslant 2$.

- In general, the solutions to $z^n = 1$ are $z = \cos\left(\dfrac{2\pi k}{n}\right) + i\sin\left(\dfrac{2\pi k}{n}\right) = e^{\frac{2\pi i k}{n}}$ for $k = 1, 2, \ldots, n$ and are known as the nth roots of unity.

If n is a positive integer, then there is an nth root of unity $\omega = e^{\frac{2\pi i}{n}}$ such that:

- the nth roots of unity are $1, \omega, \omega^2, \ldots, \omega^{n-1}$

- $1, \omega, \omega^2, \ldots, \omega^{n-1}$ form the **vertices** of a regular n-gon

- $1 + \omega + \omega^2 + \ldots + \omega^{n-1} = 0$

Example 14

Solve the equation $z^4 = 2 + 2i\sqrt{3}$

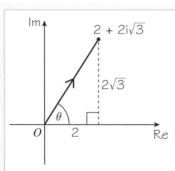

modulus $= \sqrt{2^2 + (2\sqrt{3})^2} = \sqrt{4 + 12} = 4$

argument $= \arctan\left(\dfrac{2\sqrt{3}}{2}\right) = \dfrac{\pi}{3}$

So $z^4 = 4\left(\cos\dfrac{\pi}{3} + i\sin\dfrac{\pi}{3}\right)$ •────────

$(r(\cos\theta + i\sin\theta))^4$

$\quad = 4\left(\cos\left(\dfrac{\pi}{3} + 2k\pi\right) + i\sin\left(\dfrac{\pi}{3} + 2k\pi\right)\right), k \in \mathbb{Z}$ •────

$r^4(\cos 4\theta + i\sin 4\theta)$

$\quad = 4\left(\cos\left(\dfrac{\pi}{3} + 2k\pi\right) + i\sin\left(\dfrac{\pi}{3} + 2k\pi\right)\right), k \in \mathbb{Z}$ •────

So $r^4 = 4 \Rightarrow r = \sqrt[4]{4} = \sqrt{2}$ •────────

$4\theta = \dfrac{\pi}{3} + 2k\pi$ •────────

$k = 0 \Rightarrow \theta = \dfrac{\pi}{12}, \qquad$ so $z_1 = \sqrt{2}\left(\cos\dfrac{\pi}{12} + i\sin\dfrac{\pi}{12}\right)$

$k = 1 \Rightarrow \theta = \dfrac{7\pi}{12}, \qquad$ so $z_2 = \sqrt{2}\left(\cos\dfrac{7\pi}{12} + i\sin\dfrac{7\pi}{12}\right)$ •────

$k = -1 \Rightarrow \theta = -\dfrac{5\pi}{12},\ $ so $z_3 = \sqrt{2}\left(\cos\left(-\dfrac{5\pi}{12}\right) + i\sin\left(-\dfrac{5\pi}{12}\right)\right)$

$k = -2 \Rightarrow \theta = -\dfrac{11\pi}{12},$ so $z_4 = \sqrt{2}\left(\cos\left(-\dfrac{11\pi}{12}\right) + i\sin\left(-\dfrac{11\pi}{12}\right)\right)$

or $z = \sqrt{2}\,e^{\frac{\pi i}{12}}$, $z = \sqrt{2}\,e^{\frac{7\pi i}{12}}$, $z = \sqrt{2}\,e^{-\frac{5\pi i}{12}}$ or $z = \sqrt{2}\,e^{-\frac{11\pi i}{12}}$ •────

To solve an equation of the form $z^n = w$, start by writing w in modulus–argument form.

Now let $z = r(\cos\theta + i\sin\theta)$, and write the general form of the argument on the RHS by adding integer multiples of 2π.

Apply de Moivre's theorem to the LHS.

Compare the modulus on both sides to get $r = \sqrt{2}$.

Compare the arguments on both sides.

When $k = 1$, $4\theta = \dfrac{\pi}{3} + 2\pi$

$\Rightarrow \theta = \dfrac{\pi}{12} + \dfrac{2\pi}{4} = \dfrac{7\pi}{12}$

Watch out Make sure you choose *n* **consecutive** values of k to get n distinct roots. If an argument is not in the interval $[-\pi, \pi]$ you can add or subtract a multiple of 2π.

These are the solutions in the form $re^{i\theta}$.

You can also use the exponential form of a complete number when solving equations.

Example 15

Solve the equation $z^3 + 4\sqrt{2} + 4i\sqrt{2} = 0$

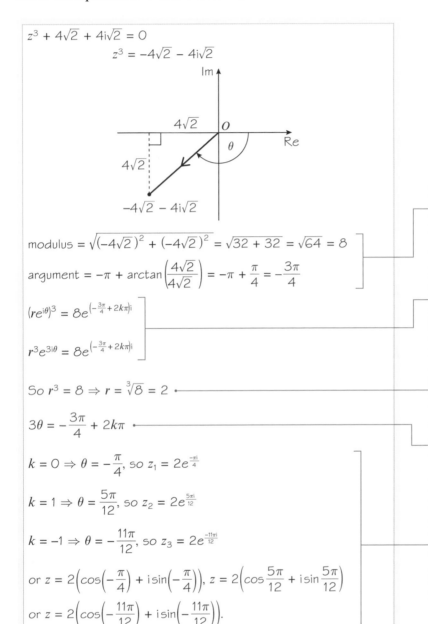

$z^3 + 4\sqrt{2} + 4i\sqrt{2} = 0$

$z^3 = -4\sqrt{2} - 4i\sqrt{2}$

$\text{modulus} = \sqrt{(-4\sqrt{2})^2 + (-4\sqrt{2})^2} = \sqrt{32 + 32} = \sqrt{64} = 8$

$\text{argument} = -\pi + \arctan\left(\dfrac{4\sqrt{2}}{4\sqrt{2}}\right) = -\pi + \dfrac{\pi}{4} = -\dfrac{3\pi}{4}$

Find the modulus and argument of $-4\sqrt{2} - 4i\sqrt{2}$.

$(re^{i\theta})^3 = 8e^{\left(-\frac{3\pi}{4} + 2k\pi\right)i}$

$r^3 e^{3i\theta} = 8e^{\left(-\frac{3\pi}{4} + 2k\pi\right)i}$

Write $z = re^{i\theta}$ and use $(re^{i\theta})n = r^n e^{in\theta}$. Remember to write the general form of the argument on the right-hand side by adding integer multiples of 2π.

So $r^3 = 8 \Rightarrow r = \sqrt[3]{8} = 2$

Compare the modulus on both sides to get $r = 2$.

$3\theta = -\dfrac{3\pi}{4} + 2k\pi$

Compare the arguments on both sides.

$k = 0 \Rightarrow \theta = -\dfrac{\pi}{4}$, so $z_1 = 2e^{\frac{-\pi i}{4}}$

$k = 1 \Rightarrow \theta = \dfrac{5\pi}{12}$, so $z_2 = 2e^{\frac{5\pi i}{12}}$

$k = -1 \Rightarrow \theta = -\dfrac{11\pi}{12}$, so $z_3 = 2e^{\frac{-11\pi i}{12}}$

or $z = 2\left(\cos\left(-\dfrac{\pi}{4}\right) + i\sin\left(-\dfrac{\pi}{4}\right)\right), z = 2\left(\cos\dfrac{5\pi}{12} + i\sin\dfrac{5\pi}{12}\right)$

or $z = 2\left(\cos\left(-\dfrac{11\pi}{12}\right) + i\sin\left(-\dfrac{11\pi}{12}\right)\right).$

Choose values of k to find three distinct roots. Either choose values that produce arguments in the interval $-\pi < \theta \leqslant \pi$, or add or subtract multiples of 2π as necessary.

Exercise **3E**

1 Solve the equations, expressing your answers for z in the form $x + iy$, where $x, y \in \mathbb{R}$.

   a $z^4 - 1 = 0$ **b** $z^3 - i = 0$ **c** $z^3 = 27$

   d $z^4 + 64 = 0$ **e** $z^4 + 4 = 0$ **f** $z^3 + 8i = 0$

2 Solve the equations, expressing the roots in the form $r(\cos\theta + i\sin\theta)$, where $-\pi < \theta \leqslant \pi$.

   a $z^7 = 1$ **b** $z^4 + 16i = 0$ **c** $z^5 + 32 = 0$

   d $z^3 = 2 + 2i$ **e** $z^4 + 2i\sqrt{3} = 2$ **f** $z^3 + 32\sqrt{3} + 32i = 0$

3 Solve the equations, expressing the roots in the form $re^{i\theta}$, where $r > 0$ and $-\pi < \theta \leqslant \pi$. Give θ to 2 decimal places.

   a $z^4 = 3 + 4i$ **b** $z^3 = \sqrt{11} - 4i$ **c** $z^4 = -\sqrt{7} + 3i$

(P) 4 **a** Find the three roots of the equation $(z + 1)^3 = -1$
   Give your answers in the form $x + iy$, where $x, y \in \mathbb{R}$.

   b Plot the points representing these three roots on an Argand diagram.

   c Given that these three points lie on a circle, find its centre and radius.

(P) 5 **a** Find the five roots of the equation $z^5 - 1 = 0$
   Give your answers in the form $r(\cos\theta + i\sin\theta)$, where $-\pi < \theta \leqslant \pi$.

   b Hence or otherwise, show that
   $$\cos\left(\frac{2\pi}{5}\right) + \cos\left(\frac{4\pi}{5}\right) = -\frac{1}{2}$$

   Problem-solving

   Use the fact that the sum of the five roots of unity is zero.

(E) 6 **a** Find the modulus and argument of $-2 - 2i\sqrt{3}$ **(2 marks)**

   b Hence find all the solutions of the equation $z^4 + 2 + 2i\sqrt{3} = 0$
   Give your answers in the form $re^{i\theta}$, where $r > 0$ and $-\pi < \theta \leqslant \pi$ and
   illustrate the roots on an Argand diagram.   **(4 marks)**

(E) 7 Find the four distinct roots of the equation $z^4 = 2(1 - i\sqrt{3})$ in exponential form, and show these
   roots on an Argand diagram.   **(7 marks)**

(E/P) **8** $z = \sqrt{6} + i\sqrt{2}$

    a Find the modulus and argument of z. **(2 marks)**

    b Find the values of w such that $w^3 = z^4$, giving your answers in the form $re^{i\theta}$, where $r > 0$ and $-\pi < \theta \leqslant \pi$. **(4 marks)**

(P) **9 a** Solve the equation

        $1 + z + z^2 + z^3 + z^4 + z^5 + z^6 + z^7 = 0$

    b Hence deduce that $(z^2 + 1)$ and $(z^4 + 1)$ are factors of

        $1 + z + z^2 + z^3 + z^4 + z^5 + z^6 + z^7$.

Problem-solving

$1 + z + z^2 + z^3 + \ldots + z^7$ is the sum of a geometric series.

Challenge

    a Find the six roots of the equation $z^6 = 1$ in the form $e^{i\theta}$, where $-\pi < \theta \leqslant \pi$.

    b Hence show that the solutions to $(z + 1)^6 = z^6$ are

        $z = -\frac{1}{2} + \frac{1}{2}i\cot\left(\frac{k\pi}{6}\right), k = 1, 2, 3, 4, 5.$

Chapter review (3)

(P) **1 a** Use $e^{i\theta} = \cos\theta + i\sin\theta$ to show that $\cos\theta = \frac{1}{2}(e^{i\theta} + e^{-i\theta})$

    b Hence prove that $\cos A \cos B \equiv \dfrac{\cos(A + B) + \cos(A - B)}{2}$

(E/P) **2** Given that $z = r(\cos\theta + i\sin\theta)$, $r \in \mathbb{R}$, prove by induction that $z^n = r^n(\cos n\theta + i\sin n\theta)$, $n \in \mathbb{Z}^+$. **(5 marks)**

3 Express $\dfrac{(\cos 3x + i\sin 3x)^2}{\cos x - i\sin x}$ in the form $\cos nx + i\sin nx$ where n is an integer to be determined.

4 Use de Moivre's theorem to evaluate:

    a $(-1 + i)^8$ **b** $\dfrac{1}{\left(\frac{1}{2} - \frac{1}{2}i\right)^{16}}$

(E/P) **5 a** Given $z = \cos\theta + i\sin\theta$, use de Moivre's theorem to show that $z^n + \dfrac{1}{z^n} = 2\cos n\theta$. **(4 marks)**

    b Express $\left(z^2 + \dfrac{1}{z^2}\right)^3$ in terms of $\cos 6\theta$ and $\cos 2\theta$. **(3 marks)**

    c Hence, or otherwise, find constants a and b such that $\cos^3 2\theta = a\cos 6\theta + b\cos 2\theta$. **(3 marks)**

    d Hence, or otherwise, show that $\displaystyle\int_0^{\frac{\pi}{6}} \cos^3 2\theta \, d\theta = k\sqrt{3}$, where k is a rational constant. **(4 marks)**

(E/P) **6 a** Show that

$$\cos^5\theta \equiv \frac{1}{16}(\cos 5\theta + 5\cos 3\theta + 10\cos\theta)$$ **(5 marks)**

The diagram shows the curve with equation $y = \cos^5 x$, $-\frac{\pi}{2} \leqslant x \leqslant \frac{\pi}{2}$. The finite region R is **bounded** by the curve and the x-axis.

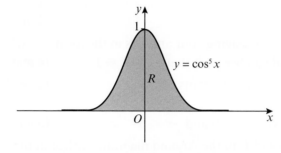

b Calculate the exact area of R.   **(6 marks)**

(E/P) **7 a** Show that

$$\sin^6\theta \equiv -\frac{1}{32}(\cos 6\theta - 6\cos 4\theta + 15\cos 2\theta - 10)$$ **(5 marks)**

b Using the substitution $\alpha = \left(\frac{\pi}{2} - \theta\right)$, or otherwise, find a similar **identity** for $\cos^6\theta$.   **(3 marks)**

c Given that $\int_0^a (\cos^6\theta + \sin^6\theta)\,d\theta = \frac{5\pi}{32}$, find the exact value of a.   **(5 marks)**

(E/P) **8** Use de Moivre's theorem to show that

$$\sin 6\theta \equiv \sin 2\theta(16\cos^4\theta - 16\cos^2\theta + 3)$$ **(5 marks)**

(E/P) **9 a** Use de Moivre's theorem to show that

$$\cos 5\theta \equiv 16\cos^5\theta - 20\cos^3\theta + 5\cos\theta$$ **(5 marks)**

b Hence find all solutions to the equation

$$16x^5 - 20x^3 + 5x + 1 = 0$$

giving your answers to 3 decimal places where necessary.   **(5 marks)**

(E/P) **10 a** Show that

$$\sin^5\theta \equiv \frac{1}{16}(\sin 5\theta - 5\sin 3\theta + 10\sin\theta)$$ **(5 marks)**

b Hence solve the equation

$$\sin 5\theta - 5\sin 3\theta + 9\sin\theta = 0 \text{ for } 0 \leqslant \theta < \pi$$ **(4 marks)**

(E/P) **11 a** Use de Moivre's theorem to show that $\cos 5\theta \equiv \cos\theta(16\cos^4\theta - 20\cos^2\theta + 5)$ **(5 marks)**

b By solving the equation $\cos 5\theta = 0$, deduce that $\cos^2\left(\frac{\pi}{10}\right) = \dfrac{5 + \sqrt{5}}{8}$ **(4 marks)**

c Hence, or otherwise, write down the exact values of $\cos^2\left(\frac{3\pi}{10}\right)$, $\cos^2\left(\frac{7\pi}{10}\right)$ and $\cos^2\left(\frac{9\pi}{10}\right)$.   **(3 marks)**

E/P **12 a** Use de Moivre's theorem to find an expression for $\tan 3\theta$ in terms of $\tan \theta$. **(4 marks)**

     b Deduce that $\cot 3\theta = \dfrac{\cot^3 \theta - 3\cot \theta}{3\cot^2 \theta - 1}$ **(2 marks)**

E **13 a** Express $4 - 4i$ in the form $r(\cos \theta + i \sin \theta)$, where $r > 0$, $-\pi < \theta \leqslant \pi$, where r and θ are exact values. **(2 marks)**

     b Hence, or otherwise, solve the equation $z^5 = 4 - 4i$, leaving your answers in the form $z = Re^{ik\pi}$, where R is the modulus of z and k is a **rational number** such that $-1 \leqslant k \leqslant 1$. **(4 marks)**

     c Show on an Argand diagram the points representing the roots. **(2 marks)**

E/P **14 a** Find the cube roots of $2 - 2i$ in the form $re^{i\theta}$ where $r > 0$ and $-\pi < \theta \leqslant \pi$. **(5 marks)**

These cube roots are represented by points A, B and C in the Argand diagram, with A in the fourth quadrant and ABC going anticlockwise. The **midpoint** of AB is M, and M represents the complex number w.

     b Draw an Argand diagram, showing the points A, B, C and M. **(2 marks)**

     c Find the modulus and argument of w. **(2 marks)**

     d Find w^6 in the form $a + bi$. **(3 marks)**

Challenge

Show that the points on an Argand diagram that represent the roots

of $\left(\dfrac{z+1}{z}\right)^6 = 1$ lie on a straight line.

Summary of key points

1 You can use **Euler's relation**, $e^{i\theta} = \cos \theta + i \sin \theta$, to write a complex number z in exponential form:

$$z = re^{i\theta}$$

where $r = |z|$ and $\theta = \arg z$.

2 For any two complex numbers $z_1 = r_1 e^{i\theta_1}$ and $z_2 = r_2 e^{i\theta_2}$

- $z_1 z_2 = r_1 r_2 e^{i(\theta_1 + \theta_2)}$

- $\dfrac{z_1}{z_2} = \dfrac{r_1}{r_2} e^{i(\theta_1 - \theta_2)}$

3 De Moivre's theorem:

For any integer n, $(r(\cos \theta + i \sin \theta))^n = r^n(\cos n\theta + i \sin n\theta)$

4 - $z + \dfrac{1}{z} = 2\cos \theta$ - $z^n + \dfrac{1}{z^n} = 2 \cos n\theta$

   - $z - \dfrac{1}{z} = 2i \sin \theta$ - $z^n - \dfrac{1}{z^n} = 2i \sin n\theta$

5 If z and w are non-zero complex numbers and n is a positive integer, then the equation $z^n = w$ has n distinct solutions.

6 For any complex number $z = r(\cos\theta + i\sin\theta)$, you can write

$z = r(\cos(\theta + 2k\pi) + i\sin(\theta + 2k\pi))$

where k is any integer.

7 In general, the solutions to $z^n = 1$ are $z = \cos\left(\dfrac{2\pi k}{n}\right) + i\sin\left(\dfrac{2\pi k}{n}\right) = e^{\frac{2\pi ik}{n}}$ for $k = 1, 2, \ldots, n$ and are known as the nth roots of unity.

If n is a positive integer, then there is an nth root of unity $\omega = e^{\frac{2\pi i}{n}}$ such that:

- The nth roots of unity are $1, \omega, \omega^2, \ldots, \omega^{n-1}$
- $1, \omega, \omega^2, \ldots, \omega^{n-1}$ form the vertices of a regular n-gon
- $1 + \omega + \omega^2 + \ldots + \omega^{n-1} = 0$

8 The nth roots of any complex number s lie on the vertices of a regular n-gon with its centre at the origin.

4 FURTHER ARGAND DIAGRAMS

3.3
3.4

Learning objectives

After completing this chapter you should be able to:

* Represent loci on an Argand diagram → **pages 47–55**
* Determine the loci of sets of points, z, in an Argand diagram given in the forms $|z - a| = k|z - b|$ and $\arg\left(\dfrac{z - a}{z - b}\right) = \beta$, where $k, \beta \in \mathbb{R}$, $k > 0, k \neq 1$ and $a, b \in \mathbb{C}$ → **pages 55–63**
* Represent regions on an Argand diagram → **pages 63–65**
* Represent regions on an Argand diagram of the forms $\alpha \leqslant \arg(z - z_1) \leqslant \beta$ and $p \leqslant \text{Re}(z) \leqslant q$, where $\alpha, \beta, p, q \in \mathbb{R}$ and $z_1 \in \mathbb{C}$ → **pages 65–69**
* Apply elementary transformations that map points from the z-plane to the w-plane, including those of the forms $w = z^2$ and $w = \dfrac{az + b}{cz + d}$ where $a, b, c, d \in \mathbb{C}$. → **pages 70–78**

Prior knowledge check

1. Show the complex numbers $z_1 = -2 + 3\text{i}$, $z_2 = 4 + \text{i}$ and $z_3 = 1 - 3\text{i}$ on an Argand diagram.
   ← Further Pure 1 Section 1.4

2. Draw the roots of the quadratic equation $z^2 + 10z + 26 = 0$ on an Argand diagram. **← Further Pure 1 Section 1.7**

3. Draw the roots of the quadratic equation $z^2 + 2z + 4 = 0$ on an Argand diagram. **← Further Pure 1 Section 1.7**

This is an image of a Julia set. Sets such as these are generated by examining the behaviour of points under the repeated application of mappings in the complex plane.

4.1　Loci in an Argand diagram

Complex numbers can be used to represent a **locus** of points on an **Argand diagram**.

■ For two complex numbers $z_1 = x_1 + iy_1$ and $z_2 = x_2 + iy_2$, $|z_2 - z_1|$ represents the distance between the points z_1 and z_2 on an Argand diagram.

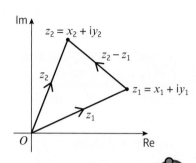

Using the above result, you can replace z_2 with the general point z. The locus of points described by $|z - z_1| = r$ is a circle with centre (x_1, y_1) and radius r.

Online　Explore the locus of z, when $|z - z_1| = r$, using GeoGebra.

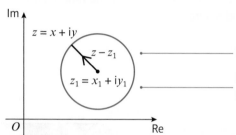

———— Locus of points.

———— Every point z, on the **circumference** of the circle, is a distance of r from the centre of the circle.

■ Given $z_1 = x_1 + iy_1$, the locus of points z on an Argand diagram such that $|z - z_1| = r$, or $|z - (x_1 + iy_1)| = r$, is a circle with centre (x_1, y_1) and radius r.

You can derive a Cartesian form of the equation of a circle from this form by squaring both sides:

$$|z - z_1| = r$$
$$|(x - x_1) + i(y - y_1)| = r$$
$$(x - x_1)^2 + (y - y_1)^2 = r^2 \quad \text{———— Since } |p + qi| = \sqrt{p^2 + q^2}$$

Links　The Cartesian equation of a circle with centre (a, b) and radius r is $(x - a)^2 + (y - b)^2 = r^2$
← **Pure 2 Section 2.5**

The locus of points that are an equal distance from two different points z_1 and z_2 is the **perpendicular bisector** of the line **segment** joining the two points.

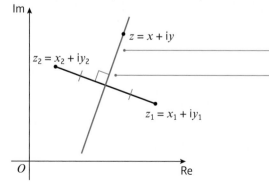

———— Locus of points.

———— Every point z on the line is an equal distance from points z_1 and z_2.

Online　Explore the locus of z, when $|z - z_1| = |z - z_2|$, using GeoGebra.

■ Given $z_1 = x_1 + iy_1$ and $z_2 = x_2 + iy_2$, the locus of points z on an Argand diagram such that $|z - z_1| = |z - z_2|$ is the perpendicular bisector of the line segment joining z_1 and z_2.

Example 1

Given that z satisfies $|z - 4| = 5$,

a sketch the locus of z on an Argand diagram.

b Find the values of z that satisfy:

  i both $|z - 4| = 5$ and $\text{Im}(z) = 0$ **ii** both $|z - 4| = 5$ and $\text{Re}(z) = 0$

a $|z - 4| = 5$ is a circle with centre (4, 0) and radius 5.

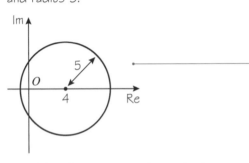

$|z - (x_1 + i y_1)| = r$ is represented by a circle with centre (x_1, y_1) and radius r.

Sketch a circle with centre (4, 0) and radius 5 on an Argand diagram.

b i $\text{Im}(z) = 0$ represents the real axis. The points where the circle cuts the real axis are (−1, 0) and (9, 0).

The values of z at these points are $z = -1$ and $z = 9$.

Centre of circle is (4, 0) and radius is 5. So consider $4 + 5 = 9$ and $4 - 5 = -1$.

Watch out Give your answers as complex numbers, not as coordinates.

ii $|z - 4| = 5 \Rightarrow (x - 4)^2 + y^2 = 5^2$

$(0 - 4)^2 + y^2 = 5^2$

$16 + y^2 = 25$

$y^2 = 9$

$y = \pm 3$

The points where the circle cuts the real axis are (0, 3) and (0, −3).

The values of z are $z = 3i$ and $z = -3i$.

This is the Cartesian equation of a circle with centre (4, 0) and radius 5.

$\text{Re}(z) = 0$ for all points on the imaginary axis, so set $x = 0$.

Example 2

A complex number z is represented by the point P in the Argand diagram.

Given that $|z - 5 - 3i| = 3$,

a sketch the locus of P **b** find the Cartesian equation of this locus

c find the maximum value of $\arg z$ in the interval $(-\pi, \pi)$.

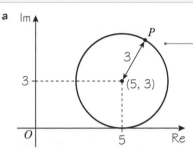

a

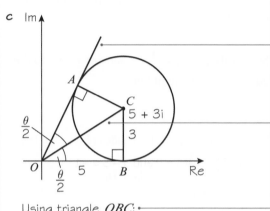

$|z - 5 - 3i|$ can be written as $|z - (5 + 3i)|$. As this distance is always equal to 3, the locus of P is a circle centre $(5, 3)$, radius 3.

The standard Cartesian equation of a circle is $(x - a)^2 + (y - b)^2 = r^2$

b The Cartesian equation of the locus is
$(x - 5)^2 + (y - 3)^2 = 9$

c

The maximum value of arg z is the angle OA makes with the positive real axis.

The line OC bisects the angle AOB.

Problem-solving

When solving geometrical problems like this one, it is helpful to draw an Argand diagram. The maximum value of arg(z) occurs when the line between the origin and P is a tangent to the circle.

Using triangle OBC:

$$\tan\left(\frac{\theta}{2}\right) = \frac{3}{5}$$

$$\theta = 2\arctan\left(\frac{3}{5}\right) = 1.08 \text{ rad (3 s.f.)}$$

Use circle properties. OB is perpendicular to BC, and triangles OBC and OAC are congruent.

Example 3

Given that the complex number $z = x + iy$ satisfies the equation $|z - 12 - 5i| = 3$, find the minimum value of $|z|$ and maximum value of $|z|$.

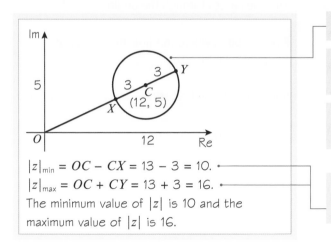

The locus of z is a circle centre $C(12, 5)$, radius 3.

$|z|$ represents the distance from the origin to any point on this locus.

$|z|_{\min}$ and $|z|_{\max}$ are represented by the distances OX and OY respectively.

$|z|_{\min} = OC - CX = 13 - 3 = 10.$
$|z|_{\max} = OC + CY = 13 + 3 = 16.$
The minimum value of $|z|$ is 10 and the maximum value of $|z|$ is 16.

The distance $OC = \sqrt{12^2 + 5^2} = 13$.
The radius $r = CX = CY = 3$.

Example **4**

Given that $|z - 3| = |z + i|$,

a sketch the locus of z and find the Cartesian equation of this locus

b find the least possible value of $|z|$.

a $|z - 3| = |z + i|$ is the perpendicular bisector of the line segment joining the points $(3, 0)$ and $(0, -1)$.

The gradient of the line joining $(0, -1)$ and $(3, 0)$ is $\frac{1}{3}$

So, the gradient of the perpendicular bisector is -3.

The midpoint of the line joining $(0, -1)$ and $(3, 0)$ is $\left(\frac{3}{2}, -\frac{1}{2}\right)$.

$$y - y_1 = m(x - x_1)$$

$$y + \frac{1}{2} = -3\left(x - \frac{3}{2}\right)$$

$$y + \frac{1}{2} = -3x + \frac{9}{2}$$

$$y = -3x + 4$$

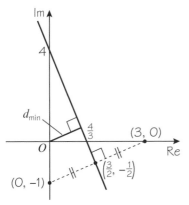

b The gradient of the line labelled d_{min} is $\frac{1}{3}$

The equation of this line is $y = \frac{1}{3}x$

$$\frac{1}{3}x = -3x + 4$$

$$\frac{10}{3}x = 4$$

$$x = \frac{6}{5} \Rightarrow y = \frac{2}{5}$$

$$d_{min} = \sqrt{\left(\frac{6}{5}\right)^2 + \left(\frac{2}{5}\right)^2}$$

$$= \frac{2\sqrt{10}}{5}$$

The locus of points z satisfying $|z - z_1| = |z - z_2|$ is the perpendicular bisector of the line segment joining z_1 to z_2.

The perpendicular bisector will pass through the midpoint.

Substitute $(x_1, y_1) = \left(\frac{3}{2}, -\frac{1}{2}\right)$ and $m = -3$ into the equation of a straight line.

Problem-solving

You could also square both sides of $|z - 3| = |z + i|$:

$$|x + iy - 3| = |x + iy + i|$$
$$|(x - 3) + iy| = |x + i(y + 1)|$$
$$(x - 3)^2 + y^2 = x^2 + (y + 1)^2$$
$$x^2 - 6x + 9 + y^2 = x^2 + y^2 + 2y + 1$$
$$y = -3x + 4$$

Problem-solving

The minimum distance is the perpendicular distance from O to the perpendicular bisector.

The line is parallel to the line joining $(0, -1)$ and $(3, 0)$.

The line passes through the origin.

Find the point where this line intersects the perpendicular bisector.

Solve to find x and substitute into $y = \frac{1}{3}x$ to find y.

Use Pythagoras' theorem.

Locus questions can also make use of the geometric property of the argument.

- Given $z_1 = x_1 + iy_1$, the locus of points z on an Argand diagram such that $\arg(z - z_1) = \theta$ is a half-line from, but not including, the fixed point z_1 making an angle θ with a line from the fixed point z_1 parallel to the real axis.

Notation   A **half-line** is a straight line extending from a point infinitely in one direction only.

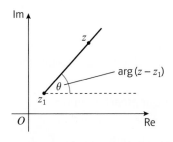

Online   Explore the locus of z, when $\arg(z - z_1) = \theta$, using GeoGebra.

You can find the Cartesian equation of the half-line corresponding to $\arg(z - z_1) = \theta$ by considering how the argument is calculated:

$$\arg(z - z_1) = \theta$$
$$\arg((x - x_1) + i(y - y_1)) = \theta$$
$$\frac{y - y_1}{x - x_1} = \tan\theta$$
$$y - y_1 = \tan\theta(x - x_1)$$

— θ is a fixed angle so $\tan\theta$ is a constant.

— This is the equation of a straight line with gradient $\tan\theta$ passing through the point (x_1, y_1).

Example (5)

Given that $\arg(z + 3 + 2i) = \dfrac{3\pi}{4}$

a sketch the locus of z on an Argand diagram

b find the Cartesian equation of the locus

c find the complex number z that satisfies both $|z + 3 + 2i| = 10$ and $\arg(z + 3 + 2i) = \dfrac{3\pi}{4}$

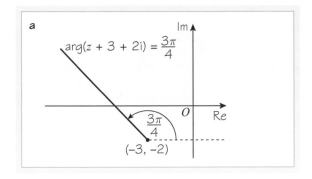

$z + 3 + 2i$ can be written as $z - (-3 - 2i)$. As $\arg(z + 3 + 2i) = \dfrac{3\pi}{4}$, the locus of z is the half-line from $(-3, -2)$ making an angle of $\dfrac{3\pi}{4}$ in an anticlockwise sense from a line in the same direction as the positive real axis.

b

$$\arg(z + 3 + 2i) = \frac{3\pi}{4}$$

$$\arg(x + iy + 3 + 2i) = \frac{3\pi}{4}$$

z can be rewritten as $z = x + iy$

$$\arg((x + 3) + i(y + 2)) = \frac{3\pi}{4}$$

Group the real and imaginary parts.

$$\frac{y + 2}{x + 3} = \tan\frac{3\pi}{4}$$

Remove the argument.

$$y + 2 = -(x + 3)$$

$\tan\dfrac{3\pi}{4} = -1$

Hence the Cartesian equation of the locus is $y = -x - 5$, $x < -3$

Watch out The locus is the half-line so you need to give a suitable range of values for *x*.

c $|z + 3 + 2i| = 10$ is a circle with centre $(-3, -2)$ and radius 10.

Use a geometric approach to find *z*.

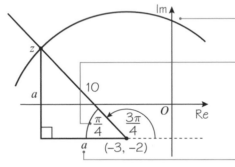

Draw part of a circle with centre $(-3, -2)$ and radius 10.

Angle inside the new triangle is $\pi - \dfrac{3\pi}{4} = \dfrac{\pi}{4}$

As the angle is $\dfrac{\pi}{4}$, the triangle is isosceles. So the two shorter sides have the same length.

$a^2 + a^2 = 10^2 \Rightarrow 2a^2 = 100$

$a = \sqrt{50} = \pm 5\sqrt{2}$

$z = (-3 - 5\sqrt{2}) + i(-2 + 5\sqrt{2})$

Problem-solving An alternative **algebraic** approach would be to substitute the equation for the half-line, $y = -x - 5$, into the equation of the circle, $(x + 3)^2 + (y + 2)^2 = 10^2$, and then solve for *x* and *y*. You would need to choose the solution which lies on the correct half-line.

Exercise **4A**

(P) 1 Sketch the locus of *z* and give the Cartesian equation of the locus of *z* when:

Hint You may choose a geometric or an algebraic approach to answer these questions.

  a $|z| = 6$ **b** $|z| = 10$ **c** $|z - 3| = 2$

  d $|z + 3i| = 3$ **e** $|z - 4i| = 5$ **f** $|z + 1| = 1$

  g $|z - 1 - i| = 5$ **h** $|z + 3 + 4i| = 4$ **i** $|z - 5 + 6i| = 5$

2 Given that *z* satisfies $|z - 5 - 4i| = 8$,

  a sketch the locus of *z* on an Argand diagram

  b find the exact values of *z* that satisfy:

    i both $|z - 5 - 4i| = 8$ and $\text{Re}(z) = 0$ **ii** both $|z - 5 - 4i| = 8$ and $\text{Im}(z) = 0$

Ⓟ **3** A complex number z is represented by the point P on the Argand diagram.
Given that $|z - 5 + 7i| = 5$,

   a sketch the locus of P

   b find the Cartesian equation of this locus

   c find the maximum value of $\arg z$ in the interval $(-\pi, \pi)$.

Ⓔ/Ⓟ **4** On an Argand diagram the point P represents the complex number z.
Given that $|z - 4 - 3i| = 8$,

   a find the Cartesian equation for the locus of P **(2 marks)**

   b sketch the locus of P **(2 marks)**

   c find the maximum and minimum values of $|z|$ for points on this locus.   **(2 marks)**

Ⓔ/Ⓟ **5** The point P represents a complex number z on an Argand diagram.
Given that $|z + 2 - 2\sqrt{3}i| = 2$,

   a sketch the locus of P on an Argand diagram   **(2 marks)**

   b write down the minimum value of $\arg z$ **(2 marks)**

   c find the maximum value of $\arg z$.   **(2 marks)**

6 Sketch the locus of z and give the Cartesian equation of the locus of z when:

   a $|z - 6| = |z - 2|$ **b** $|z + 8| = |z - 4|$

   c $|z| = |z + 6i|$ **d** $|z + 3i| = |z - 8i|$

   e $|z - 2 - 2i| = |z + 2 + 2i|$ **f** $|z + 4 + i| = |z + 4 + 6i|$

   g $|z + 3 - 5i| = |z - 7 - 5i|$ **h** $|z + 4 - 2i| = |z - 8 + 2i|$

   i $\dfrac{|z + 3|}{|z - 6i|} = 1$ **j** $\dfrac{|z + 6 - i|}{|z - 10 - 5i|} = 1$

Ⓔ/Ⓟ **7** Given that $|z - 3| = |z - 6i|$,

   a sketch the locus of z **(3 marks)**

   b find the exact least possible value of $|z|$.   **(4 marks)**

Ⓔ/Ⓟ **8** Given that $|z + 3 + 3i| = |z - 9 - 5i|$,

   a sketch the locus of z **(3 marks)**

   b find the Cartesian equation of this locus   **(3 marks)**

   c find the exact least possible value of $|z|$.   **(3 marks)**

9 Sketch the locus of z and give the Cartesian equation of the locus of z when:

   a $|2 - z| = 3$ **b** $|5i - z| = 4$ **c** $|3 - 2i - z| = 3$

10 Sketch the locus of z when:

   a $\arg z = \dfrac{\pi}{3}$ **b** $\arg(z + 3) = \dfrac{\pi}{4}$ **c** $\arg(z - 2) = \dfrac{\pi}{2}$

   d $\arg(z + 2 + 2i) = -\dfrac{\pi}{4}$ **e** $\arg(z - 1 - i) = \dfrac{3\pi}{4}$ **f** $\arg(z + 3i) = \pi$

   g $\arg(z - 1 + 3i) = \dfrac{2\pi}{3}$ **h** $\arg(z - 3 + 4i) = -\dfrac{\pi}{2}$ **i** $\arg(z - 4i) = -\dfrac{3\pi}{4}$

(P) **11** Given that z satisfies $|z + 2i| = 3$,

    a sketch the locus of z on an Argand diagram

    b find $|z|$ that satisfies both $|z + 2i| = 3$ and $\arg z = \dfrac{\pi}{6}$

(E/P) **12** Given that the complex number z satisfies the equation $|z + 6 + 6i| = 4$,

    a find the exact maximum and minimum value of $|z|$ **(3 marks)**

    b find the range of values for θ, $-\pi < \theta < \pi$, for which $\arg(z - 4 + 2i) = \theta$ and
       $|z + 6 + 6i| = 4$ have no common solutions.   **(4 marks)**

(E/P) **13** The point P represents a complex number z on an Argand diagram such that $|z| = 5$.

    The point Q represents a complex number z on an Argand diagram such that $\arg(z + 4) = \dfrac{\pi}{2}$

    a Sketch, on the same Argand diagram, the locus of P and the locus of Q as z varies.   **(2 marks)**

    b Find the complex number for which both $|z| = 5$ and $\arg(z + 4) = \dfrac{\pi}{2}$ **(2 marks)**

(E/P) **14** Given that the complex number z satisfies $|z - 2 - 2i| = 2$,

    a sketch, on an Argand diagram, the locus of z **(2 marks)**

    Given further that $\arg(z - 2 - 2i) = \dfrac{\pi}{6}$,

    b find the value of z in the form $a + ib$, where $a, b \in \mathbb{R}$.   **(4 marks)**

(E/P) **15** Sketch on the same Argand diagram the locus of points satisfying:

    a $|z - 2i| = |z - 8i|$ **(2 marks)**

    b $\arg(z - 2 - i) = \dfrac{\pi}{4}$ **(3 marks)**

    The complex number z satisfies both $|z - 2i| = |z - 8i|$ and $\arg(z - 2 - i) = \dfrac{\pi}{4}$ **(2 marks)**

    c Use your answers to parts **a** and **b** to find the value of z.

(E/P) **16** Sketch on the same Argand diagram the locus of points satisfying:

    a $|z - 3 + 2i| = 4$ **(2 marks)**

    b $\arg(z - 1) = -\dfrac{\pi}{4}$ **(3 marks)**

    The complex number z satisfies both $|z - 3 + 2i| = 4$ and $\arg(z - 1) = -\dfrac{\pi}{4}$

    Given that $z = a + ib$, where $a, b \in \mathbb{R}$,

    c find the exact value of a and the exact value of b.   **(3 marks)**

(E/P) **17** If the complex number z satisfies both $\arg z = \dfrac{\pi}{3}$ and $\arg(z - 4) = \dfrac{\pi}{2}$

    a find the value of z in the form $a + ib$, where $a, b \in \mathbb{R}$.   **(3 marks)**

    b Hence, find $\arg(z - 8)$.   **(2 marks)**

(E/P) **18** Given that $\arg(z + 4) = \dfrac{\pi}{3}$

    a sketch the locus of z on an Argand diagram   **(3 marks)**

    b find the minimum value of $|z|$ for points on this locus.   **(2 marks)**

E/P **19** A complex number z is represented by the point P on the Argand diagram. Given $|z + 8 - 4i| = 2$,

    a sketch the locus of P **(2 marks)**

    b show that the maximum value of $\arg(z + 15 - 2i)$ in the interval $(-\pi, \pi)$

        is $2\arcsin\left(\dfrac{2}{\sqrt{53}}\right)$ **(3 marks)**

    c find the exact values of the complex numbers that satisfy both $|z + 8 - 4i| = 2$

        and $\arg(z + 4i) = \dfrac{3\pi}{4}$ **(3 marks)**

Challenge

The complex number z satisfies both $|z + i| = 5$ and $\arg(z - 2i) = \theta$, where θ is a real constant such that $-\pi < \theta \leqslant \pi$.
Given that $|z - 4i| < 3$, find the range of possible values of θ.

4.2 **Further loci in an Argand diagram**

You need to be able to determine the locus of a set of points whose distances from two fixed points are in a **constant ratio**.

Consider a circle with centre O and radius r. The fixed point A lies inside the circle, and the fixed point B lies on the straight line through OA and is such that $OA \times OB = r^2$.

For any point P on the circumference of the circle:

$$OA \times OB = OP^2 \text{ so } \frac{OB}{OP} = \frac{OP}{OA}$$

This means that triangle OPA and triangle OBP are similar, since they have two corresponding sides in the same ratio with an equal included angle (SAS). Hence $\dfrac{BP}{AP} = \dfrac{OB}{OP}$ which is constant for all points P on the circumference of the circle. Hence $BP = kAP$ for some constant k, and the locus of points which satisfies this relationship is a circle.

For example, the set of points that are exactly twice the distance from $(0, 1)$ as from the point $(3, -2)$. It is not intuitive, but this locus of points is a circle with its centre at $(4, -3)$.

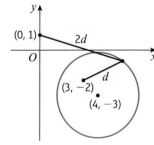

If you replaced the coordinate axes above with an Argand diagram, this would be equivalent to the set of points that were twice as far from i as from $3 - 2i$. You could write this locus as the set of points z that satisfy $|z - i| = 2|z - (3 - 2i)|$.

The locus of points z that satisfy $|z - a| = k|z - b|$, where $a, b \in \mathbb{C}$ and $k \in \mathbb{R}, k > 0, k \neq 1$ is a circle.

You can find the centre and radius of the circle by finding its Cartesian equation.

Example 6

Given that $|z - 6| = 2|z + 6 - 9i|$,
a use algebra to show that the locus of z is a circle, stating its centre and its radius
b sketch the locus of z on an Argand diagram.

Online   Explore the locus of z when $|z - a| = k|z - b|$ using GeoGebra.

a $|z - 6| = 2|z + 6 - 9i|$

$\Rightarrow |x + iy - 6| = 2|x + iy + 6 - 9i|$ — z can be written as $z = x + iy$.

$\Rightarrow |(x - 6) + iy| = 2|(x + 6) + i(y - 9)|$ — Group the real and imaginary parts.

$\Rightarrow |(x - 6) + iy|^2 = 2^2|(x + 6) + i(y - 9)|^2$

$\Rightarrow (x - 6)^2 + y^2 = 4((x + 6)^2 + (y - 9)^2)$ — Square both sides.

$\Rightarrow x^2 - 12x + 36 + y^2 = 4(x^2 + 12x + 36 + y^2 - 18y + 81)$

$\Rightarrow x^2 - 12x + 36 + y^2 = 4x^2 + 48x + 144 + 4y^2 - 72y + 324$ — Remove the moduli.

$\Rightarrow 3x^2 + 60x + 3y^2 - 72y + 432 = 0$

$\Rightarrow x^2 + 20x + y^2 - 24y + 144 = 0$

$\Rightarrow (x + 10)^2 - 100 + (y - 12)^2 - 144 + 144 = 0$ — Complete the square twice for x and for y.

$\Rightarrow (x + 10)^2 + (y - 12)^2 = 100$

So the locus of z is a circle with centre $(-10, 12)$ and radius 10.

Circle $(x - a)^2 + (y - b)^2 = r^2$ with $(a, b) = (-10, 12)$ and $r = 10$.

b

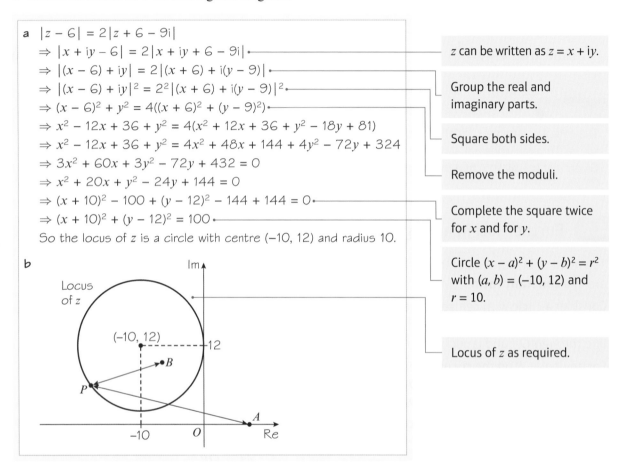

Locus of z as required.

Problem-solving

$|z - 6|$ represents the distance from the point $A(6, 0)$ to P.
$|z + 6 - 9i| = |z - (-6 + 9i)|$ represents the distance from the point $B(-6, 9)$ to P.
$|z - 6| = 2|z + 6 - 9i|$ gives $AP = 2BP$. This means that P is the locus of points such that the distance AP is twice the distance BP.
One of the points will always be inside the circle and the other will always be outside the circle.

Another previous result for loci in an Argand diagram makes use of the geometric property of the argument of a complex number.

■ Given $z_1 = x_1 + iy_1$, the locus of points z on an Argand diagram such that $\arg(z - z_1) = \theta$ is a **half-line** from, but not including, the fixed point z_1, making an angle θ with a line from the fixed point z_1 **parallel** to the real axis.

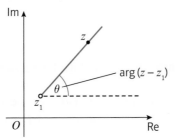

Watch out The endpoint z_1 is **not** included in the locus. You show this by drawing it with an open circle.

You can make use of the following circle properties to determine more complicated loci given in terms of arguments.

- **Angles subtended at an arc in the same segment are equal.**

- **The angle in a semicircle is a right angle.**

- **The angle subtended at the centre of the circle is twice the angle at the circumference.**

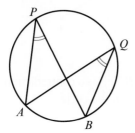 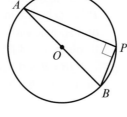 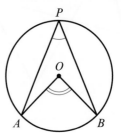

$$\angle APB = \angle AQB \qquad \angle APB = \frac{\pi}{2} \qquad \angle AOB = 2\angle APB$$

■ The locus of points z that satisfy $\arg\left(\dfrac{z-a}{z-b}\right) = \theta$, where $\theta \in \mathbb{R}$, $\theta > 0$ and $a, b \in \mathbb{C}$, is an arc of a circle with endpoints A and B representing the complex numbers a and b, respectively.

Watch out The endpoints of the arc, A and B, are **not** included in the locus.

You can see why this locus is the arc of a circle by drawing points A and B on an Argand diagram, and drawing a point P such that $\angle APB = \theta$, where θ is a positive, constant angle.

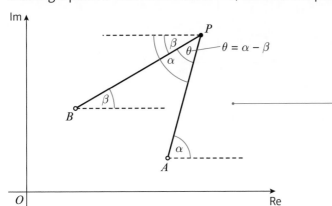

$\theta = \alpha - \beta$

The solution shown for Example 2 below illustrates the same approach developed here.

From knowing the locus for an equation of the form $\arg(z - z_1) = \theta$, you can conclude that $\arg(z - a) = \alpha$ and $\arg(z - b) = \beta$. It follows that

$\angle APB = \alpha - \beta$ ———————— This is due to the properties of parallel lines.

$\theta = \alpha - \beta$

$\quad = \arg(z - a) - \arg(z - b)$

$\quad = \arg\left(\dfrac{z - a}{z - b}\right)$ ———————— $\arg\left(\dfrac{z_1}{z_2}\right) = \arg z_1 - \arg z_2$ ← **Further Pure 1 Section 2.3**

As P moves, $\angle APB$ is always equal to the constant θ. By the **converse** of the first circle property on the previous page, $\angle APB$ must be the angle subtended in the arc of a circle. The locus of P is the arc of a circle that is drawn **anticlockwise** from A to B.

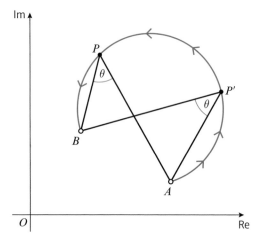

Problem-solving

To prove the converse of the first circle property, suppose P' did not lie on the circle through A, B and P. Let Q be the intersection of this circle with the line through A and P'. Then $\angle AQB = \theta$ and $\angle AQB \neq \angle AP'B$. This is a contradiction since $\angle AP'B = \theta$, so P' must lie on the circle.

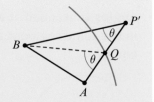

If $\theta < \dfrac{\pi}{2}$, then the locus is a **major arc** of the circle.

If $\theta > \dfrac{\pi}{2}$, then the locus is a **minor arc** of the circle.

If $\theta = \dfrac{\pi}{2}$, then the locus is a **semicircle**.

In these two examples, $a = 2\mathrm{i}$ and $b = -3$. The arcs are drawn **anticlockwise** from A to B.

$\arg\left(\dfrac{z - 2\mathrm{i}}{z + 3}\right) = \dfrac{\pi}{3}$

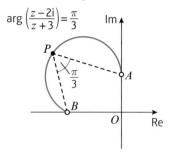

$\arg\left(\dfrac{z - 2\mathrm{i}}{z + 3}\right) = \dfrac{2\pi}{3}$

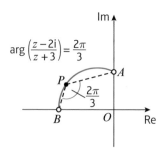

In the following two examples the values of a and b are reversed.

$\arg\left(\dfrac{z + 3}{z - 2\mathrm{i}}\right) = \dfrac{\pi}{3}$

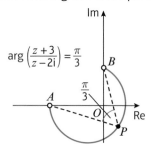

$\arg\left(\dfrac{z + 3}{z - 2\mathrm{i}}\right) = \dfrac{2\pi}{3}$

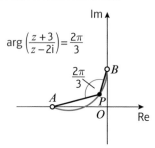

Finding the centre of the circle on which the major or minor arc is located requires algebraic and/or geometric working. This is illustrated in Example 2.

Example 7

Given that $\arg\left(\dfrac{z-6}{z-2}\right) = \dfrac{\pi}{4}$

Online Explore the locus of z when $\arg\left(\dfrac{z-a}{z-b}\right) = \theta$ using GeoGebra.

a sketch the locus of $P(x, y)$ which is represented by z on an Argand diagram

b find the Cartesian equation of this locus.

You must show your reasoning clearly.

a $\arg\left(\dfrac{z-6}{z-2}\right) = \arg(z-6) - \arg(z-2) = \dfrac{\pi}{4}$

Let L_1 be the half-line satisfying $\arg(z-6) = \alpha$

and let L_2 be the half-line satisfying $\arg(z-2) = \beta$.

It follows that $\alpha - \beta = \dfrac{\pi}{4}$ **(1)**

Use $\arg\left(\dfrac{z_1}{z_2}\right) = \arg z_1 - \arg z_2$.

Use $\arg(z-6) - \arg(z-2) = \dfrac{\pi}{4}$

All points on L_1 satisfy $\arg(z-6) = \alpha$

All points on L_2 satisfy $\arg(z-2) = \beta$

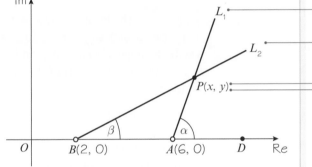

Therefore the point P is found lying on both L_1 and L_2 where $\alpha - \beta = \dfrac{\pi}{4}$
As P lies on L_1 and L_2, it is found where L_1 and L_2 intersect.

From $\triangle ABP$, it follows that

$\angle BPA + \angle PBA = \angle PAD$

$\Rightarrow \angle BPA + \beta = \alpha$

$\Rightarrow \angle BPA = \alpha - \beta$

$\Rightarrow \angle BPA = \dfrac{\pi}{4}$

As α and β vary, $\angle BPA$ is constant and is $\dfrac{\pi}{4}$

The exterior angle of a triangle is the sum of the two opposite interior angles.

From the diagram, $\angle PBA = \beta$ and $\angle PAD = \alpha$.

Use $\alpha - \beta = \dfrac{\pi}{4}$ **(1)**

P can vary but $\angle BPA$ must always be $\dfrac{\pi}{4}$

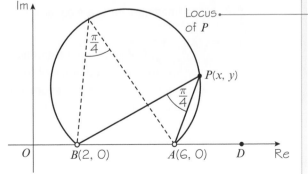

From the circle theorems, angles in the same segment of a circle are equal.
Therefore as P varies, $\angle BPA$ will always be equal to $\dfrac{\pi}{4}$
So, since $\dfrac{\pi}{4} < \dfrac{\pi}{2}$ it follows that P must lie on the **major arc** starting at $(6, 0)$ and finishing at $(2, 0)$, but **not** including the points $(6, 0)$ and $(2, 0)$.

b Method 1: Geometric

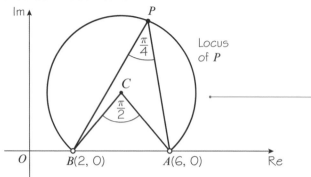

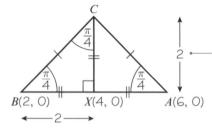

$AX = CX = 2 \Rightarrow AC = \sqrt{2^2 + 2^2} = 2\sqrt{2}$ and C is the point $(4, 2)$.

So the Cartesian equation of the locus of P is
$(x - 4)^2 + (y - 2)^2 = 8$, where $y > 0$.

Method 2: Algebraic

$$\frac{z - 6}{z - 2} = \frac{x - 6 + iy}{x - 2 + iy}$$

$$= \frac{(x - 6 + iy)(x - 2 - iy)}{(x - 2 + iy)(x - 2 - iy)}$$

$$= \frac{x^2 - 8x + 12 + y^2 + 4iy}{(x - 2)^2 + y^2}$$

$$= \left(\frac{x^2 - 8x + 12 + y^2}{(x - 2)^2 + y^2}\right) + \left(\frac{4y}{(x - 2)^2 + y^2}\right)i$$

So $\arg\left(\left(\frac{x^2 - 8x + 12 + y^2}{(x - 2)^2 + y^2}\right) + \left(\frac{4y}{(x - 2)^2 + y^2}\right)i\right) = \frac{\pi}{4}$

$$\Rightarrow \frac{x^2 - 8x + 12 + y^2}{(x - 2)^2 + y^2} = \frac{4y}{(x - 2)^2 + y^2}$$

$$\Rightarrow x^2 - 8x + 12 + y^2 = 4y$$

$$\Rightarrow (x - 4)^2 + (y - 2)^2 = 8, \text{ where } y > 0$$

$\angle BPA = \frac{\pi}{4} \Rightarrow \angle ACB = \frac{\pi}{2}$, as the angle subtended at the centre of the circle is twice the angle at the circumference.

As CA and CB are both radii, then the radius is $r = CA = CB$.

This implies that $\triangle CAB$ is isosceles and $\angle CAB = \angle CBA = \frac{\pi}{4}$

Let X be the midpoint of AB. Hence $\angle CXA = \frac{\pi}{2}$ and $\angle XCA = \angle CAX = \frac{\pi}{4}$
So $\triangle CAX$ is isosceles and $AX = CX = 2$.

Since the locus is the major arc of the circle which lies above the real axis, then the Cartesian equation for the locus must include the condition that $y > 0$.

Watch out The locus is only a part of a circle (an arc), so you need to give a suitable range of values for x and/or y to indicate which part of the circle is included.

Problem-solving

In order to deal with $\arg\left(\frac{z - 6}{z - 2}\right)$ algebraically, you need to identify its real and imaginary parts. Write $z = x + iy$ then multiply the numerator and denominator by $(z - 2)^*$.

If $\arg w = \theta$, then $\frac{\text{Im}(w)}{\text{Re}(w)} = \tan\theta$. In this case, $\theta = \frac{\pi}{4}$ and $\tan\frac{\pi}{4} = 1$, so the real and imaginary parts are equal.

Watch out If you use an algebraic method to find the equation of the circle, you still need to use geometric considerations to work out which arc of the circle satisfies the given condition. In this case $y > 0$.

Example **8**

Given the equation $\arg\left(\dfrac{z}{z-4i}\right) = \dfrac{\pi}{2}$

a sketch the locus of points z that satisfy the equation on an Argand diagram.

b Hence write down the range of possible values of Re(z).

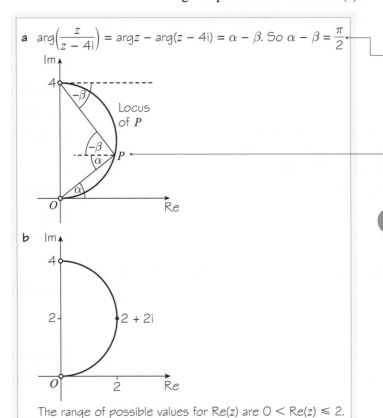

a $\arg\left(\dfrac{z}{z-4i}\right) = \arg z - \arg(z-4i) = \alpha - \beta$. So $\alpha - \beta = \dfrac{\pi}{2}$.

Locus of P

> $\arg z = \alpha$ and $\arg(z-4i) = \beta$
> $\arg\left(\dfrac{z}{z-4i}\right) = \dfrac{\pi}{2}$
> $\alpha - \beta = \dfrac{\pi}{2}$ and $\alpha < \dfrac{\pi}{2} \Rightarrow \beta < 0$.

> Since the constant angle at P is $\dfrac{\pi}{2}$, the locus of P is a semicircle from $(0, 0)$ anticlockwise to $(0, 4)$, not including $(0, 0)$ and $(0, 4)$.

Problem-solving

> The point on the locus furthest to the right is $2 + 2i$, so the largest possible value of Re(z) is 2. The endpoints of the semicircle are at 0 and $4i$. These points are not included in the locus of z, so use a strict inequality to show the smallest possible value of Re(z).

b

The range of possible values for Re(z) are $0 < \text{Re}(z) \leqslant 2$.

Exercise **4B**

1 Sketch the locus of z and give the Cartesian equation of the locus of z when:

  a $|z + 3| = 3|z - 5|$ **b** $|z - 3| = 4|z + 1|$

  c $|z - i| = 2|z + i|$ **d** $|z + 2 - 7i| = 2|z - 10 + 2i|$

  e $|z + 4 - 2i| = 2|z - 2 - 5i|$ **f** $|z| = 2|2 - z|$

2 Sketch the locus of z when:

  a $\arg\left(\dfrac{z}{z+3}\right) = \dfrac{\pi}{4}$ **b** $\arg\left(\dfrac{z-3i}{z+4}\right) = \dfrac{\pi}{6}$

  c $\arg\left(\dfrac{z}{z-2}\right) = \dfrac{\pi}{3}$ **d** $\arg\left(\dfrac{z-3i}{z-5}\right) = \dfrac{\pi}{4}$

  e $\arg z - \arg(z - 2 + 3i) = \dfrac{\pi}{3}$ **f** $\arg\left(\dfrac{z-4i}{z+4}\right) = \dfrac{\pi}{2}$

(E) **3** The complex number $z = x + iy$ satisfies the equation $|z + 1 + i| = 2|z + 4 - 2i|$
The complex number z is represented by the point P on the Argand diagram.

   a Show that the locus of P is a circle with centre $(-5, 3)$.   **(4 marks)**

   b Find the exact radius of this circle.   **(1 mark)**

(E/P) **4** The point P represents a complex number z in an Argand diagram.

   Given that $\arg z - \arg(z + 4) = \dfrac{\pi}{4}$ is a locus of points P lying on an arc of a circle C,

   a sketch the locus of points P **(2 marks)**

   b find the coordinates of the centre of C **(3 marks)**

   c find the radius of C **(2 marks)**

   d find a Cartesian equation for the circle C **(1 mark)**

   e find the finite area bounded by the locus of P and the x-axis.   **(3 marks)**

(E/P) **5** A curve F is described by the equation $|z| = 2|z + 4|$

   a Show that F is a circle, and find its centre and radius.   **(5 marks)**

   b Sketch F on an Argand diagram.   **(2 marks)**

   c Given that z lies on F, find the range of possible values of $\text{Im}(z)$.   **(3 marks)**

(E/P) **6** The set of points z lie on the curve defined by $|z - 8| = 2|z - 2 - 6i|$. Find the range of possible values of $\arg(z)$.   **(7 marks)**

(E/P) **7** A curve S is described by the equation $\arg\left(\dfrac{w - 8i}{w + 6}\right) = \dfrac{\pi}{2},\ w \in \mathbb{C}$.

   a Sketch S on an Argand diagram.   **(2 marks)**

   b Find the Cartesian equation for S.   **(3 marks)**

   c Given that z lies on S, find the largest value of a and the smallest value of b that satisfy $a < \arg(z) < b$.   **(2 marks)**

   d State the range of possible values of $\text{Re}(z)$.   **(1 mark)**

(E/P) **8** The point P represents the complex number z that satisfies the equation

$$\arg(z - 1) - \arg(z + 3) = \frac{3\pi}{4},\ z \neq -3$$

   Use a geometric approach to find the Cartesian equation of the locus of P.   **(5 marks)**

(E/P) **9** Each of the three Argand diagrams below shows an arc of a circle drawn from point A to point B that is the locus of a set of complex numbers z. Write down a complex equation for each locus.   **(6 marks)**

a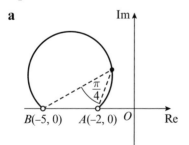

b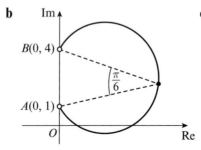

c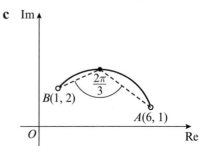

(E) **10** The curve C has equation $|z + 3| = 3|z - 5|$, $z \in \mathbb{C}$.

     a Show that C is a circle with equation $x^2 + y^2 - 12x + 27 = 0$ **(2 marks)**

     b Sketch C on an Argand diagram.   **(2 marks)**

     c The point z_1 lies on C such that $\arg z_1 = \dfrac{\pi}{6}$. Express z_1 in the form $r(\cos\theta + i\sin\theta)$.   **(3 marks)**

(E/P) **11** In an Argand diagram, points A and B represent the numbers 6i and 3 respectively. As z varies, the locus of points P satisfying the equation $|z - z_1| = k|z - z_2|$, where $z_1, z_2 \in \mathbb{C}$ and $k \in \mathbb{R}$, is the circle C such that each point P on the circle is twice the distance from point A than it is from point B.

     a Write down the complex numbers z_1 and z_2, and the value of k.   **(2 marks)**   **Hint** $AP = 2BP$

     b Show that the Cartesian equation of circle C is $x^2 + y^2 - 8x + 4y = 0$ **(2 marks)**

     The locus of points w satisfying the equation $\arg(w - 6) = \alpha$ where $\alpha \in \mathbb{R}$ passes through the centre of circle C and intersects it at point Q.

     c Find the value of α.   **(3 marks)**

     d Find the exact coordinates of Q.   **(3 marks)**

Challenge

Fully describe the locus of points z that satisfy the equation $|z - a| + |z + a| = b$, where a and b are real constants and $b > 2a$.

4.3   Regions in an Argand diagram

You can use complex numbers to represent regions on an Argand diagram.

Example   **9**

a On separate Argand diagrams, shade in the regions represented by:

     i $|z - 4 - 2i| \leqslant 2$ **ii** $|z - 4| < |z - 6|$ **iii** $0 \leqslant \arg(z - 2 - 2i) \leqslant \dfrac{\pi}{4}$

b Hence, on the same Argand diagram, shade the region which satisfies

$$\{z \in \mathbb{C} : |z - 4 - 2i| \leqslant 2\} \cap \{z \in \mathbb{C} : |z - 4| < |z - 6|\} \cap \left\{z \in \mathbb{C} : 0 \leqslant \arg(z - 2 - 2i) \leqslant \dfrac{\pi}{4}\right\}$$

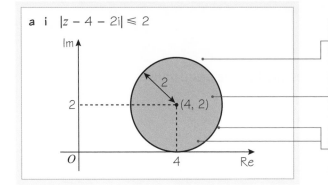

a   **i** $|z - 4 - 2i| \leqslant 2$

$|z - 4 - 2i| = 2$ represents a circle centre $(4, 2)$, radius 2.

$|z - 4 - 2i| < 2$ represents the region on the inside of this circle.

$|z - 4 - 2i| \leqslant 2$ represents the **boundary** inside of this circle.

ii $|z - 4| < |z - 6|$

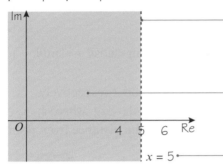

$|z - 4| = |z - 6|$ is represented by the line $x = 5$. This line is the perpendicular bisector of the line segment joining $(4, 0)$ to $(6, 0)$.

$|z - 4| < |z - 6|$ represents the region $x < 5$. All points in this region are closer to $(4, 0)$ than to $(6, 0)$.

Note this region does not include the line $x = 5$. So $x = 5$ is represented by a dashed line.

iii $0 \leqslant \arg(z - 2 - 2i) \leqslant \dfrac{\pi}{4}$

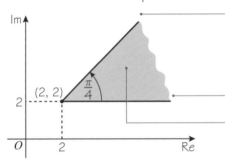

$\arg(z - 2 - 2i) = \dfrac{\pi}{4}$ is the half-line from the point $(2, 2)$ at angle $\dfrac{\pi}{4}$ to the horizontal.

$\arg(z - 2 - 2i) = 0$ is the other half-line shown from the point $(2, 2)$.

$0 \leqslant \arg(z - 2 - 2i) \leqslant \dfrac{\pi}{4}$ is represented by the region in between and including these two half-lines.

Notation The symbol $\cap$ is the symbol for the **intersection** of two sets. You need to find the region of points that lie in all three sets.

b $|z - 4 - 2i| \leqslant 2, \ |z - 4| < |z - 6|$
and $0 \leqslant \arg(z - 2 - 2i) \leqslant \dfrac{\pi}{4}$

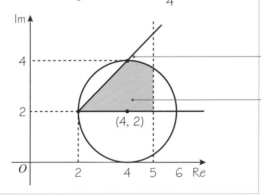

The line $\arg(z - 2 - 2i) = \dfrac{\pi}{4}$ and the circle $|z - 4 - 2i| = 2$ both go through the point $(4, 4)$.

The region shaded is satisfied by all three of
$|z - 4 - 2i| \leqslant 2$
$|z - 4| < |z - 6|$
$0 \leqslant \arg(z - 2 - 2i) \leqslant \dfrac{\pi}{4}$

Online Explore this region using GeoGebra.

Exercise 4C

1 On an Argand diagram, shade in the regions represented by the inequalities:

a $|z| < 3$　　　　**b** $|z - 2i| > 2$　　　**c** $|z + 7| \geqslant |z - 1|$　　**d** $|z + 6| > |z + 2 + 8i|$

e $2 \leqslant |z| \leqslant 3$　　　**f** $1 \leqslant |z + 4i| \leqslant 4$　　**g** $3 \leqslant |z - 3 + 5i| \leqslant 5$

E/P **2** The complex number z is represented by a point P on an Argand diagram.

Given that $|z + 1 - i| \leqslant 1$ and $0 \leqslant \arg z \leqslant \frac{3\pi}{4}$, shade the locus of P. **(6 marks)**

E/P **3** Shade on an Argand diagram the region satisfied by

$$\{z \in \mathbb{C} : |z| \leqslant 3\} \cap \left\{z \in \mathbb{C} : \frac{\pi}{4} \leqslant \arg(z + 3) \leqslant \pi\right\}$$ **(6 marks)**

E/P **4 a** Sketch on the same Argand diagram:

    i the locus of points representing $|z - 2| = |z - 6 - 8i|$ **(2 marks)**

    ii the locus of points representing $\arg(z - 4 - 2i) = 0$ **(2 marks)**

    iii the locus of points representing $\arg(z - 4 - 2i) = \frac{\pi}{2}$ **(2 marks)**

  b Shade on an Argand diagram the set of points

$$\{z \in \mathbb{C} : |z - 2| \leqslant |z - 6 - 8i|\} \cap \left\{z \in \mathbb{C} : 0 \leqslant \arg(z - 4 - 2i) \leqslant \frac{\pi}{2}\right\}$$ **(2 marks)**

E/P **5 a** Find the Cartesian equations of:

    i the locus of points representing $|z + 10| = |z - 6 - 4i\sqrt{2}|$

    ii the locus of points representing $|z + 1| = 3$ **(6 marks)**

  b Find the two values of z that satisfy both $|z + 10| = |z - 6 - 4i\sqrt{2}|$ and $|z + 1| = 3$ **(2 marks)**

  c Hence shade in the region R on an Argand diagram which satisfies both $|z + 10| \leqslant |z - 6 - 4i\sqrt{2}|$ and $|z + 1| \leqslant 3$ **(4 marks)**

Challenge

The sets A, B and C are defined as:

$A = \{z \in \mathbb{C} : |z + 5 + 8i| \leqslant 5\}$

$B = \{z \in \mathbb{C} : |z + 8 + 4i| \leqslant |z + 2 + 12i|\}$

$C = \left\{z \in \mathbb{C} : 0 \leqslant \arg(z + 10 + 8i) \leqslant \frac{\pi}{4}\right\}$

Shade the set of points $A \cap B \cap C'$, that are in set A and in set B, but not in set C.

4.4 **Further regions in an Argand diagram**

You can use inequalities to represent regions in the Argand diagram.

- The inequality $\theta_1 \leqslant \arg(z - z_1) \leqslant \theta_2$ describes a region in an Argand diagram that is **enclosed** by the two half-lines $\arg(z - z_1) = \theta_1$ and $\arg(z - z_1) = \theta_2$, and also includes the two half-lines, but does not include the point represented by z_1.

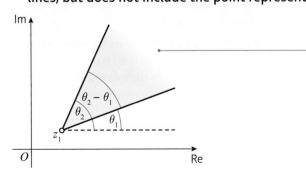

Imagine that the enclosed region in the diagram, represented by $\theta_1 \leqslant \arg(z - z_1) \leqslant \theta_2$, is formed by rotating the half-line with argument θ_1 anti-clockwise by the angle $\theta_2 - \theta_1$ about the point z_1.

Watch out The region described by $\theta_1 < \arg(z - z_1) < \theta_2$ would not include the two half-lines. You would use dotted lines to represent them.

Example **10**

Describe algebraically, in terms of z, the region shown in each Argand diagram.

a

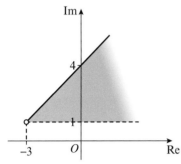

b

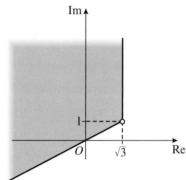

c

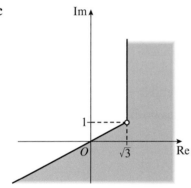

d

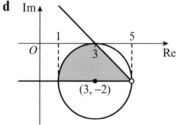

a The region is enclosed by the two half-lines
$\arg(z - (-3 + i)) = 0$ and $\arg(z - (-3 + i)) = \frac{\pi}{4}$ •
The region is described by the inequality
$0 < \arg(z + 3 - i) \leq \frac{\pi}{4}$ •

b The region is enclosed by the two half-lines
$\arg(z - (\sqrt{3} + i)) = \frac{\pi}{2}$ and $\arg(z - (\sqrt{3} + i)) = -\frac{5\pi}{6}$

The region is described by the inequality
$\frac{\pi}{2} \leq \arg(z - \sqrt{3} - i) \leq \frac{7\pi}{6}$

c The initial half-line is $\arg(z - \sqrt{3} - i) = -\frac{5\pi}{6}$

and the terminal half-line is $\arg(z - \sqrt{3} - i) = \frac{\pi}{2}$ •

The region is described by the inequality
$-\frac{5\pi}{6} \leq \arg(z - \sqrt{3} - i) \leq \frac{\pi}{2}$

The initial half-line is horizontal, so $\theta_1 = 0$.
The gradient of the terminal half-line is 1
since it extends from $(-3, 1)$ through $(0, 4)$. so
$\theta_2 = \frac{\pi}{4}$

Since the initial half-line is dashed it is not
included ($<$) in the region. The terminal half-line is solid so it is included ($\leq$) in the region.

Watch out The argument θ of any complex
number is usually given in the range
$-\pi < \theta \leq \pi$. This is called the principal
argument. However, you could also give the
second half-line as $\arg(z - (\sqrt{3} + i)) = \frac{7\pi}{6}$
It makes more sense to use this value in the
final inequality so that the second upper
value is greater than the lower value.

← **Further Pure 2 Section 3**

These are the same half-lines as part **b**. You can
consider this region as being formed by
rotating the half-line $\arg(z - \sqrt{3} - i) = -\frac{5\pi}{6}$
anticlockwise about the point $(\sqrt{3}, 1)$ from an
angle of $-\frac{5\pi}{6}$ to an angle of $\frac{\pi}{2}$

d The shaded region in the diagram is the intersection of a circle and its interior with the region between two half-lines.

The circle and its interior is given by

$|z - 3 + 2i| \leqslant 2$

The equation for the initial half-line is $\arg(z - 5 + 2i) = \dfrac{3\pi}{4}$ and the equation for the terminal half-line is $\arg(z - 5 + 2i) = \pi$. So the region between the two half-lines is described by the inequality $\dfrac{3\pi}{4} \leqslant \arg(z - 5 + 2i) \leqslant \pi$.

The shaded region is given by

$\{z \in \mathbb{C} : |z - 3 + 2i| \leqslant 2\}$

$\cap \left\{z \in \mathbb{C} : \dfrac{3\pi}{4} \leqslant \arg(z - 5 + 2i) \leqslant \pi\right\}$

> The set of points z satisfying the inequality $|z - z_1| \leqslant r$ is a circle and its interior with radius r and centre at the point representing z_1.

> The initial half-line extends from $(5, -2)$ through $(3, 0)$, so $\theta_1 = \dfrac{3\pi}{4}$
> The terminal half-line extends horizontally to the left, so $\theta_2 = \pi$.

> **Notation**　Use set notation, with the symbol $\cap$ denoting the **intersection** of the two sets.

Example 11

On separate Argand diagrams, shade the region satisfied by each set of points:

a $\left\{z \in \mathbb{C} : \dfrac{2\pi}{3} \leqslant \arg z \leqslant \pi\right\} \cap \{z \in \mathbb{C} : |z + 3 - 4i| \leqslant 5\}$

b $\{z \in \mathbb{C} : 2|z - 4| \leqslant |z|\} \cap \{z \in \mathbb{C} : 4 \leqslant \text{Re}(z) \leqslant 6\}$

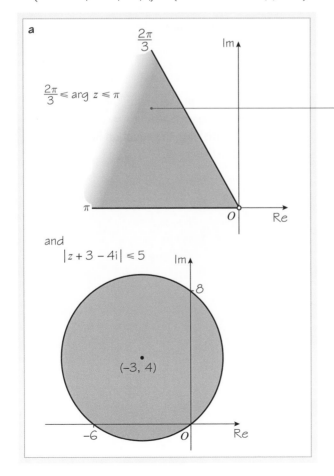

a

$\dfrac{2\pi}{3} \leqslant \arg z \leqslant \pi$

and

$|z + 3 - 4i| \leqslant 5$

$(-3, 4)$

> The region described by the inequality $\dfrac{2\pi}{3} \leqslant \arg z \leqslant \pi$ is between the two half-lines $\arg z = \dfrac{2\pi}{3}$ and $\arg z = \pi$.

> **Problem-solving**
>
> If you have to sketch a union or intersection of regions on an Argand diagram, it is helpful to sketch each region separately first.

Therefore the intersection is

$$\left\{z \in \mathbb{C} : \frac{2\pi}{3} \leqslant \arg z \leqslant \pi\right\} \cap \{z \in \mathbb{C} : |z + 3 - 4i| \leqslant 5\}$$

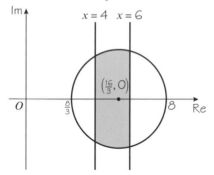

Online Explore this region using GeoGebra.

b Let $z = x + iy$.

$$2|x - 4 + iy| \leqslant |x + iy|$$
$$2^2|(x - 4) + iy|^2 \leqslant |x + iy|^2$$
$$4(x^2 - 8x + 16 + y^2) \leqslant x^2 + y^2$$
$$3x^2 + 3y^2 - 32x + 64 \leqslant 0$$
$$x^2 + y^2 - \frac{32}{3}x + \frac{64}{3} \leqslant 0$$
$$\left(x - \frac{16}{3}\right)^2 + y^2 \leqslant \frac{256}{9} - \frac{64}{3}$$
$$\left(x - \frac{16}{3}\right)^2 + y^2 \leqslant \frac{64}{9}$$

Therefore $2|z - 4| \leqslant |z|$ describes the region consisting of the circle with centre $\left(\frac{16}{3}, 0\right)$ and radius $\frac{8}{3}$ and its interior.

The region described by $4 \leqslant \text{Re}(z) \leqslant 6$ is the region between, and including, the vertical lines $x = 4$ and $x = 6$.

So $\{z \in \mathbb{C} : 2|z - 4| \leqslant |z|\}$
$\cap \{z \in \mathbb{C} : 4 \leqslant \text{Re}(z) \leqslant 6\}$
describes the region shaded below.

Problem-solving

The equation $2|z - 4| = |z|$ represents a circle, so the inequality $2|z - 4| \leqslant |z|$ represents a region consisting of either a circle and its interior, or a circle and the region outside it. You need to use an algebraic approach to find the centre and radius of the circle.

Complete the square.

The locus of points satisfying the equation $\text{Re}(z) = 4$ is the vertical line $x = 4$, and the locus of points satisfying the equation $\text{Re}(z) = 6$ is the vertical line $x = 6$.

Exercise 4D

1 On separate Argand diagrams, shade the regions, R, described by:

a $0 \leqslant \arg(z - 4 - i) \leqslant \dfrac{\pi}{2}$

b $-1 \leqslant \text{Im}(z) \leqslant 2$

c $\dfrac{1}{2} \leqslant |z| < 1$

d $-\dfrac{\pi}{3} \leqslant \arg(z + i) \leqslant \dfrac{\pi}{4}$

2 The region R in an Argand diagram is satisfied by the inequalities $|z| \leqslant 5$ and $|z| \leqslant |z - 6i|$. Draw an Argand diagram and shade in the region R.

3 Shade on an Argand diagram the region satisfied by the set of points $P(x, y)$, where $|z + 1 - i| \leqslant 1$ and $0 \leqslant \arg z < \dfrac{3\pi}{4}$

4 Shade on an Argand diagram the region, R, satisfied by the set of points $P(x, y)$, where $|z| < 3$ and $\dfrac{\pi}{4} \leqslant \arg(z + 3) \leqslant \pi$

(E) 5 On separate Argand diagrams, shade the regions, R, defined by the sets of points:

a $\left\{z \in \mathbb{C} : -\dfrac{\pi}{2} \leqslant \arg(z + 1 + i) \leqslant -\dfrac{\pi}{4}\right\} \cap \{z \in \mathbb{C} : |z + 1 + 2i| \leqslant 1\}$ **(4 marks)**

b $\{z \in \mathbb{C} : 2|z - 6| \leqslant |z - 3|\} \cap \{z \in \mathbb{C} : \text{Re}(z) \leqslant 7\}$ **(4 marks)**

(E/P) 6 **a** Shade on an Argand diagram the region defined by $|z + 6| \leqslant 3$ **(2 marks)**

b The complex number z satisfies $|z + 6| \leqslant 3$. Find the range of possible values of $\arg z$.   **(4 marks)**

(E/P) 7 **a** Indicate on an Argand diagram the region consisting of the set of points satisfying both $\dfrac{3\pi}{4} \leqslant \arg(z - 8) \leqslant \pi$ and $\text{Im}(z) \leqslant \text{Re}(z)$.   **(3 marks)**

b Find the exact area of this region.   **(3 marks)**

(E/P) 8 **a** Shade on an Argand diagram the region R defined by

$$\{z \in \mathbb{C} : |z - 3 + 2i| \geqslant \sqrt{2}|z - 1|\} \cap \left\{z \in \mathbb{C} : 0 \leqslant \arg(z + 1 + 2i) \leqslant \dfrac{\pi}{3}\right\}$$ **(4 marks)**

b Find the exact area of region R.   **(3 marks)**

c The complex number z lies in region R. Find the maximum value of $\text{Im}(z)$.   **(5 marks)**

Challenge

On an Argand diagram, shade the set of points
$\{z \in \mathbb{C} : 6 \leqslant \text{Re}((2 - 3i)z) < 12\} \cap \{z \in \mathbb{C} : (\text{Re}z)(\text{Im}z) \geqslant 0\}$

4.5 Transformations of the complex plane

You need to be able to **transform** simple loci, such as lines and circles, from one complex **plane** (the z-plane) to another complex plane (the w-plane). **Transformations** will map points in the z-plane to points in the w-plane by applying a formula relating $z = x + iy$ to $w = u + iv$.

> **Notation** The **convention** is to use u for the real part and v for the imaginary part of a complex number in the w-plane.

It is helpful to be able to recognise the type of transformation – **translation**, **enlargement** or **rotation** – from the formula for some simple transformations.

Example 12

The point P represents the complex number z on an Argand diagram, where $|z| = 2$. T_1, T_2 and T_3 represent transformations from the z-plane, where $z = x + iy$, to the w-plane where $w = u + iv$. Describe the locus of the image of P under the transformations:

a $T_1: w = z - 2 + 4i$ **b** $T_2: w = 3z$ **c** $T_3: w = \frac{1}{2}z + i$

The locus of P in the z-plane is a circle with centre $(0, 0)$ and radius 2.
This is the locus of P in the z-plane before any transformations have been applied.

Rearrange to make z the subject.

Apply the modulus to both sides of the equation.

Use $|z| = 2$

a $T_1: w = z - 2 + 4i$
$\Rightarrow w + 2 - 4i = z$
$\Rightarrow |w + 2 - 4i| = |z|$
$\Rightarrow |w + 2 - 4i| = 2$

The image of the locus of P under T_1 is $|w + 2 - 4i| = 2$. This is a circle with centre $(-2, 4)$ and radius 2.

> **Problem-solving**
> The transformation $T_1: w = z - 2 + 4i$ represents a **translation** of z by the vector $\begin{pmatrix} -2 \\ 4 \end{pmatrix}$.

Apply the modulus to both sides of the equation.

Use $|z_1 z_2| = |z_1||z_2|$

b $T_2: w = 3z$
$\Rightarrow |w| = |3z|$
$\Rightarrow |w| = |3||z|$
$\Rightarrow |w| = 3(2) = 6$

Use $|z| = 2$

> **Online** Explore these transformations using GeoGebra.

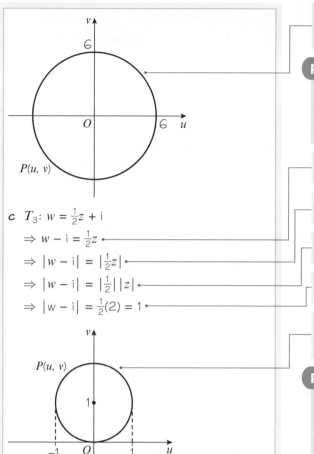

The image of the locus of P under T_2 is $|w| = 6$. This is a circle with centre $(0, 0)$ and radius 6.

Problem-solving

The transformation T_2: $w = 3z$ represents an **enlargement** of z by **scale factor** 3 with centre $(0, 0)$.

Rearrange to make $\frac{1}{2}z$ the subject.

Apply the modulus to both sides of the equation.

Use $|z_1 z_2| = |z_1||z_2|$

Use $|z| = 2$

c T_3: $w = \frac{1}{2}z + i$

$\Rightarrow w - i = \frac{1}{2}z$

$\Rightarrow |w - i| = |\frac{1}{2}z|$

$\Rightarrow |w - i| = |\frac{1}{2}||z|$

$\Rightarrow |w - i| = \frac{1}{2}(2) = 1$

The image of the locus of P under T_3 is $|w - i| = 1$. This is a circle with centre $(0, 1)$ and radius 1.

Problem-solving

The transformation T_3: $w = \frac{1}{2}z + i$ represents an enlargement of z by scale factor $\frac{1}{2}$ about the point $(0, 0)$, followed by a translation by the vector $\begin{pmatrix} 0 \\ 1 \end{pmatrix}$

Example 13

For the transformation $w = iz - 1$, find the locus of w when z lies on the half-line $\arg(z + 2) = \dfrac{\pi}{4}$

$w = iz - 1$

$\Rightarrow iz = w + 1$

$\Rightarrow z = \dfrac{w}{i} + \dfrac{1}{i}$

$\Rightarrow z = -iw - i$

Rearrange the transformation formula $w = iz - 1$ to make z the subject.

$\arg(z + 2) = \dfrac{\pi}{4}$

$\Rightarrow \arg(-iw - i + 2) = \dfrac{\pi}{4}$

Substitute $-iw - i$ for z.

$\Rightarrow \arg(-iw + 2 - i) = \dfrac{\pi}{4}$

$\Rightarrow \arg(-i(w + 2i + 1)) = \dfrac{\pi}{4}$

$\Rightarrow \arg(-i) + \arg(w + 1 + 2i) = \dfrac{\pi}{4}$

Use $\arg(z_1 z_2) = \arg(z_1) + \arg(z_2)$

$\Rightarrow -\dfrac{\pi}{2} + \arg(w + 1 + 2i) = \dfrac{\pi}{4}$

$\Rightarrow \arg(w + 1 + 2i) = \dfrac{3\pi}{4}$

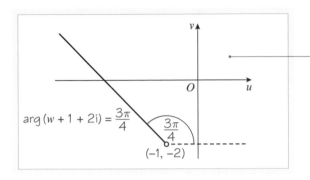

The locus of points in the w-plane is the half-line, $\arg(w + 1 + 2i) = \dfrac{3\pi}{4}$, that extends from the point $(-1, -2)$ at an angle of $\dfrac{3\pi}{4}$ to the horizontal extending to the left of $(-1, -2)$.

Problem-solving

The transformation $w = iz - 1$ represents an anticlockwise rotation through $\dfrac{\pi}{2}$ about the origin followed by a translation by the vector $\begin{pmatrix} -1 \\ 0 \end{pmatrix}$.

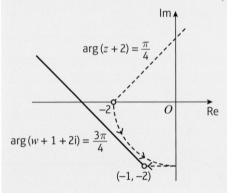

Examples 6 and 7 lead to the following general results:

- $w = z + a + ib$ represents a translation by the vector $\begin{pmatrix} a \\ b \end{pmatrix}$, where $a, b \in \mathbb{R}$.

- $w = kz$, where $k \in \mathbb{R}$, represents an enlargement by scale factor k with centre $(0, 0)$, where $k \in \mathbb{R}$.

- $w = iz$ represents an anticlockwise rotation through $\dfrac{\pi}{2}$ about the origin.

Compound transformations, such as the one in Example 7, are represented by transformation formulae which combine more than one of the characteristics listed above. For example, the transformation formula $w = kz + a + ib$ represents an enlargement by scale factor k with centre $(0, 0)$ followed by a translation by the vector $\begin{pmatrix} a \\ b \end{pmatrix}$, where $a, b, k \in \mathbb{R}$.

Example 14

A transformation from the z-plane to the w-plane is given by $w = z^2$, where $z = x + iy$ and $w = u + iv$. Describe the locus of w and give its Cartesian equation when z lies on:

a a circle with equation $x^2 + y^2 = 16$
b the line with equation $x = 1$

Notation   A Cartesian equation for a locus in the z-plane will be in terms of x and y because $z = x + iy$. However, a Cartesian equation for a locus in the w-plane will be in terms of u and v because $w = u + iv$.

a $|z| = 4$

$w = z^2 \Rightarrow |w| = |z^2|$

$\Rightarrow |w| = |z||z|$

$\Rightarrow |w| = 4 \times 4$

$\Rightarrow |w| = 16$

Hence the locus of w is a circle with centre $(0, 0)$ and radius 16, and the Cartesian equation for the locus of w is

$u^2 + v^2 = 16^2 = 256$

b Let $z = 1 + iy$

$w = z^2 \Rightarrow w = (1 + iy)^2$

$\Rightarrow w = (1 - y^2) + 2yi$

So $u = 1 - y^2$ and $v = 2y$

$-4u = -4 + 4y^2$ and $v^2 = 4y^2$

The Cartesian equation for w is

$v^2 = -4u + 4$

The locus of w is a parabola that is symmetric about the real axis, with vertex at $(1, 0)$, as shown in the diagram.

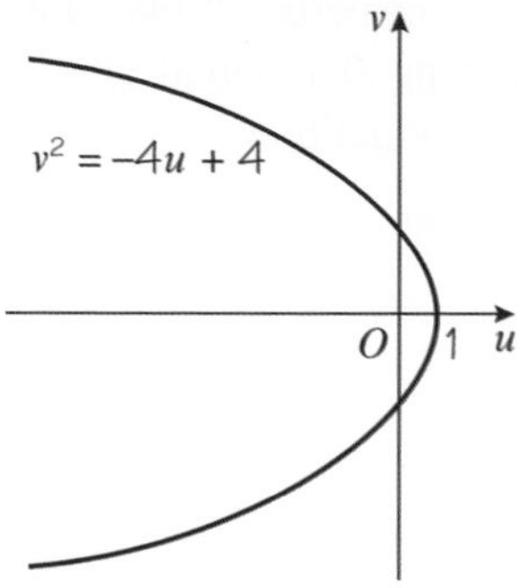

This has Cartesian equation $x^2 + y^2 = 16$

Take the modulus of each side of the equation.

Use $|z_1 z_2| = |z_1||z_2|$, where $z_1 = z_2 = z$

Use $|z| = 4$

The line $x = 1$ in the z-plane is the locus of $\text{Re}(z) = 1$

This is a **parametric equation** of a curve in the w-plane with y as the parameter.

Problem-solving

A Cartesian equation in the w-plane should be in terms of u and v. You need to eliminate y from the equations.

- You need to be able to apply transformation formulae of the form $w = \dfrac{az + b}{cz + d}$ where $a, b, c, d \in \mathbb{C}$, that map points in the z-plane to points in the w-plane.

Example 15

The transformation T from the z-plane, where $z = x + iy$, to the w-plane, where $w = u + iv$, is given by $w = \dfrac{5iz + i}{z + 1}$, $z \neq -1$.

a Show that the image, under T, of the circle $|z| = 1$ in the z-plane is a line l in the w-plane.

b Sketch l on an Argand diagram.

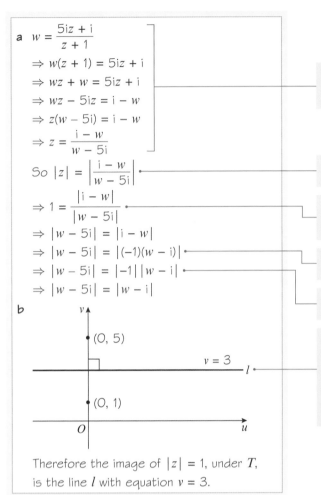

a $w = \dfrac{5iz + i}{z + 1}$

$\Rightarrow w(z + 1) = 5iz + i$

$\Rightarrow wz + w = 5iz + i$

$\Rightarrow wz - 5iz = i - w$

$\Rightarrow z(w - 5i) = i - w$

$\Rightarrow z = \dfrac{i - w}{w - 5i}$

So $|z| = \left|\dfrac{i - w}{w - 5i}\right|$

$\Rightarrow 1 = \dfrac{|i - w|}{|w - 5i|}$

$\Rightarrow |w - 5i| = |i - w|$

$\Rightarrow |w - 5i| = |(-1)(w - i)|$

$\Rightarrow |w - 5i| = |-1||w - i|$

$\Rightarrow |w - 5i| = |w - i|$

| Rearrange the transformation equation to make z the subject of the equation. |

| Take the modulus of each side of the equation. |

| Use $|z| = 1$ and $\left|\dfrac{z_1}{z_2}\right| = \dfrac{|z_1|}{|z_2|}$ |

| Take out a factor of -1 on the RHS. |

| Use $|z_1 z_2| = |z_1||z_2|$ |

b

Therefore the image of $|z| = 1$, under T, is the line l with equation $v = 3$.

| As you are working in the w-plane, plot v against u. $|w - 5i| = |w - i|$ is in the form $|w - w_1| = |w - w_2|$ so represents points on the perpendicular bisector of the line segment joining $(0, 1)$ and $(0, 5)$. Therefore the line l has equation $v = 3$ |

Example 16

The transformation T from the z-plane, where $z = x + iy$, to the w-plane, where $w = u + iv$, is given by $w = \dfrac{3z - 2}{z + 1}, z \neq -1$.

Show that the image, under T, of the circle with equation $x^2 + y^2 = 4$ in the z-plane is a circle C in the w-plane. State the centre and radius of C.

$w = \dfrac{3z - 2}{z + 1}$

$\Rightarrow w(z + 1) = 3z - 2$

$\Rightarrow wz + w = 3z - 2$

$\Rightarrow w + 2 = 3z - wz$

$\Rightarrow w + 2 = z(3 - w)$

$\Rightarrow \dfrac{w + 2}{3 - w} = z$

| Rearrange the transformation equation $w = \dfrac{3z - 2}{z + 1}$ to make z the subject of the equation. |

$x^2 + y^2 = 4$ can also be written as $|z| = 2$. $x^2 + y^2 = 4$ is the equation of a circle with centre $(0, 0)$ and radius 2.

$\left|\dfrac{w + 2}{3 - w}\right| = |z| = 2$

$\Rightarrow \dfrac{|w + 2|}{|3 - w|} = 2$ Take the modulus of each side of the equation.

$\Rightarrow |w + 2| = 2|3 - w|$

$\Rightarrow |w + 2| = 2|-1||w - 3|$ Use $\left|\dfrac{z_1}{z_2}\right| = \dfrac{|z_1|}{|z_2|}$ and $|z| = 2$.

$\Rightarrow |w + 2| = 2|w - 3|$

$\Rightarrow |u + iv + 2| = 2|u + iv - 3|$ Write w as $u + iv$.

$\Rightarrow |(u + 2) + iv| = 2|(u - 3) + iv|$ Group the real and imaginary parts.

$\Rightarrow |(u + 2) + iv|^2 = 2^2|(u - 3) + iv|^2$

$\Rightarrow (u + 2)^2 + v^2 = 4((u - 3)^2 + v^2)$ Square both sides.

$\Rightarrow u^2 + 4u + 4 + v^2 = 4(u^2 - 6u + 9 + v^2)$

$\Rightarrow u^2 + 4u + 4 + v^2 = 4u^2 - 24u + 36 + 4v^2$ Remove the moduli.

$\Rightarrow 3u^2 - 28u + 3v^2 + 32 = 0$

$\Rightarrow u^2 - \dfrac{28}{3}u + v^2 + \dfrac{32}{3} = 0$

$\Rightarrow \left(u - \dfrac{14}{3}\right)^2 - \dfrac{196}{9} + v^2 + \dfrac{32}{3} = 0$ Complete the square for u.

$\Rightarrow \left(u - \dfrac{14}{3}\right)^2 + v^2 = \dfrac{100}{9}$

Therefore the image of $x^2 + y^2 = 4$, under T, is a circle C with centre $\left(\dfrac{14}{3}, 0\right)$ and radius $\dfrac{10}{3}$

Example **17**

A transformation T of the z-plane to the w-plane is given by $w = \dfrac{iz - 2}{1 - z}$, $z \neq 1$.

Show that as z lies on the real axis in the z-plane, then w lies on a line l in the w-plane. Sketch l on an Argand diagram.

$w = \dfrac{iz - 2}{1 - z}$

$\Rightarrow w(1 - z) = iz - 2$

$\Rightarrow w - wz = iz - 2$

$\Rightarrow w + 2 = wz + iz$ Rearrange the transformation equation $w = \dfrac{iz - 2}{1 - z}$ to make z the subject of the equation.

$\Rightarrow w + 2 = z(w + i)$

$\Rightarrow \dfrac{w + 2}{w + i} = z$

So $z = \dfrac{u + iv + 2}{u + iv + i}$ Write w as $u + iv$.

$\Rightarrow z = \dfrac{(u + 2) + iv}{u + i(v + 1)}$ Group the real and imaginary parts.

$\Rightarrow z = \dfrac{(u + 2) + iv}{u + i(v + 1)} \times \dfrac{u - i(v + 1)}{u - i(v + 1)}$ Multiply the numerator and denominator by the **complex conjugate** of $u + i(v + 1)$.

$\Rightarrow z = \dfrac{u(u + 2) - i(u + 2)(v + 1) + iuv + v(v + 1)}{u^2 + (v + 1)^2}$ Use the difference of two squares.

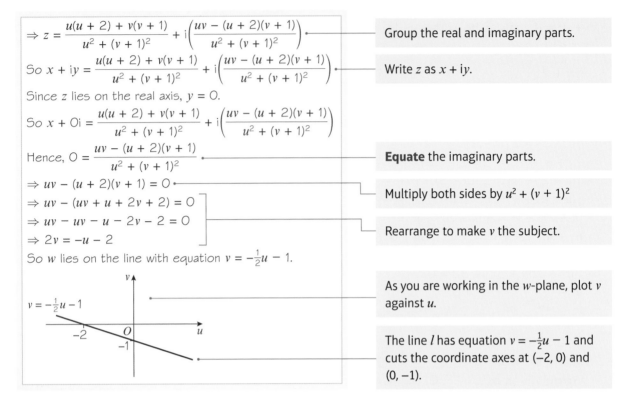

$$\Rightarrow z = \frac{u(u + 2) + v(v + 1)}{u^2 + (v + 1)^2} + i\left(\frac{uv - (u + 2)(v + 1)}{u^2 + (v + 1)^2}\right)$$

Group the real and imaginary parts.

So $x + iy = \frac{u(u + 2) + v(v + 1)}{u^2 + (v + 1)^2} + i\left(\frac{uv - (u + 2)(v + 1)}{u^2 + (v + 1)^2}\right)$

Write z as $x + iy$.

Since z lies on the real axis, $y = 0$.

So $x + 0i = \frac{u(u + 2) + v(v + 1)}{u^2 + (v + 1)^2} + i\left(\frac{uv - (u + 2)(v + 1)}{u^2 + (v + 1)^2}\right)$

Hence, $0 = \frac{uv - (u + 2)(v + 1)}{u^2 + (v + 1)^2}$

Equate the imaginary parts.

$\Rightarrow uv - (u + 2)(v + 1) = 0$

Multiply both sides by $u^2 + (v + 1)^2$

$\Rightarrow uv - (uv + u + 2v + 2) = 0$

$\Rightarrow uv - uv - u - 2v - 2 = 0$

$\Rightarrow 2v = -u - 2$

Rearrange to make v the subject.

So w lies on the line with equation $v = -\frac{1}{2}u - 1$.

As you are working in the w-plane, plot v against u.

The line l has equation $v = -\frac{1}{2}u - 1$ and cuts the coordinate axes at $(-2, 0)$ and $(0, -1)$.

Exercise 4E

1 Consider the triangle shown on the right in the z-plane. For each of the transformation formulae:
   i sketch the image of the triangle by plotting the images of z_1, z_2 and z_3, in the w-plane
   ii give a geometrical description of the **mapping** from the z-plane to the w-plane.

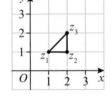

   a $w = z - 3 + 2i$ b $w = 2z$ c $w = iz - 2 + i$ d $w = 3z - 2i$

2 A transformation T from the z-plane to the w-plane is a translation by the vector $\begin{pmatrix} -2 \\ 3 \end{pmatrix}$ followed by an enlargement with scale factor 4 and centre O. Write down the transformation T in the form $w = az + b$, where $a, b \in \mathbb{C}$.

3 Determine the formula for a transformation from the z-plane to the w-plane in such a way that the locus of w points is the image of the locus of z points rotated 90° anticlockwise and enlarged by a scale factor of 4, both about the point $(0, 0)$.

4 For the transformation $w = 2z - 5 + 3i$, find the Cartesian equation of the locus of w as z moves on the circle $|z - 2| = 4$.

5 For the transformation $w = z - 1 + 2i$, sketch on separate Argand diagrams the locus of w when z lies on:

   a the circle $|z - 1| = 3$ b the half-line $\arg(z - 1 + i) = \frac{\pi}{4}$
   c the line $y = 2x$

6   For the transformation $w = \dfrac{1}{z}$, $z \neq 0$, describe the locus of w when z lies on:

    a   the circle $|z| = 2$ **b**   the half-line with equation $\arg z = \dfrac{\pi}{4}$

    c   the line with equation $y = 2x + 1$

(E)   7   For the transformation $w = z^2$,

    a   show that as z moves once round a circle with centre $(0, 0)$ and radius 3, w moves twice round a circle with centre $(0, 0)$ and radius 9   **(6 marks)**

    b   find the locus of w when z lies on the real axis   **(2 marks)**

    c   find the locus of w when z lies on the imaginary axis.   **(2 marks)**

(E)   8   The transformation T from the z-plane to the w-plane is given by $w = \dfrac{2}{i - 2z}$, $z \neq \dfrac{i}{2}$

    The circle with equation $|z| = 1$ is mapped by T onto the curve C.

    a   **i**   Show that C is a circle.

         ii   Find the centre and radius of C.   **(8 marks)**

    The region $|z| \leqslant 1$ in the z-plane is mapped by T onto the region R in the w-plane.

    b   Shade the region R on an Argand diagram.   **(2 marks)**

(E/P)   9   For the transformation $w = \dfrac{1}{2 - z}$, $z \neq 2$, show that the image, under T, of the circle with centre O, and radius 2 in the z-plane is a line l in the w-plane. Sketch l on an Argand diagram.   **(6 marks)**

(E)   10   A transformation from the z-plane to the w-plane is given by $w = \dfrac{z - i}{z + i}$, $z \neq -i$.

     a   Show that the circle with equation $|z - i| = 1$ in the z-plane is mapped to a circle in the w-plane, giving an equation for this circle.   **(5 marks)**

     b   Sketch the new circle on an Argand diagram.   **(1 mark)**

(E/P)   11   The transformation T from the z-plane, where $z = x + iy$, to the w-plane where $w = u + iv$, is given by $w = \dfrac{3}{2 - z}$, $z \neq 2$.

     Show that, under T, the straight line with equation $2y = x$ is transformed to a circle in the w-plane with centre $\left(\dfrac{3}{4}, \dfrac{3}{2}\right)$ and radius $\dfrac{3\sqrt{5}}{4}$ **(7 marks)**

(E/P)   12   The transformation T from the z-plane, where $z = x + iy$, to the w-plane, where $w = u + iv$, is given by $w = \dfrac{-iz + i}{z + 1}$, $z \neq -1$.

     a   The transformation T maps the points on the circle with equation $x^2 + y^2 = 1$ in the z-plane, to points on a line l in the w-plane. Find the Cartesian equation of l.   **(4 marks)**

     b   Hence, or otherwise, shade and label on an Argand diagram the region R of the w-plane which is the image of $|z| \leqslant 1$ under T.   **(2 marks)**

     c   Show that the image, under T, of the circle with equation $x^2 + y^2 = 4$ in the z-plane is a circle C in the w-plane. Find the equation of C.   **(4 marks)**

(E)   13   The transformation T from the z-plane, where $z = x + iy$, to the w-plane, where $w = u + iv$, is given by $w = \dfrac{4z - 3i}{z - 1}$, $z \neq 1$.

     Show that the circle $|z| = 3$ is mapped by T onto a circle C, and state the centre and radius of C.   **(6 marks)**

(E) **14** The transformation T from the z-plane, where $z = x + iy$, to the w-plane, where $w = u + iv$, is given by $w = \dfrac{1}{z+i}$, $z \neq -i$.

    a Show that the image, under T, of the real axis in the z-plane is a circle C_1 in the w-plane and find the equation of C_1. **(5 marks)**

    b Show that the image, under T, of the line $x = 4$ in the z-plane is a circle C_2 in the w-plane, and find the equation of C_2. **(5 marks)**

(E/P) **15** The transformation T from the z-plane, where $z = x + iy$, to the w-plane where $w = u + iv$, is given by $w = z + \dfrac{4}{z}$, $z \neq 0$.

    Show that the transformation T maps the points on a circle $|z| = 2$ to points in the interval $[-k, k]$ on the real axis. State the value of the constant k. **(7 marks)**

(E/P) **16** The transformation T from the z-plane, where $z = x + iy$, to the w-plane, where $w = u + iv$, is given by $w = \dfrac{1}{z+3}$, $z \neq -3$.

    Show that T maps the line with equation $2x - 2y + 7 = 0$ onto a circle C, and state the centre and the exact radius of C. **(6 marks)**

Challenge

A transformation $T: w = az + b$, $a, b \in \mathbb{C}$ maps the complex numbers 0, 1 and $1 + i$ in the z-plane to the points $2i$, $3i$ and $-1 + 3i$, respectively, in the w-plane. Find a and b.

Chapter review **4**

(E/P) **1** The point P represents a complex number z in an Argand diagram.

    Given that $|z + 1 - i| = 1$

    a find a Cartesian equation for the locus of P **(2 marks)**

    b sketch the locus of P on an Argand diagram **(2 marks)**

    c find the greatest and least possible values of $|z|$ **(2 marks)**

    d find the greatest and least possible values of $|z - 1|$. **(2 marks)**

(P) **2** Given that $\arg(z - 2 + 4i) = \dfrac{\pi}{4}$

    a sketch the locus of $P(x, y)$ which represents z on an Argand diagram

    b find the minimum value of $|z|$ for points on this locus.

(E/P) **3** The complex number z satisfies $|z + 3 - 6i| = 3$. Show that the exact maximum value of $\arg z$ in the interval $(-\pi, \pi)$ is $\dfrac{\pi}{2} + 2\arcsin\left(\dfrac{1}{\sqrt{5}}\right)$ **(4 marks)**

(E/P) **4** A complex number z is represented by the point P on the Argand diagram.

    Given that $|z - 5| = 4$,

    a sketch the locus of P. **(2 marks)**

    b Find the complex numbers that satisfy both $|z - 5| = 4$ and $\arg(z + 3i) = \dfrac{\pi}{3}$ giving your answers in radians to 2 decimal places. **(6 marks)**

    c Given that $\arg(z + 5) = \theta$ and $|z - 5| = 4$ have no common solutions, find the range of possible values of θ, $-\pi < \theta < \pi$. **(3 marks)**

(E/P) **5** Given that $|z + 5 - 5i| = |z - 6 - 3i|$

    a sketch the locus of z **(3 marks)**

    b find the Cartesian equation of this locus **(3 marks)**

    c find the least possible value of $|z|$. **(3 marks)**

(E/P) **6 a** Find the Cartesian equation of the locus of points that satisfies $|z - 4| = |z - 8i|$ **(3 marks)**

    b Find the value of z that satisfies both $|z - 2| = |z - 4i|$ and $\arg z = \dfrac{\pi}{4}$ **(3 marks)**

    c Shade on an Argand diagram the set of points

       $\{z \in \mathbb{C} : |z - 4| \leqslant |z - 8i|\} \cap \left\{z \in \mathbb{C} : \dfrac{\pi}{4} \leqslant \arg z \leqslant \pi\right\}$ **(3 marks)**

(E/P) **7 a** Find the Cartesian equations of:

      i the locus of points representing $|z - 3 + i| = |z - 1 - i|$

      ii the locus of points representing $|z - 2| = 2\sqrt{2}$ **(6 marks)**

    b Find the two values of z that satisfy both $|z - 3 + i| = |z - 1 - i|$ and $|z - 2| = 2\sqrt{2}$ **(2 marks)**

    The region R is defined by the inequalities $|z - 3 + i| \geqslant |z - 1 - i|$ and $|z - 2| \leqslant 2\sqrt{2}$

    c Show the region R on an Argand diagram. **(4 marks)**

8 For each equation:

    i use an algebraic approach to determine a Cartesian equation for the locus of z on an Argand diagram

    ii describe the locus geometrically.

    a $|z| = |z - 4|$

    b $|z| = 2|z - 4|$

(E/P) **9 a** Sketch the locus of points that satisfies the equation $|z - 2 + i| = \sqrt{3}$ **(3 marks)**

    The half-line L with equation $y = mx - 1$, $x \geq 0$, $m > 0$ is tangent to the locus from part **a** at point A.

    b Find the value of m. **(3 marks)**

    c Write an equation for L in the form $\arg(z - z_1) = \theta$, $z_1 \in \mathbb{C}$, $-\pi < \theta \leqslant \pi$. **(2 marks)**

    d Find the complex number a represented by point A. **(3 marks)**

(E) **10 a** Find the Cartesian equation of the locus of points representing $|z + 2| = |2z - 1|$ **(3 marks)**

    b Find the value of z which satisfies both $|z + 2| = |2z - 1|$ and $\arg z = \dfrac{\pi}{4}$ **(3 marks)**

    c Hence shade in the region R on an Argand diagram which satisfies both $|z + 2| \geqslant |2z - 1|$ and $\dfrac{\pi}{4} \leqslant \arg z \leqslant \pi$ **(2 marks)**

(E) **11** Given that $\arg\left(\dfrac{z - 4 - 2i}{z - 6i}\right) = \dfrac{\pi}{2}$

    a sketch the locus of $P(x, y)$ which represents z on an Argand diagram **(4 marks)**

    b deduce the exact value of $|z - 2 - 4i|$. **(2 marks)**

(E/P) **12** A curve has equation $2|z + 3| = |z - 3|$, where $z \in \mathbb{C}$.

    a Show that the curve is a circle with equation $x^2 + y^2 + 10x + 9 = 0$ **(2 marks)**

    b Sketch the curve on an Argand diagram. **(2 marks)**

    The line L has equation $bz^* + b^*z = 0$, where $b \in \mathbb{C}$ and $z \in \mathbb{C}$.

    c Given that the line L is a tangent to the curve and that $\arg b = \theta$, find the possible values of $\tan\theta$. **(5 marks)**

(E/P) **13** A curve S is described by the equation $\arg\left(\dfrac{z-5-2i}{z-1-6i}\right) = \dfrac{\pi}{2}$

    a Show that S is a semicircle, and find its centre and radius. **(5 marks)**

    b Find the maximum value of $|z|$, and express it exactly. **(4 marks)**

(E) **14 a** Indicate on an Argand diagram the region, R, consisting of the set of points satisfying the inequality $2 \leqslant |z - 2 - 3i| \leqslant 3$ **(3 marks)**

    b Find the exact area of region R. **(2 marks)**

    c Determine whether or not the point represented by $4 + i$ lies inside R. **(3 marks)**

(E) **15** The transformation T from the z-plane, where $z = x + iy$, to the w-plane where $w = u + iv$, is given by $w = \dfrac{1}{z}$, $z \neq 0$.

    a Show that the image, under T, of the line with equation $x = \frac{1}{2}$ in the z-plane is a circle C in the w-plane. Find the equation of C. **(4 marks)**

    b Hence, or otherwise, shade and label on an Argand diagram the region R of the w-plane which is the image of $x \geqslant \frac{1}{2}$ under T. **(3 marks)**

(E) **16** The point P represents the complex number z on an Argand diagram.

    Given that $|z + 4i| = 2$

    a sketch the locus of P on an Argand diagram. **(2 marks)**

    b Hence find the maximum value of $|z|$. **(3 marks)**

    T_1, T_2, T_3 and T_4 represent transformations from the z-plane to the w-plane. Describe the locus of the image of P under the transformations:

    c   **i** $T_1: w = 2z$

        ii $T_2: w = iz$

        iii $T_3: w = -iz$

        iv $T_4: w = z^*$ **(8 marks)**

(E) **17** The transformation T from the z-plane, where $z = x + iy$, to the w-plane where $w = u + iv$, is given by $w = \dfrac{z+2}{z+i}$, $z \neq -i$.

    a Show that the image, under T, of the imaginary axis in the z-plane is a line l in the w-plane. Find the equation of l. **(4 marks)**

    b Show that the image, under T, of the line $y = x$ in the z-plane is a circle C in the w-plane. Find the centre of C and show that the radius of C is $\dfrac{\sqrt{10}}{2}$ **(5 marks)**

(E/P) **18** The transformation T from the z-plane, where $z = x + iy$, to the w-plane where $w = u + iv$, is given by $w = \dfrac{4-z}{z+i}$, $z \neq -i$.

    The circle $|z| = 1$ is mapped by T onto a line l. Show that l can be written in the form $au + bv + c = 0$, where a, b and c are integers to be determined. **(5 marks)**

(E/P) **19** The transformation T from the z-plane, where $z = x + iy$, to the w-plane where $w = u + iv$, is given by $w = \dfrac{3iz+6}{1-z}$, $z \neq 1$.

    Show that the circle $|z| = 2$ is mapped by T onto a circle C. State the centre of C and show that the radius of C can be expressed in the form $k\sqrt{5}$ where k is an integer to be determined. **(5 marks)**

(E/P) **20** The mapping from the z-plane to the w-plane given by $w = \dfrac{az+b}{z+c}$, $z, w \in \mathbb{C}$, $a, b, c \in \mathbb{R}$

maps the origin onto itself, and reflects the point $1 + 2i$ in the real axis.

a Find the values of a, b and c. **(5 marks)**

A second complex number ω is also mapped to itself.

b Find ω. **(5 marks)**

(E/P) **21** A transformation from the z-plane to the w-plane is defined by $w = \dfrac{az+b}{z+c}$, where $a, b, c \in \mathbb{R}$.

Given that $w = 1$ when $z = 0$ and that $w = 3 - 2i$ when $z = 2 + 3i$,

a find the values of a, b and c **(5 marks)**

b find the exact values of the two points in the complex plane which remain **invariant**
under the transformation. **(5 marks)**

22 The transformation T from the z-plane, where $z = x + iy$, to the w-plane where $w = u + iv$,
is given by $w = \dfrac{z+i}{z}$, $z \neq 0$.

a The transformation T maps the points on the line with equation $y = x$ in the z-plane, other
than $(0, 0)$, to points on the line l in the w-plane. Find an equation of l. **(4 marks)**

b Show that the image, under T, of the line with equation $x + y + 1 = 0$ in the z-plane
is a circle in the w-plane, where C has equation $u^2 + v^2 - u + v = 0$. **(4 marks)**

c On the same Argand diagram, sketch l and C. **(3 marks)**

Challenge

1 The complex number z satisfies $\arg(z - 3 + 3i) = -\dfrac{\pi}{4}$

The complex number w is such that $|w - z| = 3$.

  a Sketch the locus of w.

  b State the exact minimum value of $|w|$.

2 The complex function f maps any point in an Argand diagram
represented by $z = x + iy$ to its reflection in the line $x + y = 1$.
Express f in the form $f(z) = az^* + b$, where $a, b \in \mathbb{C}$.

Summary of key points

1 You can represent complex numbers on an **Argand diagram**. The x-axis on an Argand
diagram is called the **real axis** and the y-axis is called the **imaginary axis**. The complex
number $z = x + iy$ is represented on the diagram by the point $P(x, y)$, where x and y are
Cartesian coordinates.

2 The complex number $z = x + iy$ can be represented as the vector $\begin{pmatrix} x \\ y \end{pmatrix}$ on an Argand diagram.

3 For two complex numbers $z_1 = x_1 + iy_1$ and $z_2 = x_2 + iy_2$, $|z_2 - z_1|$ represents the distance
between the points z_1 and z_2 on an Argand diagram.

4 Given $z_1 = x_1 + iy_1$, the locus of points z on an Argand diagram such that $|z - z_1| = r$, or
$|z - (x_1 + iy_1)| = r$, is a circle with centre (x_1, y_1) and radius r.

5 Given $z_1 = x_1 + iy_1$ and $z_2 = x_2 + iy_2$, the locus of points z on an Argand diagram such that $|z - z_1| = |z - z_2|$ is the perpendicular bisector of the line segment joining z_1 and z_2.

6 Given $z_1 = x_1 + iy_1$, the locus of points z on an Argand diagram such that $\arg(z - z_1) = \theta$ is a half-line from, but not including, the fixed point z_1 making an angle θ with a line from the fixed point z_1 parallel to the real axis.

7 The locus of points z that satisfy $|z - a| = k|z - b|$, where $a, b \in \mathbb{C}$ and $k \in \mathbb{R}, k > 0, k \neq 1$ is a circle.

8 The locus of points z that satisfy $\arg\left(\dfrac{z - a}{z - b}\right) = \theta$, where $\theta \in \mathbb{R}, \theta > 0$ and $a, b \in \mathbb{C}$, is an arc of a circle with endpoints A and B representing the complex numbers a and b, respectively. The endpoints of the arc are not included in the locus.

- If $\theta < \dfrac{\pi}{2}$, then the locus is a major arc of the circle.

- If $\theta > \dfrac{\pi}{2}$, then the locus is a minor arc of the circle.

- If $\theta = \dfrac{\pi}{2}$, then the locus is a semicircle.

9 The inequality $\theta_1 \leqslant \arg(z - z_1) \leqslant \theta_2$ describes a region in an Argand diagram that is enclosed by the two half-lines $\arg(z - z_1) = \theta_1$ and $\arg(z - z_1) = \theta_2$, and also includes the two half-lines, but does not include the point represented by z_1.

10 · $w = z + a + ib$ represents a translation by the vector $\begin{pmatrix} a \\ b \end{pmatrix}$, where $a, b \in \mathbb{R}$.

- $w = kz$, where $k \in \mathbb{R}$, represents an enlargement by scale factor k with centre $(0, 0)$, where $k \in \mathbb{R}$.

- $w = iz$ represents an anticlockwise rotation through $\dfrac{\pi}{2}$ about the origin.

11 You need to be able to apply transformation formulae of the form $w = \dfrac{az + b}{cz + d}$, where $a, b, c, d \in \mathbb{C}$, that map points in the z-plane to points in the w-plane.

Review exercise

1

(E/P) **1** Use algebra to solve $\dfrac{2}{x-2} < \dfrac{1}{x+1}$ **(6)**

← **Further Pure 2 Section 1.1**

(E) **2** Find the set of values of x for which

$$\dfrac{x^2}{x-2} > 2x$$ **(5)**

← **Further Pure 2 Section 1.1**

(E) **3** Find the set of values of x for which

$$\dfrac{x^2-12}{x} > 1$$ **(5)**

← **Further Pure 2 Section 1.1**

(E) **4** Find the set of values of x for which

$$2x - 5 > \dfrac{3}{x}$$

giving your answer using set notation. **(5)**

← **Further Pure 2 Section 1.1**

(E/P) **5** Given that k is a constant and that $k > 0$, find, in terms of k, the set of values of

x for which $\dfrac{x+k}{x+4k} > \dfrac{k}{x}$ **(7)**

← **Further Pure 2 Section 1.1**

(E) **6 a** On the same set of axes, sketch the graphs of

$$y = 2 - x \text{ and } y = -\dfrac{2}{x-1}$$ **(3)**

  b Find the points of intersection of

$$y = 2 - x \text{ and } y = -\dfrac{2}{x-1}$$ **(2)**

  c Write down the solution to the inequality

$$2 - x > -\dfrac{2}{x-1}$$ **(2)**

← **Further Pure 2 Section 1.2**

(E) **7 a** On the same set of axes sketch the

graphs of $y = \dfrac{4x}{2-x}$ and $y = \dfrac{2x}{(x+1)^2}$ **(4)**

  b Find the points of intersection of

$$y = \dfrac{4x}{2-x} \text{ and } y = \dfrac{2x}{(x+1)^2}$$ **(2)**

  c Hence, or otherwise, solve the inequality

$$\dfrac{4x}{2-x} \leqslant \dfrac{2x}{(x+1)^2}$$

giving your answer using set notation.
(2)

← **Further Pure 2 Section 1.2**

(E) **8 a** On the same set of axes, sketch the graphs of

$y = |x - 5|$ and $y = |3x - 2|$ **(3)**

  b Finds the coordinates of the points of intersection of $y = |x - 5|$ and

$y = |3x - 2|$ **(3)**

  c Write down the solution to the inequality

$$|x - 5| < |3x - 2|$$ **(2)**

← **Further Pure 2 Section 1.3**

(E) **9 a** Sketch the graph of $y = |x + 2|$ **(2)**

  b Use algebra to solve the inequality

$2x > |x + 2|$ **(4)**

← **Further Pure 2 Section 1.3**

(E) **10 a** Sketch the graph of $y = |x - 2a|$, given that $a > 0$ **(2)**

  b Solve $|x - 2a| > 2x + a$, where $a > 0$ **(4)**

← **Further Pure 2 Section 1.3**

(E/P) **11** Solve the inequality $\left|\dfrac{x}{x-3}\right| < 8 - x$,

giving your answer in set notation. **(6)**

← **Further Pure 2 Section 1.3**

(E) **12 a** On the same set of axes, sketch the graphs of $y = x$ and $y = |2x - 1|$ **(3)**

  b Use algebra to find the coordinates of the points of intersection of the two graphs. **(2)**

  c Hence, or otherwise, find the set of values of x for which $|2x - 1| > x$ **(4)**

← **Further Pure 2 Section 1.3**

(E/P) **13** Use algebra to find the set of real values of x for which $|x - 3| > 2|x + 1|$ **(5)**

← Further Pure 2 Section 1.3

(E/P) **14** Solve, for x, the inequality $|5x + a| \leq |2x|$, where $a > 0$ **(6)**

← Further Pure 2 Section 1.3

(E/P) **15 a** Using the same set of axes, sketch the curve with equation $y = |x^2 - 6x + 8|$ and the line with equation $2y = 3x - 9$ State the coordinates of the points where the curve and the line meet the x-axis. **(4)**

b Use algebra to find the coordinates of the points where the curve and the line intersect and, hence, solve the inequality $2|x^2 - 6x + 8| > 3x - 9$ **(5)**

← Further Pure 2 Section 1.3

(E) **16 a** Sketch, on the same set of axes, the graph of $y = |(x - 2)(x - 4)|$, and the line with equation $y = 6 - 2x$ **(3)**

b Find the exact values of x for which $|(x - 2)(x - 4)| = 6 - 2x$ **(3)**

c Hence solve the inequality $|(x - 2)(x - 4)| < 6 - 2x$ **(2)**

← Further Pure 2 Section 1.3

(E/P) **17**

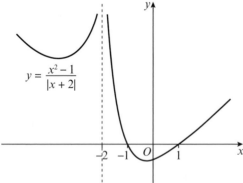

The diagram above shows a sketch of the curve with equation
$$y = \frac{x^2 - 1}{|x + 2|}, \quad x \neq -2$$
The curve crosses the x-axis at $x = 1$ and $x = -1$ and the line $x = -2$ is an asymptote of the curve.

a Use algebra to solve the equation
$$\frac{x^2 - 1}{|x + 2|} = 3(1 - x)$$ **(6)**

b Hence, or otherwise, find the set of values of x for which
$$\frac{x^2 - 1}{|x + 2|} < 3(1 - x)$$
Give your answer using set notation. **(2)**

← Further Pure 2 Section 1.3

(E/P) **18** Prove that
$$\sum_{r=1}^{n} \frac{2}{(r + 1)(r + 2)} = \frac{n}{n + 2}$$ **(5)**

← Further Pure 2 Section 2.1

(E/P) **19** Prove that
$$\sum_{r=1}^{n} \frac{2}{(r + 1)(r + 3)} = \frac{n(an + b)}{c(n + 2)(n + 3)}$$
where a, b and c are constants to be found. **(5)**

← Further Pure 2 Section 2.1

(E/P) **20 a** Show that
$$\frac{r + 1}{r + 2} - \frac{r}{r + 1} \equiv \frac{1}{(r + 1)(r + 2)}, \quad r \in \mathbb{Z}^+$$ **(2)**

b Hence, or otherwise, find
$$\sum_{r=1}^{n} \frac{1}{(r + 1)(r + 2)}$$ giving your answer as a single fraction in terms of n. **(3)**

← Further Pure 2 Section 2.1

(E/P) **21** $f(x) = \dfrac{2}{(x + 1)(x + 2)(x + 3)}$

a Express $f(x)$ in partial fractions. **(2)**

b Hence find $\displaystyle\sum_{r=1}^{n} f(r)$. **(3)**

← Further Pure 2 Section 2.1

(E/P) **22 a** Express as a simplified single fraction
$$\frac{1}{(r - 1)^2} - \frac{1}{r^2}$$ **(2)**

b Hence prove, by the method of differences, that
$$\sum_{r=2}^{n} \frac{2r - 1}{r^2(r - 1)^2} = 1 - \frac{1}{n^2}$$ **(3)**

← Further Pure 2 Section 2.1

(E/P) **23 a** Prove that
$$\sum_{r=1}^{n} \frac{4}{r(r+2)} = \frac{n(an+b)}{(n+1)(n+2)}$$
where a and b are constants to be found. **(5)**

b Find the value of $\displaystyle\sum_{r=50}^{100} \frac{4}{r(r+2)}$, to 4 decimal places. **(2)**

← Further Pure 2 Section 2.1

(E/P) **24 a** Prove that
$$\sum_{r=1}^{n} \frac{2}{4r^2 - 1} = 1 - \frac{1}{2n+1}$$ **(5)**

b Hence find the exact value of
$$\sum_{r=11}^{20} \frac{2}{4r^2 - 1}$$ **(2)**

← Further Pure 2 Section 2.1

(E) **25** Given that for all real values of r,
$$(2r+1)^3 - (2r-1)^3 = Ar^2 + B$$
where A and B are constants,

a find the value of A and the value of B. **(2)**

b Hence show that
$$\sum_{r=1}^{n} r^2 = \tfrac{1}{6}n(n+1)(2n+1)$$ **(3)**

c Calculate $\displaystyle\sum_{r=1}^{40} (3r-1)^2$. **(2)**

← Further Pure 2 Section 2.1

(E/P) **26** Prove that
$$\sum_{r=1}^{2n} \frac{1}{r(r+1)(r+2)} = \frac{n(an+b)}{c(n+1)(2n+1)}$$
where a, b and c are constants to be found. **(6)**

← Further Pure 2 Section 2.1

(E) **27 a** Show that
$$\frac{r^3 - r + 1}{r(r+1)} \equiv r - 1 + \frac{1}{r} - \frac{1}{r+1}$$
for $r \neq 0, -1$. **(2)**

b Find $\displaystyle\sum_{r=1}^{n} \frac{r^3 - r + 1}{r(r+1)}$, expressing your answer as a single fraction in its simplest form. **(3)**

← Further Pure 2 Section 2.1

(E/P) **28** Find $\displaystyle\sum_{r=1}^{n} \frac{2r+3}{3^r(r+1)}$ **(5)**

← Further Pure 2 Section 2.1

(E) **29** Show that
$$\frac{\cos 2x + i\sin 2x}{\cos 9x - i\sin 9x}$$
can be expressed in the form $\cos nx + i\sin nx$, where n is an integer to be found. **(4)**

← Further Pure 2 Section 3.2

(E/P) **30 a** Use de Moivre's theorem to show that
$$\cos 5\theta = 16\cos^5\theta - 20\cos^3\theta + 5\cos\theta \quad \textbf{(4)}$$

b Hence find 3 distinct solutions of the equation $16x^5 - 20x^3 + 5x + 1 = 0$, giving your answers to 3 decimal places where appropriate. **(5)**

← Further Pure 2 Section 3.4

(E/P) **31 a** Use de Moivre's theorem to show that
$$\sin 5\theta = \sin\theta(16\cos^4\theta - 12\cos^2\theta + 1)$$ **(4)**

b Hence, or otherwise, solve, for $0 \leqslant \theta < \pi$, $\sin 5\theta + \cos\theta \sin 2\theta = 0$ **(5)**

← Further Pure 2 Section 3.4

(E/P) **32 a** Use de Moivre's theorem to show that
$$\sin^5\theta = \tfrac{1}{16}(\sin 5\theta - 5\sin 3\theta + 10\sin\theta)$$ **(4)**

b Hence, or otherwise, show that
$$\int_0^{\frac{\pi}{2}} \sin^5\theta \, d\theta = \frac{8}{15}$$ **(6)**

← Further Pure 2 Section 3.4

(E/P) **33 a** Given that $z = \cos\theta + i\sin\theta$, show that
$$z^n + z^{-n} = 2\cos n\theta$$ **(2)**

b Express $\cos^6\theta$ in terms of cosines of multiples of θ. **(4)**

c Hence show that
$$\int_0^{\frac{\pi}{2}} \cos^6\theta \, d\theta = \frac{5\pi}{32}$$ **(6)**

← Further Pure 2 Section 3.4

(E) 34 a Solve the equation

$$z^5 = 4 + 4i$$

giving your answers in the form $z = re^{ik\pi}$, where r is the modulus of z and k is a rational number such that $0 \leqslant k \leqslant 2$. **(6)**

b Show on an Argand diagram the points representing your solutions. **(2)**

← **Further Pure 2 Section 3.5**

(E) 35 a Solve the equation

$$z^3 = 32 + 32\sqrt{3}i$$

giving your answers in the form $re^{i\theta}$, where $r > 0$, $-\pi < \theta \leqslant \pi$. **(6)**

b Show that your solutions satisfy the equation

$$z^9 + 2^k = 0$$

for an integer k, the value of which should be stated. **(3)**

← **Further Pure 2 Section 3.5**

(E) 36 Solve the equation $z^5 = i$, giving your answers in the form $\cos\theta + i\sin\theta$. **(6)**

← **Further Pure 2 Section 3.5**

(E) 37 a Find, in the form $re^{i\theta}$, the solutions to the equation

$$z^5 - 16 - 16i\sqrt{3} = 0$$ **(5)**

The solutions form the vertices of a polygon in the Argand diagram.

b State the name of the polygon formed. **(1)**

← **Further Pure 2 Section 3.5**

(E/P) 38 The point P represents the complex number z in an Argand diagram.

Given that $|z - 2 + i| = 3$,

a sketch the locus of P in an Argand diagram **(2)**

b find the exact values of the maximum and minimum of $|z|$. **(2)**

← **Further Pure 2 Section 4.1**

(E/P) 39 Given that z stisfies $|z - 2i| = 2$,

a sketch the locus of z on an Argand diagram **(2)**

b find the maximum value of $|z|$. **(2)**

← **Further Pure 2 Section 4.1**

(E/P) 40 A complex number z is represented by the point P in an Argand diagram.

Given that $|z - 3i| = 3$,

a sketch the locus of P **(2)**

b find the complex number z which satisfies both $|z - 3i| = 3$ and

$$\arg(z - 3i) = \frac{3\pi}{4}$$ **(3)**

← **Further Pure 2 Section 4.1**

(E) 41 Sketch, on an Argand diagram, the locus of the point P representing a complex number z such that

$$\arg(z + 3 + i) = \frac{\pi}{2}$$ **(3)**

← **Further Pure 2 Section 4.1**

(E/P) 42 The complex number z satisfies the equation $|z + 3 + i| = |z - 2 + i|$.

a Sketch the locus of z. **(2)**

b Find the minimum value of $|z|$. **(1)**

c Find the value of z that also satisfies

$$\arg z = -\frac{3\pi}{4}$$ **(2)**

← **Further Pure 2 Section 4.1**

(E/P) 43 A complex number z is represented by the point P on an Argand diagram.

Given that $\arg\left(\dfrac{z + i}{z - i}\right) = \dfrac{\pi}{4}$,

a without calculation, explain why the locus of P forms a major arc. **(1)**

b determine the location of the centre of the circle containing this arc. **(4)**

← **Further Pure 2 Section 4.2**

(E/P) 44 The diagram shows the sector of a circle drawn on an Argand diagram.

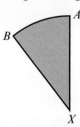

The centre of the circle, X, represents the complex number $-1 - 2i$, and the arc AB is the locus of points $z \in \mathbb{C}$ that satisfy the equation $\arg\left(\dfrac{z - 3i + 1}{z - b}\right) = \theta$, where $b \in \mathbb{C}$, $\theta \in \mathbb{R}$.

a Write down the complex number represented by the point A. **(1)**

b Given that the sector has area $\dfrac{25\pi}{12}$, find the values of b and θ. **(6)**

← **Further Pure 2 Section 4.2**

(E) 45 On an Argand diagram a circle is defined by $|z - 1| = \sqrt{2}|z - i|$ for $z \in \mathbb{C}$.

Determine the radius and centre of this circle. **(4)**

← **Further Pure 2 Section 4.2**

(E) 46 A curve P is described by the equation $\arg\left(\dfrac{z - 2i}{z + 2}\right) = \dfrac{\pi}{2}$, $z \in \mathbb{C}$.

a Sketch the locus of P **(4)**

b Deduce the value of $|z + 1 - i|$ **(2)**

← **Further Pure 2 Section 4.2**

(E) 47 A curve L is defined in the complex plane by $|z - 4| = \sqrt{5}|z + 2i|$ for $z \in \mathbb{C}$.

A curve M is defined in the complex plane by $|z - 6| = \sqrt{7}|z + 6i|$ for $z \in \mathbb{C}$.

a Explain why L and M are similar. **(2)**

b Find the exact scale factor of enlargement from L to M. **(2)**

← **Further Pure 2 Section 4.2**

(E) 48 A curve P is described by the equation $\arg\left(\dfrac{z + 1}{z}\right) = \dfrac{\pi}{4}$, $z \in \mathbb{C}$.

Find the exact length of this curve. **(6)**

← **Further Pure 2 Section 4.2**

(E/P) 49 A circle with circumference of 24π is plotted on an Argand diagram.

This circle is known to be defined by the equation $|z - i| = \sqrt{p}|z + 1|$, where $p > 1$, $p \in \mathbb{R}$ and $z \in \mathbb{C}$.

Find the exact value of p. **(7)**

← **Further Pure 2 Section 4.2**

(E) 50 Sketch, on an Argand diagram, the region which satisfies the following condition.

$$\frac{\pi}{4} \leqslant \arg(z - 1) \leqslant \frac{2\pi}{3} \qquad \textbf{(3)}$$

← **Further Pure 2 Section 4.3**

(E/P) 51 Shade on an Argand diagram the set of points

$$\left\{ z \in \mathbb{C} : -\frac{\pi}{2} < \arg(z - 3 - 3i) \leqslant \frac{3\pi}{4} \right\}$$

$$\cap \{ z \in \mathbb{C} : |z - 3i| \leqslant 3 \} \qquad \textbf{(6)}$$

← **Further Pure 2 Section 4.3**

(E/P) 52 Using an Argand diagram shade the region satisfied by

$$\left\{ z \in \mathbb{C} : \frac{\pi}{3} \leqslant \arg(z - 5) \leqslant \pi \right\}$$

$$\cap \left\{ z \in \mathbb{C} : 0 \leqslant \arg(z - 10) \leqslant \frac{5\pi}{6} \right\} \qquad \textbf{(4)}$$

← **Further Pure 2 Section 4.4**

(E/P) 53 Drawn on an Argand diagram, a shaded semicircle is defined by

$$\{ z \in \mathbb{C} : |z - 6i| \leqslant 2|z - 3| \}$$

$$\cap \{ z \in \mathbb{C} : \text{Re}(z) \leqslant k \}$$

where $k \in \mathbb{R}$.

a Find k. **(4)**

b Find the exact area of the semicircle. **(2)**

← **Further Pure 2 Section 4.4**

(E/P) 54 On an Argand diagram a triangular region is defined by

$$\left\{z \in \mathbb{C} : 0 \leqslant \arg(z - p) \leqslant \frac{\pi}{4}\right\}$$
$$\cap \{z \in \mathbb{C} : |z - p| \leqslant |z - q|\}$$

where $p, q \in \mathbb{R}$.

The region has an area of x, $x > 0$.

Prove that $q = p + \sqrt{8x}$.   **(6)**

← Further Pure 2 Section 4.4

(E/P) 55 Three points in the z-plane form the vertices A, B and C of an isosceles triangle. This triangle has area 8 and a line of symmetry defined by $\text{Im}(z) = 4$.

A transformation T from the z-plane to the w-plane is defined by $w = 3z + 4 - 2i$

a Find the area of the image of triangle ABC under T in the w-plane.   **(2)**

b Define, as a locus, the line of symmetry of the image of triangle ABC under T in the w-plane.   **(3)**

← Further Pure 2 Section 4.5

(E/P) 56 A transformation from the z-plane to the w-plane is given by

$$w = \frac{2z - 1}{z - 2}$$

Show that the circle $|z| = 1$ is mapped onto the circle $|w| = 1$.   **(5)**

← Further Pure 2 Section 4.5

(E/P) 57 A transformation from the z-plane to the w-plane is given by

$$w = \frac{z - i}{z}$$

a Show that under this transformation the line $\text{Im}\, z = \frac{1}{2}$ is mapped to the circle with equation $|w| = 1$ **(5)**

b Hence, or otherwise, find, in the form $w = \dfrac{az + b}{cz + d}$, where a, b, c and $d \in \mathbb{C}$, the transformation that maps the line $\text{Im}\, z = \frac{1}{2}$ to the circle with centre $3 - i$ and radius 2.   **(4)**

← Further Pure 2 Section 4.5

(E/P) 58 The transformation T from the z-plane to the w-plane is defined by

$$w = \frac{z + 1}{z + i},\ z \neq i$$

a Show that T maps points on the half-line $\arg z = \dfrac{\pi}{4}$ in the z-plane onto points on the circle $|w| = 1$ in the w-plane.   **(4)**

b Find the image under T in the w-plane of the circle $|z| = 1$ in the z-plane.   **(4)**

c Sketch, on separate diagrams, the circle $|z| = 1$ in the z-plane and its image under T in the w-plane.   **(2)**

d Mark on your sketches the point P where $z = i$ and its image Q under T in the w-plane.   **(3)**

← Further Pure 2 Section 4.5

(E/P) 59 A transformation of the z-plane to the w-plane, T, is given by

$$w = az + \frac{1}{z},\ z \in \mathbb{C},\ z \neq 0,\ a \in \mathbb{Z},\ a > 1$$

where $z = x + iy$ and $w = u + iv$

The locus of the points in the z-plane that satisfy the equation $|z| = \dfrac{1}{a}$ is mapped under T onto a curve C in the w-plane.

a Given that $|z| = \dfrac{1}{a}$, express z in exponential form.   **(1)**

b Hence prove that C may be defined by a Cartesian equation in the w-plane as $(1 - a)^2 u^2 + (1 + a)^2 v^2 = (1 - a^2)^2$ **(6)**

c T produces an image in the w-plane which forms an ellipse with equation

$$\frac{u^2}{16} + \frac{v^2}{4} = 1$$

Sketch the locus of the points on the z-plane which have been transformed under T to create this image.   **(3)**

← Further Pure 2 Section 4.5

Challenge

1 Solve in the range $0 < x < 2\pi$, $\dfrac{1}{1 - \sin x} < \dfrac{1}{\sin x}$ ← **Further Pure 2 Section 1.2**

2 a Show that if $\omega = e^{\frac{2\pi i}{3}}$, then

$$\frac{1^n + \omega^n + (\omega^2)^n}{3} = \begin{cases} 1 & \text{if } n \text{ is zero or a multiple of 3} \\ 0 & \text{otherwise} \end{cases}$$

Let $f(x)$ be a finite polynomial whose largest power of x is a multiple of 3, so that

$f(x) = a_0 + a_1 x + a_2 x^2 + \ldots + a_{3k} x^{3k}$ where $a_i \in \mathbb{R}$, $k \in \mathbb{N}$. The sum S is given by

$$S = a_0 + a_3 + a_6 + \ldots + a_{3k} = \sum_{r=0}^{k} a_{3r}$$

b By considering a general term of $f(x)$, show that $S = \dfrac{f(1) + f(\omega) + f(\omega^2)}{3}$

c Hence, by considering the binomial expansion of $(1 + x)^{45}$, show that $\displaystyle\sum_{r=0}^{15} \binom{45}{3r} = \dfrac{2^{45} - 2}{3}$

← **Further Pure 2 Section 2.1**

5 FIRST-ORDER DIFFERENTIAL EQUATIONS

4.1
4.2
4.3

Learning objectives

After completing this chapter you should be able to:

● Solve first-order differential equations by separation of variables and sketching members of the family of solution curves
→ pages 91–94

● Solve first-order differential equations using an integrating factor
→ pages 95–98

● Use a given substitution to transform a differential equation into one that can be solved
→ pages 98–102

Prior knowledge check

1 Find the general solution to the differential equation $\dfrac{dy}{dx} = xe^x$
← Pure 4 Section 6.6

2 Find the particular solution to the differential equation $\dfrac{dy}{dx} = -\dfrac{x}{y}$ given that $y = 0$ when $x = 2$
← Pure 4 Section 6.6

3 Find:

a $\displaystyle\int \dfrac{3}{50 - 2t}\, dt$

b $\displaystyle\int \tan 4x\, dx$
← Pure 3 Section 7.2

Population growth can be modelled by a differential equation. For example, the rate of change of the population of bacteria in a petri dish is proportional to the number of bacteria present, subject to the limiting factor of the amount of space on the dish.

5.1   First-order differential equations with separable variables

If a **first-order differential equation** can be written in the form $\dfrac{\mathrm{d}y}{\mathrm{d}x} = f(x)g(y)$ then you can solve it by writing $\displaystyle\int \frac{1}{g(y)}\,\mathrm{d}y = \int f(x)\,\mathrm{d}x$

Links This process is called **separating the variables**.   ← Pure 4 Section 6.6

When you have integrated and found the general solution, you can let the arbitrary constant take different numerical values, thus generating particular solutions. You can then sketch a graph for each of these solutions. **The curves that are sketched are called a family of solution curves.**

In some questions you will be given a boundary condition, such as $y = 1$ when $x = 0$.

You can use this to find the arbitrary constant. Different boundary conditions will give rise to different particular solutions. The graph of each solution belongs to the family of solution curves.

Example   1

Find the general solution of the differential equation
$$\frac{\mathrm{d}y}{\mathrm{d}x} = 2$$
and sketch members of the family of solution curves represented by the general solution.

Integrating gives $y = 2x + C$
which is the general solution.
The solution 'curves' corresponding to
$C = -2, -1, 0, 1,$ and 2 are shown below.

This is a straight line equation.

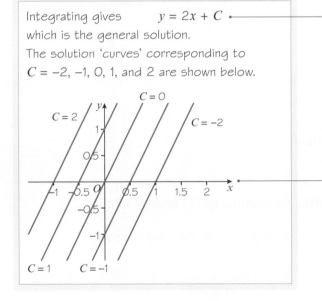

The graphs of $y = 2x + C$ form the family of solution 'curves' for this differential equation.

These are a set of straight lines with gradient 2 and intercept C.

Example 2

Find the general solution of the differential equation

$$\frac{dy}{dx} = -\frac{x}{y}$$

and sketch members of the family of solution curves represented by the general solution.

$\int y\,dy = -\int x\,dx$ ————— Separate the variables and integrate.

$\therefore \frac{1}{2}y^2 = -\frac{1}{2}x^2 + C$

which is the general solution.

This can be written as $x^2 + y^2 = r^2$, ————— This is a circle equation.
where $r^2 = 2C$.

The solution curves corresponding to
$C = 0.5, \quad 1.125, \quad 2, \quad 4.5$ are shown below.

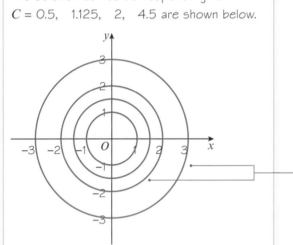

The graphs of $x^2 + y^2 = 2C$ form the family of solution curves for this differential equation.

These are a set of circles with centre at the origin and with radius r, where $r^2 = 2C$.

Example 3

Find the general solution to the differential equation

$$\frac{dy}{dx} = -\frac{y}{x}$$

and sketch members of the family of solution curves represented by the general solution.

$\int \frac{1}{y}\,dy = -\int \frac{1}{x}\,dx$ ————— Separate the variables and integrate.

$\ln|y| = -\ln|x| + c$

$\ln|y| + \ln|x| = c$ ————— Collect the ln terms together and combine using the laws of logarithms.

$\ln|xy| = c$

$|xy| = e^c$

$y = \pm\frac{A}{x}$, where $A = e^c$

Problem-solving

If c is a constant of integration, then $A = e^c$ can also be used as a constant. Writing the equation in this form helps you determine the family of solution curves.

Some solution curves corresponding to different values of A are shown below.

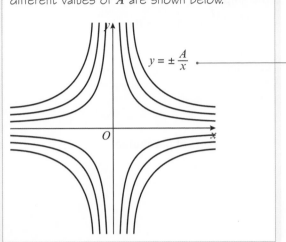

$y = \pm\dfrac{A}{x}$

The graphs of $y = \pm\dfrac{A}{x}$ form the family of solution curves for this differential equation.

Online   Explore families of solution curves using GeoGebra.

Example **4**

a Find the general solution of the differential equation

$$\frac{dx}{dt} = \sqrt{x}, \qquad t \geq 0$$

b Find the particular solutions which satisfy the initial conditions

i $x = 0$ when $t = 0$ **ii** $x = 1$ when $t = 0$

iii $x = 4$ when $t = 0$ **iv** $x = 9$ when $t = 0$

c Sketch the members of the family of solution curves represented by these particular solutions.

a $\displaystyle\int \frac{1}{\sqrt{x}}\, dx = \int dt$

Separate the variables, which in this question are x and t.

t usually denotes time.

$2x^{\frac{1}{2}} = t + c$

$x = \left(\dfrac{t + c}{2}\right)^2,\ t \geq 0$

Integrate and make x the subject of the formula.

b i Substituting $x = 0$ when $t = 0$ gives $c = 0$

$\therefore x = \dfrac{t^2}{4},\ t \geq 0$

Substitute the initial conditions, i.e. the values of x when $t = 0$, to find c.

ii Substituting $x = 1$ when $t = 0$ gives $c = 2$

$\therefore x = \dfrac{(t + 2)^2}{4},\ t \geq 0$

iii Substituting $x = 4$ when $t = 0$ gives $c = 4$

$\therefore x = \dfrac{(t \pm 4)^2}{4},\ t \geq 0$

iv Substituting $x = 9$ when $t = 0$ gives $c = 6$

$\therefore x = \dfrac{(t \pm 6)^2}{4},\ t \geq 0$

Write the equations of the particular solutions.

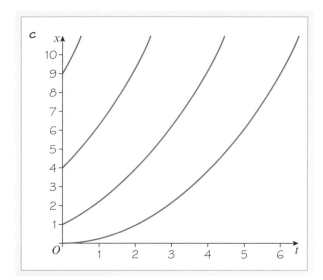

The graphs of
$$x = \left(\frac{t+c}{2}\right)^2, t \geqslant 0,$$ form the
family of solution curves for this differential equation.

These are parts of **parabolae**.

Exercise 5A

In questions 1–8 find the general solution of the differential equation and sketch the family of solution curves represented by the general solution.

1 $\dfrac{dy}{dx} = 2x$

2 $\dfrac{dy}{dx} = y$

3 $\dfrac{dy}{dx} = x^2$

4 $\dfrac{dy}{dx} = \dfrac{1}{x}, x > 0$

5 $\dfrac{dy}{dx} = \dfrac{2y}{x}$

6 $\dfrac{dy}{dx} = \dfrac{x}{y}$

7 $\dfrac{dy}{dx} = e^y$

8 $\dfrac{dy}{dx} = \dfrac{y}{x(x+1)}, \qquad x > 0$

9 $\dfrac{dy}{dx} = \cos x$

10 $\dfrac{dy}{dx} = y \cot x, \quad 0 < x < \pi$

11 $\dfrac{dy}{dt} = \sec^2 t, -\dfrac{\pi}{2} < t < \dfrac{\pi}{2}$

12 $\dfrac{dy}{dx} = x(1-x), \qquad 0 < x < 1$

13 Given that a is an arbitrary constant, show that $y^2 = 4ax$ is the general solution of the differential equation $\dfrac{dy}{dx} = \dfrac{y}{2x}$.

  a Sketch the members of the family of solution curves for which $a = \dfrac{1}{4}$, 1 and 4.

  b Find also the particular solution which passes through the point $(1, 3)$, and add this curve to your diagram of solution curves.

14 Given that k is an arbitrary positive constant, show that $y^2 + kx^2 = 9k$ is the general solution of the differential equation $\dfrac{dy}{dx} = \dfrac{-xy}{9 - x^2} \qquad |x| \leqslant 3$.

  a Find the particular solution, which passes through the point $(2, 5)$.

  b Sketch the family of solution curves for $k = \dfrac{1}{9}, \dfrac{4}{9}$, 1 and include your particular solution in the diagram.

5.2 First-order linear differential equations of the form $\frac{dy}{dx} + Py = Q$ where P and Q are functions of x

Example 5

Find the general solution to the differential equation

$$x^3\frac{dy}{dx} + 3x^2y = \sin x$$

$x^3\dfrac{dy}{dx} + 3x^2y = \sin x$

So $\dfrac{d}{dx}(x^3y) = \sin x$

$\Rightarrow x^3y = \int \sin x \, dx$

$\quad\quad = -\cos x + c$

So $\quad y = -\dfrac{1}{x^3}\cos x + \dfrac{c}{x^3}$

You can use the product rule

$u\dfrac{dv}{dx} + v\dfrac{du}{dx} = \dfrac{d}{dx}(uv)$, with $u = x^3$ and $v = y$, to

recognise that $x^3\dfrac{dy}{dx} + 3x^2y = \dfrac{d}{dx}(x^3y)$.

Use integration as the **inverse** process of differentiation.

Integrate each side of the equation, including an **arbitrary constant** on the right-hand side.

Make y the subject by dividing each of the terms on the right-hand side by x^3.

One side of the differential equation in the example above is an exact derivative of a product in the form

$$f(x)\frac{dy}{dx} + f'(x)y = \frac{d}{dx}(f(x)y)$$

You can solve some first-order differential equations by turning them into equations of this form.

Example 6

Find the general solution of the equation

$$\frac{dy}{dx} + \frac{3y}{x} = \frac{\sin x}{x^3}$$

$\dfrac{dy}{dx} + \dfrac{3y}{x} = \dfrac{\sin x}{x^3}$

Multiply this equation by x^3

$\quad x^3\dfrac{dy}{dx} + 3x^2\, y = \sin x$

The solution is $\quad y = -\dfrac{1}{x^3}\cos x + \dfrac{c}{x^3}$

You can multiply this equation by x^3 to make it into an exact equation.

x^3 is called an integrating factor.

This is an exact equation which was solved as Example 5.

Example 7

Solve the general equation $\dfrac{dy}{dx} + Py = Q$, where P and Q are functions of x.

Multiply the equation by the integrating factor f(x).	You do this to make the equation exact.
Then $f(x) \dfrac{dy}{dx} + f(x)\, Py = f(x)Q$ (1)	Compare the left-hand side of your differential equation with the format for an exact differential equation.
The equation is now exact and so the left-hand side is of the form $$f(x) \dfrac{dy}{dx} + f'(x)y$$	Compare the coefficients of y and put them equal.
So $f(x)\dfrac{dy}{dx} + f(x)Py = f(x)\dfrac{dy}{dx} + f'(x)y$	
$\therefore$ $f'(x) = f(x)P$	This is a ln integral as the numerator is the derivative of the denominator.
Dividing by f(x) and integrating $$\int \dfrac{f'(x)}{f(x)}\, dx = \int P\, dx$$	You need to learn this formula for the integrating factor.
$\therefore$ $\ln\|f(x)\| = \int P\, dx$ $\therefore$ $f(x) = e^{\int P\, dx}$	
Equation (1) becomes	This will lead to a solution provided that these integrals can be found.
$e^{\int P\, dx}\dfrac{dy}{dx} + e^{\int P\, dx}\, Py = e^{\int P\, dx}Q$	
$\therefore$ $\dfrac{d}{dx}(e^{\int P\, dx}\, y) = e^{\int P\, dx}Q$	The left-hand side will always be $y \times$ integrating factor.
$\therefore$ $e^{\int P\, dx}\, y = \int e^{\int P\, dx}Q\, dx + C$	This is the solution to the differential equation.

- For the general equation $\dfrac{dy}{dx} + Py = Q$, where P and Q are functions of x, you obtain the integrating factor by finding $e^{\int P\, dx}$

- You obtain the general solution to the differential equation by using $e^{\int P\, dx} y = \int e^{\int P\, dx} Q\, dx + C$

Example 8

Find the general solution of the differential equation
$$\dfrac{dy}{dx} - 4y = e^x$$

	Find the integrating factor.
The integrating factor is $e^{\int P(x)} = e^{\int (-4)\, dx} = e^{-4x}$	Multiply each term by the integrating factor.
$e^{-4x}\dfrac{dy}{dx} - 4e^{-4x}\, y = e^x e^{-4x}$	
$\Rightarrow$ $\dfrac{d}{dx}(e^{-4x}\, y) = e^{-3x}$	Express the LHS as the derivative of a product.
$\Rightarrow$ $e^{-4x}\, y = \int e^{-3x}\, dx$	Integrate to get the general solution.
$= -\dfrac{1}{3}e^{-3x} + c$	
So $y = -\dfrac{1}{3}e^x + ce^{4x}$	Divide every term, including the constant, by the integrating factor to make y the subject.

Example 9

Find the general solution of the differential equation $\cos x \dfrac{dy}{dx} + 2y \sin x = \cos^4 x$

Divide through by $\cos x$:

$\dfrac{dy}{dx} + 2y \tan x = \cos^3 x$ (1)

The integrating factor is

$e^{\int P(x)dx} = e^{\int 2\tan x\, dx} = e^{2\ln \sec x} = e^{\ln \sec^2 x}$

$= \sec^2 x$

$\sec^2 x \dfrac{dy}{dx} + 2y \sec^2 x \tan x = \sec^2 x \cos^3 x$

So $\dfrac{d}{dx}(y\sec^2 x) = \cos x$

$\Rightarrow \qquad y\sec^2 x = \int \cos x \, dx$

$\Rightarrow \qquad y\sec^2 x = \sin x + c$

$\Rightarrow \qquad\qquad y = \cos^2 x(\sin x + c)$

Divide by $\cos x$ so that equation is in the form $\dfrac{dy}{dx} + P(x) = Q(x)$

Use properties of $\ln$ to simplify the integrating factor.

Multiply equation **(1)** by the integrating factor and simplify the right-hand side.

Integrate to get the general solution and multiply through by $\cos^2 x$.

Exercise 5B

1 Find the general solutions to these differential equations.

a $x\dfrac{dy}{dx} + y = \cos x$

b $e^{-x}\dfrac{dy}{dx} - e^{-x}y = xe^x$

c $\sin x \dfrac{dy}{dx} + y\cos x = 3$

d $\dfrac{1}{x}\dfrac{dy}{dx} - \dfrac{1}{x^2}y = e^x$

e $x^2 e^y \dfrac{dy}{dx} + 2xe^y = x$

f $4xy\dfrac{dy}{dx} + 2y^2 = x^2$

Ⓔ **2 a** Find the general solution to the differential equation $\dfrac{dy}{dx} + 2xy = e^{-x^2}$ **(4 marks)**

  b Describe the behaviour of y as $x \to \infty$.   **(1 mark)**

3 a Find the general solution to the differential equation

   $x^2\dfrac{dy}{dx} + 2xy = 2x + 1$

  b Find the three particular solutions which pass through the points with coordinates $(-\tfrac{1}{2}, 0)$, $(-\tfrac{1}{2}, 3)$ and $(-\tfrac{1}{2}, 19)$ respectively and sketch their solution curves for $x < 0$.

4 a Find the general solution to the differential equation

   $\ln x \dfrac{dy}{dx} + \dfrac{y}{x} = \dfrac{1}{(x+1)(x+2)} \qquad x > 1$

  b Find the particular solution which passes through the point $(2, 2)$.

5 Find the general solutions to these differential equations by using an integrating factor.

a $\dfrac{dy}{dx} + 2y = e^x$

b $\dfrac{dy}{dx} + y\cot x = 1$

c $\dfrac{dy}{dx} + y \sin x = e^{\cos x}$

d $\dfrac{dy}{dx} - y = e^{2x}$

e $\dfrac{dy}{dx} + y \tan x = x \cos x$

f $\dfrac{dy}{dx} + \dfrac{y}{x} = \dfrac{1}{x^2}$

g $x^2 \dfrac{dy}{dx} - xy = \dfrac{x^3}{x+2}, \ x > -2$

h $3x \dfrac{dy}{dx} + y = x$

i $(x+2) \dfrac{dy}{dx} - y = x + 2$

j $x \dfrac{dy}{dx} + 4y = \dfrac{e^x}{x^2}$

6 Find y in terms of x given that $x\dfrac{dy}{dx} + 2y = e^x$ and that $y = 1$ when $x = 1$.   **(8 marks)**

7 Solve the differential equation, giving y in terms of x, where $x^3 \dfrac{dy}{dx} - x^2 y = 1$
and $y = 1$ at $x = 1$.   **(8 marks)**

8 a Find the general solution to the differential equation

$\left(x + \dfrac{1}{x}\right) \dfrac{dy}{dx} + 2y = 2(x^2 + 1)^2$

giving y in terms of x.   **(6 marks)**

b Find the particular solution which satisfies the condition that $y = 1$ at $x = 1$.   **(2 marks)**

9 a Find the general solution to the differential equation

$\cos x \dfrac{dy}{dx} + y = 1, \ -\dfrac{\pi}{2} < x < \dfrac{\pi}{2}$ **(6 marks)**

b Find the particular solution which satisfies the condition that $y = 2$ at $x = 0$.   **(2 marks)**

(E) **10 a** Find the general solution to the differential equation

$\cos x \dfrac{dy}{dx} + y \sin x = 1$ **(6 marks)**

b Find the particular solution such that $y = 3$ when $x = \pi$.   **(2 marks)**

c Show that the points $\left(\dfrac{\pi}{2}, 1\right)$ and $\left(\dfrac{3\pi}{2}, -1\right)$ lie on all possible solution curves.   **(3 marks)**

(E/P) **11** Find a general solution to the equation $a\dfrac{dy}{dx} + by = 0$ in terms of a and b.   **(6 marks)**

5.3 Reducible first-order differential equations

You can use a substitution to reduce a first-order differential equation into a form that you know how to solve, either by separating the variables, or by using an integrating factor.

Example 10

a Show that the substitution $y = xz$ transforms the differential equation

$$\frac{dy}{dx} = \frac{x^2 + 3y^2}{2xy}$$

into

$$x\frac{dz}{dx} = \frac{1 + z^2}{2z}$$

b Hence find the general solution to the original equation, giving y^2 in terms of x.

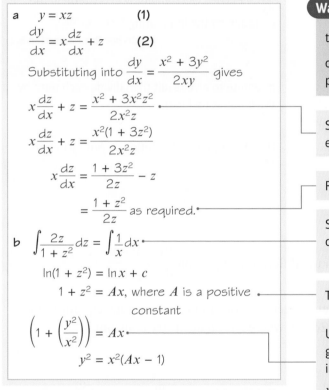

a $y = xz$ (1)

$$\frac{dy}{dx} = x\frac{dz}{dx} + z \quad (2)$$

Substituting into $\dfrac{dy}{dx} = \dfrac{x^2 + 3y^2}{2xy}$ gives

$$x\frac{dz}{dx} + z = \frac{x^2 + 3x^2z^2}{2x^2z}$$

$$x\frac{dz}{dx} + z = \frac{x^2(1 + 3z^2)}{2x^2z}$$

$$x\frac{dz}{dx} = \frac{1 + 3z^2}{2z} - z$$

$$= \frac{1 + z^2}{2z} \text{ as required.}$$

b $\displaystyle\int \frac{2z}{1 + z^2}\,dz = \int \frac{1}{x}\,dx$

$$\ln(1 + z^2) = \ln x + c$$

$$1 + z^2 = Ax, \text{ where } A \text{ is a positive}$$
$$\text{constant}$$

$$\left(1 + \left(\frac{y^2}{x^2}\right)\right) = Ax$$

$$y^2 = x^2(Ax - 1)$$

Watch out Using the substitution, differentiate to get $\dfrac{dy}{dx}$ in terms of $\dfrac{dz}{dx}$. Note that z is a function of x and y, not a constant, so you must use the product rule.

Substitute into the differential equation using equations **(1)** and **(2)**.

Rearrange and simplify your equation.

Separate the variables, then integrate including a constant of integration.

← **Further Pure 2 Section 5.1**

Take exponentials and let $A = e^c$.

Use the original substitution to transform the general solution in z back into a general solution in x and y.
$y = xz$, so $z = \dfrac{y}{x}$ and $z^2 = \left(\dfrac{y}{x}\right)^2$.

Example 11

a Use the substitution $z = y^{-1}$ to transform the differential equation $\dfrac{dy}{dx} + xy = xy^2$ into a differential equation in z and x.

b Solve the new equation, using an integrating factor.

c Find the general solution to the original equation, giving y in terms of x.

a As $z = y^{-1}$, $y = z^{-1}$ ——————————————— Rearrange the substitution to make y the subject.

$$\frac{dy}{dx} = -\frac{1}{z^2}\frac{dz}{dx}$$

Substituting into $\frac{dy}{dx} + xy = xy^2$ gives ——————— Differentiate to give $\frac{dy}{dx}$ in terms of $\frac{dz}{dx}$

$$-\frac{1}{z^2}\frac{dz}{dx} + xz^{-1} = xz^{-2}$$

$$\Rightarrow \frac{dz}{dx} - xz = -x$$ ——————————————— Rearrange and simplify your equation.

b The integrating factor is $e^{\int -x\,dx} = e^{-\frac{x^2}{2}}$

$$e^{-\frac{x^2}{2}}\frac{dz}{dx} - xe^{-\frac{x^2}{2}}z = -xe^{-\frac{x^2}{2}}$$

To solve a differential equation in the form $\frac{dy}{dx} + P(x)y = Q(x)$, multiply every term in the equation by the integrating factor $e^{\int P(x)dx}$.

$$\frac{d}{dx}(e^{-\frac{x^2}{2}}z) = -xe^{-\frac{x^2}{2}}$$

$$e^{-\frac{x^2}{2}}z = -\int xe^{-\frac{x^2}{2}}\,dx$$

← **Further Pure 2 Section 5.2**

$$e^{-\frac{x^2}{2}}z = e^{-\frac{x^2}{2}} + c$$

$$z = 1 + ce^{\frac{x^2}{2}}$$

Integrate to give result then divide each term by the integrating factor.

c As $y = z^{-1}$,

$$y = \frac{1}{1 + ce^{\frac{x^2}{2}}}$$

Use the original substitution to write y in terms of x.

Example **12**

a Use the substitution $u = y - x$ to transform the differential equation $\dfrac{dy}{dx} = \dfrac{y - x + 2}{y - x + 3}$ into a differential equation in u and x.

b By first solving this new equation, show that the general solution to the original equation may be written in the form $(y - x)^2 + 6y - 4x - 2c = 0$, where c is an arbitrary constant.

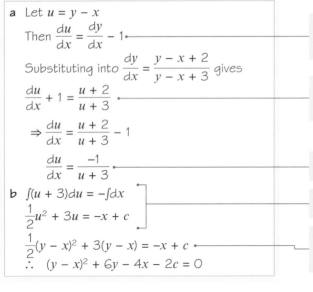

a Let $u = y - x$

Then $\dfrac{du}{dx} = \dfrac{dy}{dx} - 1$ ——————————————— Differentiate to give $\dfrac{du}{dx}$ in terms of $\dfrac{dy}{dx}$

Substituting into $\dfrac{dy}{dx} = \dfrac{y - x + 2}{y - x + 3}$ gives

$$\frac{du}{dx} + 1 = \frac{u + 2}{u + 3}$$ ——————— Make $\dfrac{dy}{dx}$ the subject and substitute.

$$\Rightarrow \frac{du}{dx} = \frac{u + 2}{u + 3} - 1$$

$$\frac{du}{dx} = \frac{-1}{u + 3}$$ ——————————————— Rearrange and simplify your equation.

b $\int(u + 3)du = -\int dx$ ——————————————— Separate the variables and integrate.

$$\frac{1}{2}u^2 + 3u = -x + c$$

$$\frac{1}{2}(y - x)^2 + 3(y - x) = -x + c$$ ——————— Substitute back to give your result in terms of x and y.

$$\therefore \quad (y - x)^2 + 6y - 4x - 2c = 0$$

Exercise 5C

1 Use the substitution $z = \dfrac{y}{x}$ to transform each differential equation into a differential equation in z and x. By first solving the transformed equation, find the general solution to the original equation, giving y in terms of x.

  a $\dfrac{dy}{dx} = \dfrac{y}{x} + \dfrac{x}{y}, \quad x > 0, y > 0$
          b $\dfrac{dy}{dx} = \dfrac{y}{x} + \dfrac{x^2}{y^2}, \quad x > 0$

  c $\dfrac{dy}{dx} = \dfrac{y}{x} + \dfrac{y^2}{x^2}, \quad x > 0$
          d $\dfrac{dy}{dx} = \dfrac{x^3 + 4y^3}{3xy^2}, \quad x > 0$

(E) **2 a** Use the substitution $z = y^{-2}$ to transform the differential equation
$$\frac{dy}{dx} + \left(\frac{1}{2}\tan x\right) y = -(2\sec x)y^3, \quad -\frac{\pi}{2} < x < \frac{\pi}{2}$$
into the differential equation $\dfrac{dz}{dx} - z\tan x = 4\sec x$.   **(5 marks)**

  b By first solving the transformed equation, find the general solution to the original equation, giving y in terms of x.   **(6 marks)**

(E) **3 a** Use the substitution $z = x^{\frac{1}{2}}$ to transform the differential equation
$$\frac{dx}{dt} + t^2 x = t^2 x^{\frac{1}{2}}$$
into the differential equation $\dfrac{dz}{dt} + \dfrac{1}{2}t^2 z = \dfrac{1}{2}t^2$.   **(4 marks)**

  b By first solving the transformed equation, find the general solution to the original equation, giving x in terms of t.   **(6 marks)**

(E) **4 a** Use the substitution $z = y^{-1}$ to transform the differential equation
$$\frac{dy}{dx} - \frac{1}{x}y = \frac{(x+1)^3}{x}y^2$$
into the differential equation $\dfrac{dz}{dx} + \dfrac{1}{x}z = -\dfrac{(x+1)^3}{x}$ **(4 marks)**

  b By first solving the transformed equation, find the general solution to the original equation, giving y in terms of x.   **(6 marks)**

(P) **5 a** Use the substitution $z = y^2$ to transform the differential equation
$$2(1 + x^2)\frac{dy}{dx} + 2xy = \frac{1}{y}$$
into a differential equation in z and x.

  By first solving the transformed equation,

  b find the general solution to the original equation, giving y in terms of x

  c find the particular solution for which $y = 2$ when $x = 0$.

(E/P) **6** Show that the substitution $z = y^{-(n-1)}$ transforms the general equation
$$\frac{dy}{dx} + P(x)y = Q(x)y^n,$$
into the linear equation $\dfrac{dz}{dx} - P(x)(n-1)z = -Q(x)(n-1)$.   **(5 marks)**

(E/P) **7 a** Use the substitution $u = y + 2x$ to transform the differential equation

$$\frac{dy}{dx} = \frac{-(1 + 2y + 4x)}{1 + y + 2x}$$

  into a differential equation in u and x. **(3 marks)**

  b By first solving this new equation, show that the general solution to the original equation may be written as $4x^2 + 4xy + y^2 + 2y + 2x = k$, where k is a constant. **(6 marks)**

Challenge

$$x^2 \frac{dy}{dx} - xy = y^2$$

By means of a suitable substitution, show that the general solution to the differential equation is given by

$$y = -\frac{x}{\ln x + C}$$

where C is a constant of integration.

Chapter review 5

(E) **1** Find the general solution to the differential equation

$$\frac{dy}{dx} + y \tan x = 2 \sec x$$

  giving your answer in the form $y = f(x)$. **(7 marks)**

(E) **2** Find the general solution to the differential equation

$$(1 - x^2)\frac{dy}{dx} + xy = 5x, \quad -1 < x < 1$$

  giving your answer in the form $y = f(x)$. **(7 marks)**

(E) **3** Find the general solution to the differential equation

$$x\frac{dy}{dx} + x + y = 0$$

  giving your answer in the form $y = f(x)$. **(7 marks)**

(E) **4** y satisfies the differential equation

$$\frac{dy}{dx} + \frac{y}{x} = \sqrt{x}$$

  Find y as a function of x. **(7 marks)**

(E) **5** y satisfies the differential equation

$$\frac{dy}{dx} + 2xy = x$$

  Find y in terms of x. **(7 marks)**

(E/P) **6** Find the general solution to the differential equation

$$x(1 - x^2)\frac{dy}{dx} + (2x^2 - 1)y = 2x^3, \quad 0 < x < 1$$

  giving your answer in the form $y = f(x)$. **(7 marks)**

(E/P) **7** Find the general solution to the equation $\dfrac{dy}{dx} - ay = Q(x)$, where a is a constant, giving your answer in terms of a, when

a $Q(x) = ke^{\lambda x}$ (k and λ are constants). **(6 marks)**

Given that $Q(x) = kx^n e^{ax}$, where k and n are constants,

b find the general solution to the differential equation. **(7 marks)**

(E/P) **8** Find, in the form $y = f(x)$, the general solution to the differential equation

$$\tan x \dfrac{dy}{dx} + y = 2\cos x \tan x, \ 0 < x < \dfrac{\pi}{2}$$ **(6 marks)**

(E) **9 a** Show that the transformation $z = y^{-1}$ transforms the differential equation

$$x\dfrac{dy}{dx} + y = y^2 \ln x \qquad \textbf{(1)}$$

into the differential equation

$$\dfrac{dz}{dx} - \dfrac{z}{x} = -\dfrac{\ln x}{x} \qquad \textbf{(2)}$$ **(4 marks)**

b By solving differential equation **(1)**, find the general solution to differential equation **(2)**. **(6 marks)**

(E) **10 a** Show that the substitution $z = y^2$ transforms the differential equation

$$2\cos x \dfrac{dy}{dx} - y\sin x + y^{-1} = 0 \qquad \textbf{(1)}$$

into the differential equation

$$\cos x \dfrac{dz}{dx} - z\sin x = -1 \qquad \textbf{(2)}$$ **(4 marks)**

b Solve differential equation **(2)** to find z as a function of x. **(6 marks)**

c Hence write down the general solution to differential equation **(1)** in the form $y^2 = f(x)$. **(1 mark)**

(E) **11 a** Show that the substitution $z = \dfrac{y}{x}$ transforms the differential equation

$$(x^2 - y^2)\dfrac{dy}{dx} - xy = 0 \qquad \textbf{(1)}$$

into the differential equation

$$x\dfrac{dz}{dx} = \dfrac{z^3}{1 - z^2} \qquad \textbf{(2)}$$ **(4 marks)**

b Solve equation **(2)** and hence obtain the general solution to equation **(1)**. **(6 marks)**

(E) **12 a** Show that the transformation $z = \dfrac{y}{x}$ transforms the differential equation

$$\dfrac{dy}{dx} = \dfrac{y(x+y)}{x(y-x)} \qquad \textbf{(1)}$$

into the differential equation

$$x\dfrac{dz}{dx} = \dfrac{2z}{z-1} \qquad \textbf{(2)}$$ **(4 marks)**

b Solve equation **(2)** and hence obtain the general solution to equation **(1)**. **(6 marks)**

(E) **13 a** Show that the substitution $z = \dfrac{y}{x}$ transforms the differential equation

$$\frac{dy}{dx} = \frac{-3xy}{y^2 - 3x^2} \qquad \textbf{(1)}$$

into the equation

$$x\frac{dy}{dx} = -\frac{z^3}{z^2 - 3} \qquad \textbf{(2)}$$ **(4 marks)**

b By solving equation **(2)**, find the general solution to equation **(1)**. **(6 marks)**

(E) **14 a** Use the substitution $u = x + y$ to show that the differential equation

$$\frac{dy}{dx} = (x + y + 1)(x + y - 1)$$

can be written as

$$\frac{du}{dx} = u^2 \qquad \textbf{(3 marks)}$$

b Hence find the general solution to the original differential equation. **(4 marks)**

(E) **15 a** Show that the transformation $u = y - x - 2$ can be used to transform the differential equation

$$\frac{dy}{dx} = (y - x - 2)^2 \qquad \textbf{(1)}$$

into the differential equation

$$\frac{du}{dx} = u^2 - 1 \qquad \textbf{(2)}$$ **(3 marks)**

b Solve equation **(2)** and hence find the general solution to equation **(1)**. **(4 marks)**

(E/P) **16** A particle is moving with velocity v at time t such that

$$t\frac{dv}{dt} + v = 2t^3 v^3, \quad 0 < t < \sqrt{3} \qquad \textbf{(1)}$$

a Use the substitution $u = v^{-2}$ to show that the differential equation can be transformed

into $\dfrac{du}{dt} - \dfrac{2u}{t} = -4t^2$ **(5 marks)**

b Given that $v = \frac{1}{2}$ when $t = 1$, show that the solution to differential equation **(1)** can

be written as $v = \sqrt{\dfrac{1}{t^2(c - 4t)}}$

where c is a constant to be found. **(8 marks)**

Summary of key points

1 You can solve a first-order differential equation of the form $\dfrac{dy}{dx} + P(x)y = Q(x)$ by multiplying every term by the **integrating factor** $e^{\int P(x)dx}$.

2 You can use a substitution to reduce a first-order differential equation into a form that you know how to solve, either by separating the variables, or by using an integrating factor.

6 SECOND-ORDER DIFFERENTIAL EQUATIONS

5.1
5.2

Learning objectives

After completing this chapter you should be able to:

* Solve second-order homogeneous differential equations using the
  auxiliary equation → **pages 106–110**

* Solve second-order non-homogeneous differential equations using the
  complementary function and the particular integral → **pages 110–115**

* Use boundary conditions to find a particular solution to a second-order
  differential equation → **pages 115–118**

* Use a given substitution to transform a second-order differential
  equation into one that can be solved → **pages 118–121**

Prior knowledge check

1 Find the general solutions of these differential equations:

a $x\dfrac{\mathrm{d}y}{\mathrm{d}x} = 2(y-1)$

← **Further Pure 2 Section 5.1**

b $\dfrac{\mathrm{d}y}{\mathrm{d}x} + \dfrac{y}{x} = 2x$

2 Find the particular solution to the differential equations

a $\dfrac{\mathrm{d}y}{\mathrm{d}x} + 3xy = \mathrm{e}^x$ when $x = 0$, $y = 2$

b $x\dfrac{\mathrm{d}y}{\mathrm{d}x} - y = x^3$ when $x = 1$, $y = 3$

← **Pure 4 Section 5.2**

Many real-life situations can be modelled using differential equations: for example, the displacement of a point on a vibrating spring from a fixed point, or the distance fallen by a parachutist.

6.1 Second-order homogeneous differential equations

A second-order differential equation contains second derivatives.

Example 1

Find the general solution to the differential equation
$$\frac{d^2y}{dx^2} = 12x$$

$$\frac{dy}{dx} = 6x^2 + A$$

$$y = 2x^3 + Ax + B$$

Watch out The general solution to this second-order differential equation needs **two** arbitrary constants. If you wanted to find a particular solution you would need to know **two** boundary conditions.

In this section you will look at techniques for solving **linear** differential equations that are of the form
$$a\frac{d^2y}{dx^2} + b\frac{dy}{dx} + cy = 0$$
where a, b and c are real constants. Equations of this form (with 0 on the right-hand side) are called **second-order homogeneous** differential equations with constant coefficients.

Notation You sometimes see differential equations of this type written as
$$ay'' + by' + cy = 0 \text{ where } y'' = \frac{d^2y}{dx^2} \text{ and } y' = \frac{dy}{dx}$$

Using the techniques from the previous section, the general solution of $a\frac{dy}{dx} + by = 0$ is of the form
$y = Ae^{kx}$, where $k = -\frac{b}{a}$. Notice that k is the solution to the equation $ak + b = 0$.

This suggests that an equation of the form $y = Ae^{kx}$ might also be a solution of the second-order differential equation $a\frac{d^2y}{dx^2} + b\frac{dy}{dx} + cy = 0$. But it cannot be the general solution, as it only contains one arbitrary constant. Since two constants are necessary for a second-order differential equation, you can try a solution of the form $y = Ae^{\lambda x} + Be^{\mu x}$, where A and B are arbitrary constants and λ and μ are constants to be determined.
$$\frac{dy}{dx} = A\lambda e^{\lambda x} + B\mu e^{\mu x}$$
$$\frac{d^2y}{dx^2} = A\lambda^2 e^{\lambda x} + B\mu^2 e^{\mu x}$$

Substituting these into the differential equation gives
$$a(A\lambda^2 e^{\lambda x} + B\mu^2 e^{\mu x}) + b(A\lambda e^{\lambda x} + B\mu e^{\mu x}) + c(Ae^{\lambda x} + Be^{\mu x}) = 0$$
$$aA\lambda^2 e^{\lambda x} + aB\mu^2 e^{\mu x} + bA\lambda e^{\lambda x} + bB\mu e^{\mu x} + cAe^{\lambda x} + cBe^{\mu x} = 0$$
$$Ae^{\lambda x}(a\lambda^2 + b\lambda + c) + Be^{\mu x}(a\mu^2 + b\mu + c) = 0$$

This shows that the equation $y = Ae^{\lambda x} + Be^{\mu x}$ will satisfy the original differential equation if both λ and μ are solutions to the quadratic equation $am^2 + bm + c = 0$.

The equation $am^2 + bm + c = 0$ is called the **auxiliary equation.**

The natures of the roots α and β of the auxiliary equation, $am^2 + bm + c = 0$ determine the

general solution to the differential equation $a\dfrac{d^2y}{dx^2} + b\dfrac{dy}{dx} + cy = 0$.

You need to consider three different cases:

- **Case 1: $b^2 > 4ac$**
  The auxiliary equation has two distinct real roots α and β. The general solution will be of the form $y = Ae^{\alpha x} + Be^{\beta x}$ where A and B are arbitrary constants.

- **Case 2: $b^2 = 4ac$**
  The auxiliary equation has one repeated root α. The general solution will be of the form $y = (A + Bx)\,e^{\alpha x}$ where A and B are arbitrary constants.

- **Case 3: $b^2 < 4ac$**
  The auxiliary equation has two complex conjugate roots α and β equal to $p \pm q$i. The general solution will be of the form $y = e^{px}(A\cos qx + B\sin qx)$ where A and B are arbitrary constants.

Links   Case 3 is equivalent to $y = Ae^{\alpha x} + Be^{\beta x}$ with complex α and β.

Notation   If the roots are purely imaginary ($p = 0$), the general solution reduces to $y = A\cos qx + B\sin qx$

Example (2)

a Find the general solution to the equation $2\dfrac{d^2y}{dx^2} + 5\dfrac{dy}{dx} + 3y = 0$.

b Verify that your answer to part **a** satisfies the equation.

a $2m^2 + 5m + 3 = 0$ — Write down the auxiliary equation.

$(2m + 3)(m + 1) = 0 \Rightarrow m = -\dfrac{3}{2}$ or $m = -1$ — Solve the auxiliary equation.

So the general solution is

$y = Ae^{-\frac{3}{2}x} + Be^{-x}$ where A and B are — Write down the general solution.

arbitrary constants

b $y = Ae^{-\frac{3}{2}x} + Be^{-x}$

$\dfrac{dy}{dx} = -\dfrac{3}{2}Ae^{-\frac{3}{2}x} - Be^{-x}$

$\dfrac{d^2y}{dx^2} = \dfrac{9}{4}Ae^{-\frac{3}{2}x} + Be^{-x}$

Write down expressions for the first and second derivatives.

$2(\dfrac{9}{4}Ae^{-\frac{3}{2}x} + Be^{-x}) + 5(-\dfrac{3}{2}Ae^{-\frac{3}{2}x} - Be^{-x})$
$\qquad + 3(Ae^{-\frac{3}{2}x} + Be^{-x})$

$= \dfrac{9}{2}Ae^{-\frac{3}{2}x} - \dfrac{15}{2}Ae^{-\frac{3}{2}x} + 3Ae^{-\frac{3}{2}x}$
$\qquad + 2Be^{-x} - 5Be^{-x} + 3Be^{-x}$

Substitute your expressions for $\dfrac{d^2y}{dx^2}, \dfrac{dy}{dx}$ and y into the differential equation, expand and simplify.

$= 0$ as required.

Example 3

Show that $y = (A + Bx)e^{3x}$ satisfies the differential equation $\dfrac{d^2y}{dx^2} - 6\dfrac{dy}{dx} + 9y = 0$

Let $y = Ae^{3x} + Bxe^{3x}$, then

$\dfrac{dy}{dx} = 3Ae^{3x} + 3Bxe^{3x} + Be^{3x}$

$\dfrac{d^2y}{dx^2} = 9Ae^{3x} + 9Bxe^{3x} + 3Be^{3x} + 3Be^{3x}$

$\qquad = 9Ae^{3x} + 9Bxe^{3x} + 6Be^{3x}$

Differentiate the expression for y twice.

$\dfrac{d^2y}{dx^2} - 6\dfrac{dy}{dx} + 9y = 9Ae^{3x} + 9Bxe^{3x} + 6Be^{3x}$

$\qquad\qquad - 6(3Ae^{3x} + 3Bxe^{3x} + Be^{3x})$

$\qquad\qquad + 9(Ae^{3x} + Bxe^{3x}) = 0$

So $y = (A + Bx)e^{3x}$ is a solution to the equation.

Substitute into the left-hand side of the differential equation and simplify to show that the result is zero.

Notation   The auxiliary equation $m^2 - 6m + 9 = 0$ has a repeated root at $m = 3$ so the general solution is in the form you expect.

Example 4

Find the general solution to the differential equation $\dfrac{d^2y}{dx^2} + 8\dfrac{dy}{dx} + 16y = 0$

$m^2 + 8m + 16 = 0$

$(m + 4)^2 = 0 \Rightarrow m = -4$

So the general solution is $y = (A + Bx)e^{-4x}$.

Write down the auxiliary equation.

Solve the auxiliary equation. In this case there is a repeated root.

Example 5

Find the general solution to the differential equation $\dfrac{d^2y}{dx^2} - 6\dfrac{dy}{dx} + 34y = 0$

$m^2 - 6m + 34 = 0 \Rightarrow m = 3 \pm 5i$

So the general solution is

$y = e^{3x}(A\cos 5x + B\sin 5x)$

Write down the auxiliary equation and solve it using the quadratic formula or by completing the square. In this case there are two complex conjugate roots.

Example 6

Find the general solution to the differential equation $\dfrac{d^2y}{dx^2} + 16y = 0$

$m^2 + 16 = 0 \Rightarrow m = \pm 4i$

So the general solution is

$y = A\cos 4x + B\sin 4x$

Write down the auxiliary equation and solve it. In this case there are two purely imaginary roots.

This is in the form $y = e^{px}(A\cos qx + B\sin qx)$ with $p = 0$.

Exercise 6A

1 Find the general solution to each differential equation.

a $\dfrac{d^2y}{dx^2} + 5\dfrac{dy}{dx} + 6y = 0$ **b** $\dfrac{d^2y}{dx^2} - 8\dfrac{dy}{dx} + 12y = 0$

c $\dfrac{d^2y}{dx^2} + 2\dfrac{dy}{dx} - 15y = 0$ **d** $\dfrac{d^2y}{dx^2} - 3\dfrac{dy}{dx} - 28y = 0$

e $\dfrac{d^2y}{dx^2} + 5\dfrac{dy}{dx} = 0$ **f** $3\dfrac{d^2y}{dx^2} + 7\dfrac{dy}{dx} + 2y = 0$

g $4\dfrac{d^2y}{dx^2} - 7\dfrac{dy}{dx} - 2y = 0$ **h** $15\dfrac{d^2y}{dx^2} - 7\dfrac{dy}{dx} - 2y = 0$

2 Find the general solution to each differential equation.

a $\dfrac{d^2y}{dx^2} + 10\dfrac{dy}{dx} + 25y = 0$ **b** $\dfrac{d^2y}{dx^2} - 18\dfrac{dy}{dx} + 81y = 0$

c $\dfrac{d^2y}{dx^2} + 2\dfrac{dy}{dx} + y = 0$ **d** $\dfrac{d^2y}{dx^2} - 8\dfrac{dy}{dx} + 16y = 0$

e $16\dfrac{d^2y}{dx^2} + 8\dfrac{dy}{dx} + y = 0$ **f** $4\dfrac{d^2y}{dx^2} - 4\dfrac{dy}{dx} + y = 0$

g $4\dfrac{d^2y}{dx^2} + 20\dfrac{dy}{dx} + 25y = 0$ **h** $\dfrac{d^2y}{dx^2} + 2\sqrt{3}\dfrac{dy}{dx} + 3y = 0$

3 Find the general solution to each differential equation.

a $\dfrac{d^2y}{dx^2} + 25y = 0$ **b** $\dfrac{d^2y}{dx^2} + 81y = 0$

c $\dfrac{d^2y}{dx^2} + y = 0$ **d** $9\dfrac{d^2y}{dx^2} + 16y = 0$

e $\dfrac{d^2y}{dx^2} + 8\dfrac{dy}{dx} + 17y = 0$ **f** $\dfrac{d^2y}{dx^2} - 4\dfrac{dy}{dx} + 5y = 0$

g $\dfrac{d^2y}{dx^2} + 20\dfrac{dy}{dx} + 109y = 0$ **h** $\dfrac{d^2y}{dx^2} + \sqrt{3}\dfrac{dy}{dx} + 3y = 0$

4 Find the general solution to each differential equation.

a $\dfrac{d^2y}{dx^2} + 14\dfrac{dy}{dx} + 49y = 0$ **b** $\dfrac{d^2y}{dx^2} + \dfrac{dy}{dx} - 12y = 0$

c $\dfrac{d^2y}{dx^2} + 4\dfrac{dy}{dx} + 13y = 0$ **d** $16\dfrac{d^2y}{dx^2} - 24\dfrac{dy}{dx} + 9y = 0$

e $9\dfrac{d^2y}{dx^2} - 6\dfrac{dy}{dx} + 5y = 0$ **f** $6\dfrac{d^2y}{dx^2} - \dfrac{dy}{dx} - 2y = 0$

(E/P) **5** Given the differential equation $\dfrac{d^2x}{dt^2} + 2k\dfrac{dx}{dt} + 9x = 0$, where k is a real constant,

    a find the general solution to the differential equation when:

        i $|k| > 3$

        ii $|k| < 3$

        iii $|k| = 3$ **(8 marks)**

    b In the case where $k = 2$,

        i find the general solution

        ii describe what happens to x as $t \to \infty$.   **(4 marks)**

(P) **6** Given that $am^2 + bm + c = 0$ has equal roots $m = \alpha$, prove that $y = (A + Bx)e^{\alpha x}$ is a solution to the differential equation $a\dfrac{d^2y}{dx^2} + b\dfrac{dy}{dx} + c = 0$.

(P) **7** Given that $y = f(x)$ and $y = g(x)$ are both solutions to the second-order differential equation $a\dfrac{d^2y}{dx^2} + b\dfrac{dy}{dx} + cy = 0$,

> **Notation**   This result is known as the **principle of superposition**.

prove that $y = Af(x) + Bg(x)$, where A and B are real constants, is also a solution.

> **Challenge**
>
> Let α and β be the roots of a real-valued quadratic equation, so that $\alpha = p + iq$ and $\beta = p - iq$, $p, q \in \mathbb{R}$. Show that it is possible to choose $A, B \in \mathbb{C}$ such that $Ae^{\alpha x} + Be^{\alpha x}$ can be written in the form $e^{px}(C\cos qx + D\sin qx)$ where C and D are arbitrary real constants.

6.2 **Second-order non-homogeneous differential equations**

A second-order differential equation of the form

$$a\frac{d^2y}{dx^2} + b\frac{dy}{dx} + cy = f(x)$$

is called a **non-homogeneous differential equation**.

> **Notation**   You sometimes see differential equations of this type written as
>
> $ay'' + by' + cy = f(x)$ where $y'' = \dfrac{d^2y}{dx^2}$ and $y' = \dfrac{dy}{dx}$

To solve an equation of this type you first find the general solution of the corresponding **homogeneous differential equation**, $a\dfrac{d^2y}{dx^2} + b\dfrac{dy}{dx} + cy = 0$. This is called the **complementary function (C.F.)**.

You then need to find a **particular integral (P.I.)**, which is a function that satisfies the differential equation. The form of the particular integral depends on the form of $f(x)$.

This table provides some particular integrals to try.

Form of $f(x)$	Form of particular integral
p	λ
$p + qx$	$\lambda + \mu x$
$p + qx + rx^2$	$\lambda + \mu x + v x^2$
pe^{kx}	λe^{kx}
$p\cos \omega x + q \sin \omega x$	$\lambda \cos \omega x + \mu \sin \omega x$

Use this form of the P.I. for functions such as $4x^2$ or $1 - x^2$.

Use this form of the P.I. for functions such as $\sin 2x$ or $5 \cos x$.

- A particular integral is a function which satisfies the original differential equation.

Example **7**

Find a particular integral of the differential equation $\dfrac{d^2y}{dx^2} - 5\dfrac{dy}{dx} + 6y = f(x)$ when $f(x)$ is:

a 3   **b** $2x$ **c** $3x^2$ **d** e^x **e** $13 \sin 3x$

a Let $y = \lambda$, then $\dfrac{dy}{dx} = 0$ and $\dfrac{d^2y}{dx^2} = 0$

Substitute into $\dfrac{d^2y}{dx^2} - 5\dfrac{dy}{dx} + 6y = 3$:

$0 - 5 \times 0 + 6\lambda = 3$

$\Rightarrow \lambda = \frac{1}{2}$

So a particular integral is $\frac{1}{2}$

When $f(x) = 3$, which is constant, choose P.I. $= \lambda$, which is also constant.

Differentiate twice and substitute the derivatives into the differential equation.

Solve equation to give the value of λ.

b Let $y = \lambda x + \mu$, then $\dfrac{dy}{dx} = \lambda$ and $\dfrac{d^2y}{dx^2} = 0$

Substitute into $\dfrac{d^2y}{dx^2} - 5\dfrac{dy}{dx} + 6y = 2x$:

$0 - 5 \times \lambda + 6(\lambda x + \mu) = 2x$

$\Rightarrow (6\mu - 5\lambda) + 6\lambda x = 2x$

$\Rightarrow 6\mu - 5\lambda = 0$ and $6\lambda = 2$

$\Rightarrow \lambda = \frac{1}{3}$ and $\mu = \frac{5}{18}$

So a particular integral is $\frac{1}{3}x + \frac{5}{18}$

When $f(x) = 2x$, which is a linear function of x, choose P.I. $= \lambda x + \mu$.

Differentiate twice and substitute the derivatives into the differential equation.

Equate the constant terms and the coefficients of x to give simultaneous equations, which you can solve to find λ and μ.

c Let $y = \lambda x^2 + \mu x + v$

Then $\dfrac{dy}{dx} = 2\lambda x + \mu$ and $\dfrac{d^2y}{dx^2} = 2\lambda$

Substitute into $\dfrac{d^2y}{dx^2} - 5\dfrac{dy}{dx} + 6y = 3x^2$:

$2\lambda - 5(2\lambda x + \mu) + 6(\lambda x^2 + \mu x + v) = 3x^2$

$\Rightarrow (2\lambda - 5\mu + 6v) + (6\mu - 10\lambda)x + 6\lambda x^2 = 3x^2$

$\Rightarrow 2\lambda - 5\mu + 6v = 0, 6\mu - 10\lambda = 0$ and $6\lambda = 3$

$\Rightarrow \lambda = \frac{1}{2}, \mu = \frac{5}{6}$ and $v = \frac{19}{36}$

So a particular integral is $\frac{1}{2}x^2 + \frac{5}{6}x + \frac{19}{36}$

As $f(x) = 3x^2$, which is a quadratic function of x let P.I. $= \lambda x^2 + \mu x + v$.

Equate the constant terms, the coefficients of x and the coefficients of x^2 to give simultaneous equations, which you can solve to find λ, μ and v.

d Let $y = \lambda e^x$, then $\dfrac{dy}{dx} = \lambda e^x$ and $\dfrac{d^2y}{dx^2} = \lambda e^x$.

As $f(x) = e^x$, which is an exponential function of x let P.I. $= \lambda e^x$.

Substitute into $\dfrac{d^2y}{dx^2} - 5\dfrac{dy}{dx} + 6y = e^x$:

$\lambda e^x - 5\lambda e^x + 6\lambda e^x = e^x$

$\Rightarrow 2\lambda e^x = e^x$

$\Rightarrow \lambda = \frac{1}{2}$

Equate coefficients of e^x to find the value of λ.

So a particular integral is $\frac{1}{2}e^x$

e Let $y = \lambda \sin 3x + \mu \cos 3x$

As $f(x) = 13 \sin 3x$, which is a trigonometric function of x let P.I. $= \lambda \sin 3x + \mu \cos 3x$, also a similar trigonometric function.

Then $\dfrac{dy}{dx} = 3\lambda \cos 3x - 3\mu \sin 3x$

and $\dfrac{d^2y}{dx^2} = -9\lambda \sin 3x - 9\mu \cos 3x$

Substitute into $\dfrac{d^2y}{dx^2} - 5\dfrac{dy}{dx} + 6y = 13 \sin 3x$:

$-9\lambda \sin 3x - 9\mu \cos 3x - 5(3\lambda \cos 3x - 3\mu \sin 3x)$
$\quad + 6(\lambda \sin 3x + \mu \cos 3x) = 13 \sin 3x$

$\Rightarrow (-9\lambda + 15\mu + 6\lambda) \sin 3x +$
$\qquad\qquad (-9\mu - 15\lambda + 6\mu) \cos 3x = 13 \sin 3x$

$\Rightarrow -9\lambda + 15\mu + 6\lambda = 13$

$\quad$ and $-9\mu - 15\lambda + 6\mu = 0$

$\Rightarrow \lambda = -\frac{1}{6}$ and $\mu = \frac{5}{6}$

So a particular integral is $-\frac{1}{6} \sin 3x + \frac{5}{6} \cos 3x$

Problem-solving

Equate coefficients of $\sin 3x$ and of $\cos 3x$ and solve simultaneous equations.

- To find the general solution to the differential equation $a\dfrac{d^2y}{dx^2} + b\dfrac{dy}{dx} + cy = f(x)$

  - Solve the corresponding homogeneous equation $a\dfrac{d^2y}{dx^2} + b\dfrac{dy}{dx} + cy = 0$ to find the complementary function (C.F.)
  - Choose an appropriate form for the particular integral (P.I.) and substitute into the original equation to find the values of any coefficients.
  - The general solution is $y =$ C.F. $+$ P.I.

Example (8)

Find the general solution to the differential equation $\dfrac{d^2y}{dx^2} - 5\dfrac{dy}{dx} + 6y = f(x)$ when $f(x)$ is:

a 3   **b** $2x$ **c** $3x^2$ **d** e^x **e** $13 \sin 3x$

$m^2 - 5m + 6 = 0$

$(m - 3)(m - 2) = 0 \Rightarrow m = 3$ or $m = 2$

Hence the complementary function is

$y = Ae^{3x} + Be^{2x}$ where A and B are arbitrary

constants.

Solve the auxiliary equation to find the values of m.

> The particular integrals were already found in
> Example 7 so the general solutions are:
>
> **a** $y = Ae^{3x} + Be^{2x} + \frac{1}{2}$
>
> **b** $y = Ae^{3x} + Be^{2x} + \frac{1}{3}x + \frac{5}{18}$
>
> **c** $y = Ae^{3x} + Be^{2x} + \frac{1}{2}x^2 + \frac{5}{6}x + \frac{19}{36}$
>
> **d** $y = Ae^{3x} + Be^{2x} + \frac{1}{2}e^x$
>
> **e** $y = Ae^{3x} + Be^{2x} - \frac{1}{6}\sin 3x + \frac{5}{6}\cos 3x$

The general solution is $y = $ C.F. + P.I.

You need to be careful if the standard form of the particular integral contains terms which form part of the complementary function. If this is the case, you need to modify your particular integral so that no two terms in the general solution have the same form.

For example, this situation occurs when f(x) is of the form pe^{kx}, and k is one of the roots of the auxiliary equation. In this case you can try a particular integral of the form, λxe^{kx}.

Example 9

Find the general solution to the differential equation $\dfrac{d^2y}{dx^2} - 5\dfrac{dy}{dx} + 6y = e^{2x}$

> As in Example 8, the complementary function is
> $y = Ae^{3x} + Be^{2x}$.
> The particular integral cannot be λe^{2x},
> as this is part of the complementary function.
>
> So let $y = \lambda xe^{2x}$
>
> Then $\dfrac{dy}{dx} = 2\lambda xe^{2x} + \lambda e^{2x}$
>
> and
>
> $\dfrac{d^2y}{dx^2} = 4\lambda xe^{2x} + 2\lambda e^{2x} + 2\lambda e^{2x} = 4\lambda xe^{2x} + 4\lambda e^{2x}$
>
> Substitute into $\dfrac{d^2y}{dx^2} - 5\dfrac{dy}{dx} + 6y = e^{2x}$:
>
> $4\lambda xe^{2x} + 4\lambda e^{2x} - 5(2\lambda xe^{2x} + \lambda e^{2x}) + 6\lambda xe^{2x} = e^{2x}$
>
> $\Rightarrow -\lambda e^{2x} = e^{2x}$
>
> $\Rightarrow \lambda = -1$
>
> So a particular integral is $-xe^{2x}$.
> The general solution is $y = Ae^{3x} + Be^{2x} - xe^{2x}$.

Watch out   The function λe^{2x} is **part of the C.F.** and satisfies the differential equation $\dfrac{d^2y}{dx^2} - 5\dfrac{dy}{dx} + 6y = 0$, so it cannot also satisfy $\dfrac{d^2y}{dx^2} - 5\dfrac{dy}{dx} + 6y = e^{2x}$

Let the P.I. be λxe^{2x} and differentiate, substitute and solve to find λ.

The general solution is $y = $ C.F. + P.I.

When one of the roots of the auxiliary equation is 0, the complementary function will contain a constant term. If f(x) is a polynomial, you will need to multiply its particular integral by x to make sure the P.I. does not also contain a constant term.

Example (10)

Find the general solution to the differential equation
$$\frac{d^2y}{dx^2} - 2\frac{dy}{dx} = 3$$

Find the complementary function by putting the right-hand side of the differential equation equal to zero, and solving this new equation.

First consider the equation $\frac{d^2y}{dx^2} - 2\frac{dy}{dx} = 0$

Write down and solve the auxiliary equation.

$m^2 - 2m = 0$

$m(m - 2) = 0$

$\Rightarrow m = 0 \text{ or } m = 2$

So the complementary function is $y = A + Be^{2x}$.

The particular integral cannot be a constant, as this is part of the complementary function, so let $y = \lambda x$.

Try to find a particular integral. The right-hand side of the original equation was 3, which was a constant and usually this would imply a constant P.I.

As the C.F. includes a constant term 'A', the P.I. cannot also be constant. A value of λ would satisfy $\frac{d^2y}{dx^2} - 2\frac{dy}{dx} = 0$ rather than $\frac{d^2y}{dx^2} - 2\frac{dy}{dx} = 3$

Then $\frac{dy}{dx} = \lambda$ and $\frac{d^2y}{dx^2} = 0$

Substitute into $\frac{d^2y}{dx^2} - 2\frac{dy}{dx} = 3$:

$0 - 2\lambda = 3$

$\Rightarrow \lambda = -\frac{3}{2}$

Multiply the 'expected' P.I. by x and try λx instead.

So a particular integral is $-\frac{3}{2}x$

The general solution is $y = A + Be^{2x} - \frac{3}{2}x$.

The general solution is $y = $ C.F. + P.I.

Exercise (6B)

1 Solve each differential equation, giving the general solution.

a $\frac{d^2y}{dx^2} + 6\frac{dy}{dx} + 5y = 10$

b $\frac{d^2y}{dx^2} - 8\frac{dy}{dx} + 12y = 36x$

c $\frac{d^2y}{dx^2} + \frac{dy}{dx} - 12y = 12e^{2x}$

d $\frac{d^2y}{dx^2} + 2\frac{dy}{dx} - 15y = 5$

e $\frac{d^2y}{dx^2} - 8\frac{dy}{dx} + 16y = 8x + 12$

f $\frac{d^2y}{dx^2} + 2\frac{dy}{dx} + y = 25\cos 2x$

g $\frac{d^2y}{dx^2} + 81y = 15e^{3x}$

h $\frac{d^2y}{dx^2} + 4y = \sin x$

i $\frac{d^2y}{dx^2} - 4\frac{dy}{dx} + 5y = 25x^2 - 7$

j $\frac{d^2y}{dx^2} - 2\frac{dy}{dx} + 26y = e^x$

(E) 2 a Find a particular integral for the differential equation
$$\frac{d^2y}{dx^2} - 5\frac{dy}{dx} + 4y = x^2 - 3x + 2$$
(6 marks)

b Hence find the general solution. **(3 marks)**

(E/P) **3** y satisfies the differential equation

$$\frac{d^2y}{dx^2} - 6\frac{dy}{dx} = 2x^2 - x + 1$$

    a Find the complementary function for this differential equation.   **(3 marks)**

    b Hence find a suitable particular integral and write down the general solution to the differential equation.   **(7 marks)**

> **Hint**   Try a particular integral of the form $\lambda x + \mu x^2 + \nu x^3$.

(E/P) **4** Find the general solution to the differential equation

$$\frac{d^2y}{dx^2} + 4\frac{dy}{dx} = 24x^2$$

    (10 marks)

(E/P) **5**   **a** Explain why λxe^x is not a suitable form for the particular integral for the differential equation

$$\frac{d^2y}{dx^2} - 2\frac{dy}{dx} + y = e^x$$

    (2 marks)

    b Find the value of λ for which $\lambda x^2 e^x$ is a particular integral for the differential equation.

    (5 marks)

    c Hence find the general solution.   **(3 marks)**

(E/P) **6** $\dfrac{d^2y}{dt^2} + 4\dfrac{dy}{dt} + 3y = kt + 5$, where k is a constant and $t > 0$.

    a Find the general solution to the differential equation in terms of k.   **(7 marks)**

For large values of t, this general solution may be approximated by a linear function.

    b Given that $k = 6$, find the equation of this linear function.   **(2 marks)**

> **Challenge**
>
> Find the general solution of the differential equation
>
> $$\frac{d^2y}{dx^2} + y = 5xe^{2x}$$

6.3   Using boundary conditions

You can use given boundary conditions to find a particular solution to a second-order differential equation. Since there are two arbitrary constants, you will need two boundary conditions to determine the complete particular solution.

Example 11

Find y in terms of x, given that $\dfrac{d^2y}{dx^2} - y = 2e^x$, and that $\dfrac{dy}{dx} = 0$ and $y = 0$ at $x = 0$.

First consider the equation $\dfrac{d^2y}{dx^2} - y = 0$.

$m^2 - 1 = 0 \Rightarrow m = \pm 1$

So the complementary function is $y = Ae^x + Be^{-x}$.

     Solve the auxiliary equation to find the values of m.

The particular integral cannot be λe^x,

as this is part of the complementary function,

so let $y = \lambda x e^x$.

Then $\dfrac{dy}{dx} = \lambda x e^x + \lambda e^x$ and $\dfrac{d^2y}{dx^2} = \lambda x e^x + \lambda e^x + \lambda e^x$

Substitute into $\dfrac{d^2y}{dx^2} - y = 2e^x$:

$\lambda x e^x + \lambda e^x + \lambda e^x - \lambda x e^x = 2e^x$

$\Rightarrow \lambda = 1$

So a particular integral is $x e^x$.

The general solution is

$y = A e^x + B e^{-x} + x e^x$

Since $y = 0$ at $x = 0$, $0 = A + B$

$\quad \Rightarrow \quad A + B = 0$

Differentiating $y = A e^x + B e^{-x} + x e^x$ with respect to x gives

$\dfrac{dy}{dx} = A e^x - B e^{-x} + e^x + x e^x$

Since $\dfrac{dy}{dx} = 0$ at $x = 0$, $0 = A - B + 1$

$\quad \Rightarrow \quad A - B = -1$

Solving the simultaneous equations gives

$A = -\tfrac{1}{2}$, and $B = \tfrac{1}{2}$

So $y = -\tfrac{1}{2}e^x + \tfrac{1}{2}e^{-x} + x e^x$ is the required solution.

As λe^x satisfies $\dfrac{d^2y}{dx^2} - y = 0$, it cannot also satisfy $\dfrac{d^2y}{dx^2} - y = 2e^x$

Substitute the boundary condition, $y = 0$ at $x = 0$, into the general solution to obtain an equation relating A and B.

Substitute the second boundary condition, $\dfrac{dy}{dx} = 0$ at $x = 0$, into the derivative of the general solution, to obtain a second equation relating A and B.

Solve the two equations to find values for A and B.

Example 12

Given that a particular integral is of the form $\lambda \sin 2t$, find the solution to the differential equation $\dfrac{d^2x}{dt^2} + x = 3\sin 2t$, for which $x = 0$ and $\dfrac{dx}{dt} = 1$ when $t = 0$.

First consider the equation $\dfrac{d^2x}{dt^2} + x = 0$.

$m^2 + 1 = 0 \Rightarrow m = \pm i$

So, the complementary function is

$x = A\cos t + B\sin t$.

The particular integral is $\lambda \sin 2t$,

so let $x = \lambda \sin 2t$.

Then $\dfrac{dx}{dt} = 2\lambda \cos 2t$ and $\dfrac{d^2x}{dt^2} = -4\lambda \sin 2t$

Substitute into $\dfrac{d^2x}{dt^2} + x = 3\sin 2t$:

$-4\lambda \sin 2t + \lambda \sin 2t = 3\sin 2t$

$\Rightarrow \lambda = -1$

Solve the auxiliary equation to find the values of m.

Watch out   Normally you would need to try a particular integral of the form $\lambda \sin 2t + \mu \cos 2t$ for this equation. However, in this case you are told that there is a particular integral in the form $\lambda \sin 2t$.

So a particular integral is $-\sin 2t$.

The general solution is

$x = A\cos t + B\sin t - \sin 2t$ •

Since $x = 0$ at $t = 0$, $A = 0$. •

Differentiating $x = B\sin t - \sin 2t$ with respect to t gives

$\dfrac{dx}{dt} = B\cos t - 2\cos 2t$

Since $\dfrac{dx}{dt} = 1$ at $t = 0$, $1 = B - 2$ •

$\Rightarrow \quad B = 3$

And so $x = 3\sin t - \sin 2t$ is the required solution.

Use general solution = complementary function + particular integral.

Substitute the initial condition, $x = 0$ at $t = 0$, into the general solution to obtain $A = 0$.

Substitute the second initial condition, $\dfrac{dx}{dt} = 1$ at $t = 0$, into the derivative of the general solution, to obtain a second equation leading to $B = 3$.

Exercise 6C

E **1 a** Find the general solution to the differential equation

$$\frac{d^2y}{dx^2} + 5\frac{dy}{dx} + 6y = 12e^x$$ **(5 marks)**

    b Hence find the particular solution that satisfies $y = 1$ and $\dfrac{dy}{dx} = 0$ when $x = 0$. **(4 marks)**

E **2 a** Find the general solution to the differential equation

$$\frac{d^2y}{dx^2} + 2\frac{dy}{dx} = 12e^{2x}$$ **(5 marks)**

    b Hence find the particular solution that satisfies $y = 2$ and $\dfrac{dy}{dx} = 6$ when $x = 0$. **(5 marks)**

E **3** Given that $y = 0$ and $\dfrac{dy}{dx} = \frac{1}{6}$ when $x = 0$, find the particular solution to the differential equation

$$\frac{d^2y}{dx^2} - \frac{dy}{dx} - 42y = 14$$ **(10 marks)**

E **4 a** Find the general solution to the differential equation

$$\frac{d^2y}{dx^2} + 9y = 16\sin x$$ **(6 marks)**

    b Hence find the particular solution that satisfies $y = 1$ and $\dfrac{dy}{dx} = 8$ when $x = 0$. **(6 marks)**

E **5 a** Find the general solution to the differential equation

$$4\frac{d^2y}{dx^2} + 4\frac{dy}{dx} + 5y = \sin x + 4\cos x$$ **(6 marks)**

    b Hence find the particular solution that satisfies $y = 0$ and $\dfrac{dy}{dx} = 0$ when $x = 0$. **(6 marks)**

E/P **6 a** Find the general solution to the differential equation

$$\frac{d^2x}{dt^2} - 3\frac{dx}{dt} + 2x = 2t - 3$$ **(6 marks)**

    b Given that $x = 1$ when $t = 0$, and $x = 2$ when $t = 1$, find a particular solution of this differential equation. **(6 marks)**

(E) 7 Find the particular solution to the differential equation

$$\frac{d^2x}{dt^2} - 9x = 10\sin t$$

that satisfies $x = 2$ and $\frac{dx}{dt} = -1$ when $t = 0$. **(10 marks)**

(E/P) 8 a i Find the value of λ for which $y = \lambda t^3 e^{2t}$ is a particular solution to the differential equation

$$\frac{d^2x}{dt^2} - 4\frac{dx}{dt} + 4x = 3te^{2t}$$

    ii Hence find the general solution to the differential equation. **(6 marks)**

  b Find the particular solution that satisfies $x = 0$ and $\frac{dx}{dt} = 1$ when $t = 0$. **(6 marks)**

(E) 9 Find the particular solution to the differential equation

$$25\frac{d^2x}{dt^2} + 36x = 18$$

that satisfies $x = 1$ and $\frac{dx}{dt} = 0.6$ when $t = 0$. **(12 marks)**

(E) 10 a Find the general solution to the differential equation

$$\frac{d^2x}{dt^2} - 2\frac{dx}{dt} + 2x = 2t^2$$ **(6 marks)**

  b Hence find the particular solution that satisfies $x = 1$ and $\frac{dx}{dt} = 3$ when $t = 0$. **(6 marks)**

(E/P) 11 a Find the general solution to the differential equation

$$\frac{d^2y}{dx^2} - 3\frac{dy}{dx} + 2y = 3e^{2x}$$ **(7 marks)**

  b Hence find the particular solution that satisfies $y = 0$, $\frac{dy}{dx} = 0$ when $x = 0$. **(6 marks)**

(E/P) 12 Solve the differential equation

$$\frac{d^2y}{dx^2} + 9y = \sin 3x$$

subject to the boundary conditions $y = 0$, $\frac{dy}{dx} = 0$ when $x = 0$. **(14 marks)**

(E/P) 13 $\frac{d^2x}{dt^2} + 5\frac{dx}{dt} + 6x = 2e^{-t}$

Given that $x = 0$ and $\frac{dx}{dt} = 2$ at $t = 0$,

  a find x in terms of t. **(8 marks)**

  b Show that the maximum value of x is $\frac{2\sqrt{3}}{9}$ and justify that this is a maximum. **(7 marks)**

6.4 Reducible second-order differential equations

You can use a given substitution to reduce second-order differential equations into differential equations of the form $a\frac{d^2y}{dx^2} + b\frac{dy}{dx} + cy = f(x)$

Example (13)

Given that $x = e^u$, show that:

a $x\dfrac{dy}{dx} = \dfrac{dy}{du}$

b $x^2\dfrac{d^2y}{dx^2} = \dfrac{d^2y}{du^2} - \dfrac{dy}{du}$

c Hence find the general solution to the differential equation

$$x^2\frac{d^2y}{dx^2} + x\frac{dy}{dx} + y = 0$$

a As $x = e^u$, $\dfrac{dx}{du} = e^u = x$

From the chain rule,

$\dfrac{dy}{du} = \dfrac{dy}{dx} \times \dfrac{dx}{du} = e^u\dfrac{dy}{dx} = x\dfrac{dy}{dx}$, as required.

> Use the chain rule to express $\dfrac{dy}{dx}$ in terms of $\dfrac{dy}{du}$

b $\dfrac{d^2y}{du^2} = \dfrac{d}{du}\left(\dfrac{dy}{du}\right)$

$= \dfrac{d}{du}\left(e^u\dfrac{dy}{dx}\right)$

> Differentiate this product using the product rule.

$= e^u\dfrac{dy}{dx} + e^u\dfrac{d^2y}{dx^2}\dfrac{dx}{du}$

$= \dfrac{dy}{du} + x^2\dfrac{d^2y}{dx^2}$, as $\dfrac{dx}{du} = e^u = x$

So $x^2\dfrac{d^2y}{dx^2} = \dfrac{d^2y}{du^2} - \dfrac{dy}{du}$ as required.

> Use the chain rule to differentiate $\dfrac{dy}{dx}$ with respect to u, by differentiating with respect to x, giving $\dfrac{d^2y}{dx^2}$, and then multiplying by $\dfrac{dx}{du}$

c Substitute the results from parts **a** and **b** into the differential equation

$$x^2\frac{d^2y}{dx^2} + x\frac{dy}{dx} + y = 0$$

to obtain $\dfrac{d^2y}{du^2} - \dfrac{dy}{du} + \dfrac{dy}{du} + y = 0$

$\dfrac{d^2y}{du^2} + y = 0$

> This is in the form $a\dfrac{d^2y}{du^2} + b\dfrac{dy}{du} + cy = 0$ with $a = 1$, $b = 0$ and $c = 1$. Find the general solution by considering the roots of the auxiliary equation.

$m^2 + 1 = 0$

$m = i$ or $m = -i$

So the general solution in terms of u is

$y = A\cos u + B\sin u$

where A and B are arbitrary constants.

$x = e^u \Rightarrow u = \ln x$ and the general solution to

the differential equation $x^2\dfrac{d^2y}{dx^2} + x\dfrac{dy}{dx} + y = 0$

is $y = A\cos(\ln x) + B\sin(\ln x)$

> The roots are complex, so the general solution will be in the form $y = e^{pu}(A\cos qu + B\sin qu)$, with $p = 0$ and $q = 1$.

> Use $u = \ln x$ to give y in terms of x.

Exercise 6D

1 Find the general solution to each differential equation using the substitution
$x = e^u$, where u is a function of x.

a $x^2\dfrac{d^2y}{dx^2} + 6x\dfrac{dy}{dx} + 4y = 0$ **b** $x^2\dfrac{d^2y}{dx^2} + 5x\dfrac{dy}{dx} + 4y = 0$ **c** $x^2\dfrac{d^2y}{dx^2} + 6x\dfrac{dy}{dx} + 6y = 0$

d $x^2\dfrac{d^2y}{dx^2} + 4x\dfrac{dy}{dx} - 28y = 0$ **e** $x^2\dfrac{d^2y}{dx^2} - 4x\dfrac{dy}{dx} - 14y = 0$ **f** $x^2\dfrac{d^2y}{dx^2} + 3x\dfrac{dy}{dx} + 2y = 0$

(E) **2 a** Show that the transformation $y = \dfrac{z}{x}$ transforms the differential equation

$$x^2\dfrac{d^2y}{dx^2} + (2 - 4x)\dfrac{dy}{dx} - 4y = 0 \qquad \textbf{(1)}$$

into the differential equation

$$\dfrac{d^2z}{dx^2} - 4\dfrac{dz}{dx} = 0 \qquad \textbf{(2)} \hspace{6cm} \textbf{(6 marks)}$$

b Find the general solution to differential equation **(2)**, giving z as a function of x.   **(4 marks)**

c Hence obtain the general solution to differential equation **(1)**.   **(1 mark)**

(E) **3 a** Show that the substitution $y = \dfrac{z}{x^2}$ transforms the differential equation

$$x^2\dfrac{d^2y}{dx^2} + 2x(x + 2)\dfrac{dy}{dx} + 2(x + 1)^2 y = e^{-x} \qquad \textbf{(1)}$$

Hint   Use a particular integral of the form λe^{-x}.   ← **Further Pure 2 Section 6.2**

into the differential equation

$$\dfrac{d^2z}{dx^2} + 2\dfrac{dz}{dx} + 2z = e^{-x} \qquad \textbf{(2)} \hspace{5cm} \textbf{(6 marks)}$$

b Find the general solution to differential equation **(2)**, giving z as a function of x.   **(7 marks)**

c Hence obtain the general solution to differential equation **(1)**.   **(1 mark)**

(E) **4 a** Use the substitution $z = \sin x$ to transform the differential equation

$$\cos x\dfrac{d^2y}{dx^2} + \sin x\dfrac{dy}{dx} - 2y\cos^3 x = 2\cos^5 x$$

into the equation

$$\dfrac{d^2y}{dz^2} - 2y = 2(1 - z^2) \hspace{7cm} \textbf{(6 marks)}$$

b Hence solve the equation $\cos x\dfrac{d^2y}{dx^2} + \sin x\dfrac{dy}{dx} - 2y\cos^3 x = 2\cos^5 x$,
giving y in terms of x.   **(8 marks)**

(E) **5 a** Show that the transformation $x = ut$ transforms the differential equation

$$t^2\frac{d^2x}{dt^2} - 2t\frac{dx}{dt} = -2(1 - 2t^2)x \qquad \textbf{(1)}$$

into the differential equation

$$\frac{d^2u}{dt^2} - 4u = 0 \qquad \textbf{(2)}$$ **(6 marks)**

b By solving differential equation **(2)**, find the general solution to differential equation **(1)** in the form $x = f(t)$. **(8 marks)**

Given that $x = 2$ and $\frac{dx}{dt} = 1$ at $t = 1$,

c find the particular solution to differential equation **(1)**. **(5 marks)**

Challenge

Use the substitution $u = \dfrac{dy}{dx}$ to find the general solution to the differential equation

$$x\frac{d^2y}{dx^2} + \frac{dy}{dx} = 12x$$

Chapter review 6

(E) **1 a** Find the general solution to the differential equation

$$\frac{dy}{dx} + y\tan x = e^x\cos x, -\frac{\pi}{2} < x < \frac{\pi}{2}$$

giving your answer in the form $y = f(x)$. **(6 marks)**

b Find the particular solution for which $y = 1$ at $x = \pi$. **(3 marks)**

(E) **2** $\dfrac{dy}{dx} - 3y = \sin x$

Given that $y = 0$ when $x = 0$, find y in terms of x. **(7 marks)**

(E) **3** $\dfrac{dy}{dx} = x(4 - y^2)$

Given that $y = 1$ when $x = 0$, find y in terms of x. **(7 marks)**

(E) **4** Find the general solution to the differential equation $\dfrac{d^2y}{dx^2} + \dfrac{dy}{dx} + y = 0$ **(6 marks)**

(E) **5** Find the general solution to the differential equation $\dfrac{d^2y}{dx^2} - 12\dfrac{dy}{dx} + 36y = 0$ **(6 marks)**

(E) **6** Find the general solution to the differential equation $\dfrac{d^2y}{dx^2} - 4\dfrac{dy}{dx} = 0$ **(6 marks)**

(E/P) **7** Find y in terms of k and x, given that $\dfrac{d^2y}{dx^2} + k^2y = 0$ where k is a constant, and $y = 1$

and $\dfrac{dy}{dx} = 1$ at $x = 0$. **(8 marks)**

Ⓔ **8** Find the solution to the differential equation $\dfrac{d^2y}{dx^2} - 2\dfrac{dy}{dx} + 10y = 0$ for which $y = 0$

and $\dfrac{dy}{dx} = 3$ at $x = 0$. **(8 marks)**

Ⓔ **9 a** Find the value of k for which $y = ke^{2x}$ is a particular integral of the differential equation

$\dfrac{d^2y}{dx^2} - 4\dfrac{dy}{dx} + 13y = e^{2x}$ **(4 marks)**

b Using your answer to part **a**, find the general solution to the differential equation. **(5 marks)**

Ⓔ/Ⓟ **10** Find the general solution of the differential equation

$\dfrac{d^2y}{dx^2} - y = 4e^x$ **(7 marks)**

Ⓔ/Ⓟ **11** The differential equation $\dfrac{d^2y}{dx^2} - 4\dfrac{dy}{dx} + 4y = 4e^{2x}$ is to be solved.

a Find the complementary function. **(3 marks)**

b Explain why neither λe^{2x} nor λxe^{2x} can be a particular integral for this equation. **(2 marks)**
A particular integral has the form kx^2e^{2x}.

c Determine the value of the constant k and find the general solution of the
equation. **(6 marks)**

Ⓔ/Ⓟ **12** Find the particular solution of the differential equation

$\dfrac{d^2y}{dt^2} + 4y = 5\cos 3t$

which satisfies the initial conditions that when $t = 0$, $y = 1$ and $\dfrac{dy}{dt} = 2$. **(12 marks)**

Ⓔ **13 a** Find the values of λ, μ and k such that $y = \lambda + \mu x + kxe^{2x}$ is a particular integral of the
differential equation

$\dfrac{d^2y}{dx^2} - 3\dfrac{dy}{dx} + 2y = 4x + e^{2x}$ **(5 marks)**

b Using your answer to part **a**, find the general solution of the differential equation. **(5 marks)**

Ⓔ/Ⓟ **14 a** Find the solution of the differential equation $16\dfrac{d^2y}{dx^2} + 8\dfrac{dy}{dx} + 5y = 5x + 23$ for which $y = 3$

and $\dfrac{dy}{dx} = 3$ at $x = 0$. **(8 marks)**

b Show that $y \approx x + 3$ for large values of x. **(2 marks)**

Ⓔ/Ⓟ **15** Find the solution of the differential equation $\dfrac{d^2y}{dx^2} - \dfrac{dy}{dx} - 6y = 3\sin 3x - 2\cos 3x$ for which

$y = 1$ at $x = 0$ and for which y remains finite as $x \to \infty$. **(8 marks)**

(E/P) **16** x satisfies the differential equation

$$\frac{d^2x}{dt^2} + 8\frac{dx}{dt} + 16x = \cos 4t, \ t \geqslant 0$$

  a Find the general solution of the differential equation. **(8 marks)**

  b Find the particular solution of this differential equation for which, at $t = 0$, $x = \frac{1}{2}$

    and $\frac{dx}{dt} = 0$. **(5 marks)**

  c Describe the behaviour of the function for large values of t. **(2 marks)**

(E/P) **17** Solve the equation $\frac{d^2y}{dx^2} + \tan x\frac{dy}{dx} + y\cos^2 x = \cos^2 x \, e^{\sin x}$, using the substitution $z = \sin x$.

  Find the solution for which $y = 1$ and $\frac{dy}{dx} = 3$ at $x = 0$. **(13 marks)**

Challenge

1 Use the substitution $z = y^2$ to transform the differential equation

$$2(1 + x^2)\frac{dy}{dx} + 2xy = \frac{1}{y}$$

into a differential equation in z and x. By first solving the transformed equation,

  a find the general solution of the original equation, giving y in terms of x.

  b Find the particular solution for which $y = 2$ when $x = 0$.

2   **a** Find the general solution of the differential equation

$$x^2\frac{d^2y}{dx^2} + 4x\frac{dy}{dx} + 2y = \ln x, \qquad x > 0,$$

    using the substitution $x = e^u$, where u is a function of x.

  b Find the equation of the solution curve passing through the point $(1, 1)$ with gradient 1.

3 By means of a suitable substitution, show that the general solution to the differential equation

$$\frac{d^2y}{dx^2} = \left(\frac{dy}{dx}\right)^2$$

is given by $y = A - \ln(x + B)$, where A and B are arbitrary constants.

Summary of key points

1 The natures of the roots α and β of the **auxiliary equation** determine the **general solution** to the second-order differential equation $a\dfrac{d^2y}{dx^2} + b\dfrac{dy}{dx} + c = 0$

You need to consider three different cases:

• **Case 1: $b^2 > 4ac$**

The auxiliary equation has two real roots α and β ($\alpha \neq \beta$). The general solution will be of the form $y = Ae^{\alpha x} + Be^{\beta x}$ where A and B are arbitrary constants.

• **Case 2: $b^2 = 4ac$**

The auxiliary equation has one repeated root α. The general solution will be of the form $y = (A + Bx)e^{\alpha x}$ where A and B are arbitrary constants.

• **Case 3: $b^2 < 4ac$**

The auxiliary equation has two complex conjugate roots α and β equal to $p \pm q$i. The general solution will be of the form $y = e^{px}(A\cos qx + B\sin qx)$ where A and B are arbitrary constants.

2 To find the general solution to the differential equation $a\dfrac{d^2y}{dx^2} + b\dfrac{dy}{dx} + cy = \mathbf{f(x)}$

• Solve the corresponding homogeneous equation $a\dfrac{d^2y}{dx^2} + b\dfrac{dy}{dx} + cy = 0$ to find the complementary function, C.F.

• Choose an appropriate form for the particular integral, P.I., and substitute into the original equation to find the values of any coefficients.

• The general solution is $y = $ C.F. + P.I.

3 You can use a substitution to reduce a first-order differential equation into a form that you know how to solve, either by separating the variables, or by using an integrating factor.

4 You can use a given substitution to reduce second-order differential equations into differential equations of the form

$$a\dfrac{d^2y}{dx^2} + b\dfrac{dy}{dx} + cy = \mathrm{f}(x)$$

7 MACLAURIN AND TAYLOR SERIES

6.1
6.2
6.3
6.4

Learning objectives

After completing this chapter you should be able to:

* Find and use higher derivatives of functions → pages 126–127
* Derive and use Maclaurin series for simple functions → pages 128–132
* Use series expansions of compound functions → pages 132–136
* Derive and use Taylor series for simple functions → pages 136–139
* Use the Taylor series method to find a series solution to a differential equation → pages 140–144

Prior knowledge check

1 Differentiate:

   a $\cos(1 + x^3)$

   b $\dfrac{1}{e^x \sin x}$ ← Pure 3 Section 6.3

2 Find the general solution to the differential equation $\dfrac{d^2y}{dx^2} + 2\dfrac{dy}{dx} + 2y = 0$

   ← Further Pure 2 Section 6.1

Taylor series can be used to approximate functions by polynomials. Mathematicians and engineers use them to approximate and model solutions to complex differential equations such as those that describe the flow of air over an aircraft wing. In this chapter you will use Taylor series to find approximate solutions to differential equations that can't be solved easily by other methods.

7.1 Higher derivatives

You need to be able to find third, and higher, **derivatives** of given functions.
You already know how to find first and second derivatives.

If $y = f(x)$, the first derivative of $f(x)$ is given by $\dfrac{dy}{dx} = f'(x)$, and the second derivative of $f(x)$ is given

by $\dfrac{d^2y}{dx^2} = \dfrac{d}{dx}\left(\dfrac{dy}{dx}\right) = f''(x)$.

Similarly, the third derivative is given by $\dfrac{d^3y}{dx^3} = \dfrac{d}{dx}\left(\dfrac{d^2y}{dx^2}\right) = f'''(x)$, and so on.

You can find the nth derivative of $f(x)$ by differentiating n times with respect to x.

Example 1

Given that $y = \ln(1 - x)$, find the value of $\dfrac{d^3y}{dx^3}$ when $x = \dfrac{1}{2}$

$\dfrac{dy}{dx} = \dfrac{1}{1-x} \dfrac{d}{dx}(1-x) = \dfrac{1}{1-x} \times (-1) = -\dfrac{1}{1-x}$ Use the **chain rule**.
                                                              ← **Pure 3 Section 6.3**

$\dfrac{d^2y}{dx^2} = \dfrac{d}{dx}\left(\dfrac{dy}{dx}\right) = \dfrac{d}{dx}(-(1-x)^{-1}) = \dfrac{1}{(1-x)^2} \times (-1) = -\dfrac{1}{(1-x)^2}$

$\dfrac{d^3y}{dx^3} = \dfrac{d}{dx}\left(\dfrac{d^2y}{dx^2}\right) = \dfrac{d}{dx}(-(1-x)^{-2}) = \dfrac{2}{(1-x)^3} \times (-1) = -\dfrac{2}{(1-x)^3}$

So when $x = \dfrac{1}{2}$, $\dfrac{d^3y}{dx^3} = \dfrac{-2}{\left(1-\frac{1}{2}\right)^3} = -16$ Substitute $x = \frac{1}{2}$

Example 2

$f(x) = e^{x^2}$

a Show that $f'(x) = 2xf(x)$

b By differentiating the result in part **a** twice more with respect to x, show that:
   i $f''(x) = 2f(x) + 2xf'(x)$ **ii** $f'''(x) = 2xf''(x) + 4f'(x)$

c **Deduce** the values of $f'(0)$, $f''(0)$ and $f'''(0)$.

a $f'(x) = e^{x^2}\dfrac{d}{dx}(x^2) = 2xe^{x^2}$ If $f(x) = e^u$, then $f'(x) = e^u\dfrac{du}{dx}$

        $= 2xf(x)$ $f(x) = e^{x^2}$

b i $f''(x) = 2f(x) + 2xf'(x)$ Use the **product rule**.   ← **Pure 3 Section 6.4**
  ii $f'''(x) = 2f'(x) + (2xf''(x) + 2f'(x))$

         $= 2xf''(x) + 4f'(x)$ **Differentiate** again.

c $f(0) = e^0 = 1$

$f'(0) = 2 \times 0 \times e^0 = 0$

$f''(0) = 2f(0) + 2 \times 0 \times f'(0)$ Substitute $x = 0$ into $f''(x)$.

$\qquad = 2f(0) = 2$

$f'''(0) = 2 \times 0 \times f''(0) + 4f'(0)$ Substitute $x = 0$ into $f'''(x)$.

$\qquad\ = 4f'(0) = 0$

Exercise 7A

1 For each function, $f(x)$, find $f'(x)$, $f''(x)$, $f'''(x)$ and $f^{(n)}(x)$.

  a e^{2x} **b** $(1 + x)^n$ **c** xe^x **d** $\ln(1 + x)$

(P) 2 a Given that $y = e^{2+3x}$ find an expression, in terms of y, for $\dfrac{d^n y}{dx^n}$

  b Hence evaluate $\dfrac{d^6 y}{dx^6}$ when $x = \ln\left(\frac{1}{9}\right)$

3 Given that $y = \sin^2 3x$,

  a show that $\dfrac{dy}{dx} = 3\sin 6x$ **b** find expressions for $\dfrac{d^2 y}{dx^2}, \dfrac{d^3 y}{dx^3}$ and $\dfrac{d^4 y}{dx^4}$

  c Hence evaluate $\dfrac{d^4 y}{dx^4}$ when $x = \dfrac{\pi}{6}$

4 $f(x) = x^2 e^{-x}$

  a Show that $f'''(x) = (6x - 6 - x^2)e^{-x}$ **b** Show that $f''''(2) = 0$

5 Given that $y = \sec x$

  a show that $\dfrac{d^2 y}{dx^2} = 2\sec^3 x - \sec x$

  b show that the value of $\dfrac{d^3 y}{dx^3}$ when $x = \dfrac{\pi}{4}$ is $11\sqrt{2}$

(P) 6 Given that y is a function of x,

  a show that $\dfrac{d^2}{dx^2}(y^2) = 2y\dfrac{d^2 y}{dx^2} + 2\left(\dfrac{dy}{dx}\right)^2$

  b Find an expression, in terms of $y, \dfrac{dy}{dx}, \dfrac{d^2 y}{dx^2}$ and $\dfrac{d^3 y}{dx^3}$, for $\dfrac{d^3}{dx^3}(y^2)$

7 Given that $f(x) = \ln\left(x + \sqrt{1 + x^2}\right)$, show that:

  a $\sqrt{1 + x^2}\, f'(x) = 1$ **b** $(1 + x^2)\, f''(x) + xf'(x) = 0$

  c $(1 + x^2)\, f'''(x) + 3xf''(x) + f'(x) = 0$ **d** Deduce the values of $f'(0), f''(0)$ and $f'''(0)$.

7.2 Maclaurin series

Many functions can be written as an **infinite** sum of terms of the form ax^n. You may have already encountered **series expansions** like these:

$$\frac{1}{1-x} = 1 + x + x^2 + x^3 + \dots, \ |x| < 1$$

$$\sqrt{1+x} = 1 + \frac{x}{2} - \frac{x^2}{8} + \frac{x^3}{16} - \dots, \ |x| < 1$$

$$e^x = 1 + x + \frac{x^2}{2} + \frac{x^3}{6} + \frac{x^4}{24} + \dots, \ x \in \mathbb{R}$$

Links The first two series expansions shown here are examples of the **binomial expansion**.   ← Pure 4 Chapter 4.3

Example 3

Given that f(x) can be differentiated infinitely many times and that it has a valid series expansion of the form $f(x) = a_0 + a_1x + a_2x^2 + a_3x^3 + \dots + a_rx^r + \dots$, where the a_i are all real constants, show that the series expansion must be

$$f(x) = f(0) + f'(0)x + \frac{f''(0)x^2}{2!} + \dots + \frac{f^{(r)}(0)x^r}{r!} + \dots$$

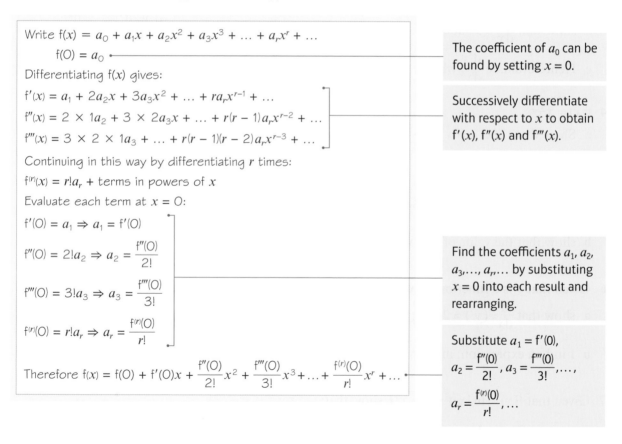

Write $f(x) = a_0 + a_1x + a_2x^2 + a_3x^3 + \dots + a_rx^r + \dots$

$f(0) = a_0$

The coefficient of a_0 can be found by setting $x = 0$.

Differentiating f(x) gives:

$f'(x) = a_1 + 2a_2x + 3a_3x^2 + \dots + ra_rx^{r-1} + \dots$

$f''(x) = 2 \times 1a_2 + 3 \times 2a_3x + \dots + r(r-1)a_rx^{r-2} + \dots$

$f'''(x) = 3 \times 2 \times 1a_3 + \dots + r(r-1)(r-2)a_rx^{r-3} + \dots$

Successively differentiate with respect to x to obtain f'(x), f''(x) and f'''(x).

Continuing in this way by differentiating r times:

$f^{(r)}(x) = r!a_r + $ terms in powers of x

Evaluate each term at $x = 0$:

$f'(0) = a_1 \Rightarrow a_1 = f'(0)$

$f''(0) = 2!a_2 \Rightarrow a_2 = \frac{f''(0)}{2!}$

$f'''(0) = 3!a_3 \Rightarrow a_3 = \frac{f'''(0)}{3!}$

$f^{(r)}(0) = r!a_r \Rightarrow a_r = \frac{f^{(r)}(0)}{r!}$

Find the coefficients a_1, a_2, a_3,..., a_r,... by substituting $x = 0$ into each result and rearranging.

Therefore $f(x) = f(0) + f'(0)x + \frac{f''(0)}{2!}x^2 + \frac{f'''(0)}{3!}x^3 + \dots + \frac{f^{(r)}(0)}{r!}x^r + \dots$

Substitute $a_1 = f'(0)$,

$a_2 = \frac{f''(0)}{2!}, a_3 = \frac{f'''(0)}{3!},\dots,$

$a_r = \frac{f^{(r)}(0)}{r!},\dots$

In this process, outlined in the worked example above, a **polynomial** in **powers** of x is being formed step by step. The process focuses on $x = 0$; substituting $x = 0$ into **successive** derivatives increases the power of the polynomial. For example, if you stop the process after finding f′(0) the polynomial is linear, $f(0) + f'(0)x$, after f″(0) it is quadratic, $f(0) + f'(0)x + \dfrac{f''(0)}{2!}x^2$, after f‴(0) it is **cubic**, $f(0) + f'(0)x + \dfrac{f''(0)}{2!}x^2 + \dfrac{f'''(0)}{3!}x^3$ and so on.

The above argument assumes that the function can be written in the given form. This is only true if the given series **converges**. The above reasoning also only holds (i.e. remains true) if the function can be differentiated an infinite number of times, and if $f^{(r)}(0)$ is always finite.

> **Watch out** Not all functions satisfy the condition that f(0), f′(0), f″(0), …, $f^{(r)}(0)$ all have finite values.
> For example, when $f(x) = \ln x$, $f'(x) = \dfrac{1}{x}$ so f′(0) is undefined and therefore does not have a finite value.

- The **Maclaurin series** expansion of a function f(x) is given by

$$f(x) = f(0) + f'(0)x + \frac{f''(0)}{2!}x^2 + \ldots + \frac{f^{(r)}(0)}{r!}x^r + \ldots$$

The series is valid provided that f(0), f′(0), f″(0), …, $f^{(r)}(0)$, … all have finite values.

The polynomial $f(0) + f'(0)x$ is a Maclaurin polynomial of **degree** 1.

The polynomial $f(0) + f'(0)x + \dfrac{f''(0)}{2!}x^2$ is a Maclaurin polynomial of degree 2.

The polynomial $f(0) + f'(0)x + \dfrac{f''(0)}{2!}x^2 + \ldots + \dfrac{f^{(r)}(0)}{r!}x^r$ is a Maclaurin polynomial of degree r.

Even when $f^{(r)}(0)$ exists and is finite for all r, a Maclaurin series expansion is only valid for values of x that give rise to a convergent series. For example, the Maclaurin series of $\dfrac{1}{1-x}$ is $1 + x + x^2 + x^3 + \ldots$.

But when $x = 2$, the series gives $1 + 2 + 4 + 8 + \ldots$ which does not converge to $\dfrac{1}{1-2} = -1$.

> **Notation** The range of validity for some individual Maclaurin series is given in the formulae booklet. If no range of validity is given in this chapter, you may assume that the expansion is valid for all $x \in \mathbb{R}$.

Example 4

a Express $\ln(1 + x)$ as an **infinite series** in **ascending** powers of x.

b Using only the first three terms of the series in part **a**, find estimates for:
　i $\ln 1.05$　　　　**ii** $\ln 1.25$　　　　**iii** $\ln 1.8$
　Comment on the accuracy of the estimates.

a $f(x) = \ln(1 + x)$ $\Rightarrow$ $f(0) = \ln 1 = 0$

$f'(x) = \dfrac{1}{1 + x} = (1 + x)^{-1}$ $\Rightarrow$ $f'(0) = 1$

$f''(x) = -(1 + x)^{-2}$ $\Rightarrow$ $f''(0) = -1$

$f'''(x) = (-1)(-2)(1 + x)^{-3}$ $\Rightarrow$ $f'''(0) = 2!$

$f^{(r)}(x) = (-1)(-2)(-3)\ldots(-(r - 1))(1 + x)^{-r}$

$\Rightarrow f^{(r)}(0) = (-1)^{r-1}(r - 1)!$

> **Problem-solving**
> The term $(-1)^r$ can be used in the general term of **alternating sequences**, in which the terms are alternately positive and negative.

So $\ln(1 + x) = 0 + 1x + \dfrac{-1}{2!}x^2 + \dfrac{(2!)}{3!}x^3 + \ldots$

$\qquad\qquad + \dfrac{(-1)^{r-1}(r-1)!}{r!}x^r + \ldots$

$\ln(1 + x) = x - \dfrac{x^2}{2} + \dfrac{x^3}{3} + \ldots + (-1)^{r-1}\dfrac{x^r}{r} + \ldots$

Substitute the values for f(0), f′(0), f″(0), etc. into the Maclaurin series for f(x).

Online This expansion is valid for $-1 < x \leqslant 1$. If you use a computer to generate the graphs of the successive Maclaurin polynomials you will see that they converge to the graph of $\ln(1 + x)$ between $x = -1$ and $x = 1$, but outside that interval they **diverge** rapidly. Explore this using GeoGebra.

b i $\ln 1.05 = 0.05 - \dfrac{0.05^2}{2} + \dfrac{0.05^3}{3} - \ldots$

$\qquad \approx 0.0487916\ldots$ This is correct to 5 d.p.

ii $\ln 1.25 = 0.25 - \dfrac{0.25^2}{2} + \dfrac{0.25^3}{3} - \ldots$

$\qquad \approx 0.223958\ldots$ This is correct to 2 d.p.

iii $\ln 1.8 = 0.8 - \dfrac{0.8^2}{2} + \dfrac{0.8^3}{3} - \ldots$

$\qquad \approx 0.6506666\ldots$ This is not correct to 1 d.p.

The further away a value is from $x = 0$, the less accurate the approximation will be and the more terms of the series you need to take to maintain a required degree of accuracy.

Example 5

a Find the first four terms in the Maclaurin series of $\sin x$.

b Using the first two terms of the series find an **approximation** for $\sin 10°$.

a $f(x) = \sin x \qquad \Rightarrow \qquad f(0) = \sin 0 = 0$

$f'(x) = \cos x \qquad \Rightarrow \qquad f'(0) = \cos 0 = 1$

$f''(x) = -\sin x \qquad \Rightarrow \qquad f''(0) = -\sin 0 = 0$

$f'''(x) = -\cos x \qquad \Rightarrow \qquad f'''(0) = -\cos 0 = -1$

$f''''(x) = \sin x \qquad \Rightarrow \qquad f''''(0) = \sin 0 = 0$

$f^{(n)} = 0$, if n is even, and the cycle of values 0, 1, 0, −1 repeats itself.

So $\sin x = x + \dfrac{-1}{3!}x^3 + \dfrac{1}{5!}x^5 + \dfrac{-1}{7!}x^7 + \ldots + \dfrac{(-1)^r}{(2r+1)!}x^{2r+1} + \ldots$

$\qquad = x - \dfrac{1}{3!}x^3 + \dfrac{1}{5!}x^5 - \dfrac{1}{7!}x^7 + \ldots$

This expansion is valid for all values of x.

Watch out x must be in **radians** in expansions of trigonometric functions.

b $\sin 10° = \sin \dfrac{\pi}{18} \approx \dfrac{\pi}{18} - \dfrac{1}{6}\left(\dfrac{\pi}{18}\right)^3$

$\qquad \approx 0.174532925 - 0.000886096$

$\qquad \approx 0.173646829$

This estimate is correct to 5 decimal places; even using $\sin x \approx x$, the approximation is correct to 2 d.p.

Exercise (7B)

1   Use the formula for the Maclaurin series and **differentiation** to show that:

> **Hint**   The binomial expansions of $(1 + x)^n$, where n is **fractional** or negative and $|x| < 1$, are the Maclaurin series of the function.

    a $(1 - x)^{-1} = 1 + x + x^2 + \ldots + x^r + \ldots$

    b $\sqrt{1 + x} = 1 + \dfrac{x}{2} - \dfrac{x^2}{8} + \dfrac{x^3}{16} - \ldots$

2   Use Maclaurin series and differentiation to show that the first three terms in the series expansion of $e^{\sin x}$ are $1 + x + \dfrac{x^2}{2}$

(P)   3   **a**   Show that the Maclaurin series of $\cos x$ is $1 - \dfrac{x^2}{2!} + \dfrac{x^4}{4!} + \ldots + (-1)^r \dfrac{x^{2r}}{(2r)!} + \ldots$

    b   Using the first three terms of the series, show that it gives a value for $\cos 30°$ correct to 3 decimal places.

> **Hint**   This expansion is valid for all values of x.

4   Using the series expansions for e^x and $\ln(1 + x)$ respectively (i.e. in the same order as what has already been mentioned), find, correct to 3 decimal places, the values of:

    a   e   **b** $\ln\left(\dfrac{6}{5}\right)$

5   Use Maclaurin series and differentiation to expand, in ascending powers of x up to and including the term in x^4,

    a e^{3x} **b** $\ln(1 + 2x)$ **c** $\sin^2 x$

(P)   6   Using the addition formula for $\cos(A - B)$ and the series expansions of $\sin x$ and $\cos x$, show that

$$\cos\left(x - \frac{\pi}{4}\right) = \frac{1}{\sqrt{2}}\left(1 + x - \frac{x^2}{2} - \frac{x^3}{6} + \frac{x^4}{24} + \ldots\right)$$

(E)   7   Given that $f(x) = (1 - x)^2 \ln(1 - x)$,

    a   show that $f''(x) = 3 + 2\ln(1 - x)$ **(2 marks)**

    b   find the values of $f(0)$, $f'(0)$, $f''(0)$, and $f'''(0)$ **(1 mark)**

    c   express $(1 - x)^2 \ln(1 - x)$ in ascending powers of x up to and including the term in x^3.   **(3 marks)**

(E/P)   8   **a**   Using the series expansions of $\sin x$ and $\cos x$, show that

        $3 \sin x - 4x \cos x + x = \dfrac{3}{2}x^3 - \dfrac{17}{120}x^5 + \ldots$ **(5 marks)**

    b   Hence, find the **limit**, as $x \to 0$, of $\dfrac{3 \sin x - 4x \cos x + x}{x^3}$ **(1 mark)**

(E) **9** Given that $f(x) = \ln \cos x$,

    a show that $f'(x) = -\tan x$ **(2 marks)**

    b find the values of $f'(0)$, $f''(0)$, $f'''(0)$ and $f''''(0)$ **(1 mark)**

    c express $\ln \cos x$ as a series in ascending powers of x up to and including the term in x^4 **(3 marks)**

    d show that using the first two terms of the Maclaurin series for $\ln \cos x$ with $x = \frac{\pi}{4}$ gives a value for $\ln 2$ of $\frac{\pi^2}{16}\left(1 + \frac{\pi^2}{96}\right)$ **(2 marks)**

(E/P) **10** Show that the Maclaurin series for $\tan x$, as far as the term in x^5, is $x + \frac{1}{3}x^3 + \frac{2}{15}x^5$ **(5 marks)**

Challenge

The **ratio test** is a sufficient condition for the convergence of an infinite series. It says that a series $\sum\limits_{r=1}^{\infty} a_r$ converges if $\lim\limits_{r \to \infty}\left|\frac{a_{r+1}}{a_r}\right| < 1$ and diverges if $\lim\limits_{r \to \infty}\left|\frac{a_{r+1}}{a_r}\right| > 1$

Use the ratio test to show that

a the Maclaurin series expansion of e^x converges for all $x \in \mathbb{R}$

b the Maclaurin series expansion of $\ln(1 + x)$ converges for $-1 < x < 1$, and diverges for $x > 1$.

Problem-solving

If $\lim\limits_{r \to \infty}\left|\frac{a_{r+1}}{a_r}\right| = 1$ or does not exist then the ratio test is inconclusive.

7.3 Series expansions of compound functions

You can find the series expansions of compound functions using known Maclaurin series. In the last exercise you found the Maclaurin series of simple compound functions, such as e^{3x} and $\ln(1 + 2x)$. However, the resulting series could also be found by replacing x by $3x$ or x by $2x$ in the known expansions of e^x and $\ln(1 + x)$ respectively. When successive derivatives of a compound function are more difficult, or when there are **products** of functions involved, it is often possible to use one of the standard results.

■ The following Maclaurin series expansions are given in the formulae booklet:

- $e^x = 1 + x + \frac{x^2}{2!} + \ldots + \frac{x^r}{r!} + \ldots$ for all x

- $\ln(1 + x) = x - \frac{x^2}{2} + \frac{x^3}{3} - \ldots + (-1)^{r+1}\frac{x^r}{r} + \ldots$ $-1 < x \leq 1$

- $\sin x = x - \frac{x^3}{3!} + \frac{x^5}{5!} - \ldots + (-1)^r\frac{x^{2r+1}}{(2r+1)!} + \ldots$ for all x

- $\cos x = 1 - \frac{x^2}{2!} + \frac{x^4}{4!} - \ldots + (-1)^r\frac{x^{2r}}{(2r)!} + \ldots$ for all x

- $\arctan x = x - \frac{x^3}{3} + \frac{x^5}{5} - \ldots + (-1)^r\frac{x^{2r+1}}{2r+1} + \ldots$ $-1 \leq x \leq 1$

Example 6

Write down the first four non-zero terms in the series expansion (in ascending powers of x) of $\cos(2x^2)$.

$$\cos(2x^2) = 1 - \frac{(2x^2)^2}{2!} + \frac{(2x^2)^4}{4!} - \frac{(2x^2)^6}{6!} + \dots$$

Substitute $2x^2$ for x in the above series for $\cos x$.

$$= 1 - 2x^4 + \frac{2}{3}x^8 - \frac{4}{45}x^{12} + \dots$$

Watch out　Make sure you simplify the coefficients as much as possible.

Example 7

Find the first three non-zero terms in the series expansion of $\ln\left(\dfrac{\sqrt{1+2x}}{1-3x}\right)$ and state the values of x for which the expansion is valid.

$$\ln\left(\frac{\sqrt{(1+2x)}}{1-3x}\right) = \ln\sqrt{1+2x} - \ln(1-3x)$$

Using $\ln\left(\dfrac{a}{b}\right) = \ln a - \ln b$

$$= \tfrac{1}{2}\ln(1+2x) - \ln(1-3x)$$

Using $\ln a^{\frac{1}{2}} = \tfrac{1}{2}\ln a$

$$\tfrac{1}{2}\ln(1+2x) = \tfrac{1}{2}\left(2x - \frac{(2x)^2}{2} + \frac{(2x)^3}{3} - \dots\right), \quad -1 < 2x \leqslant 1$$

Substitute $2x$ for x in the expansion of $\ln(1+x)$

$$= x - x^2 + \tfrac{4}{3}x^3 - \dots \qquad -\tfrac{1}{2} < x \leqslant \tfrac{1}{2}$$

Problem-solving

You are substituting $2x$ into the series expansion of $\ln(1+x)$, so the series is now only valid for $-1 < 2x \leqslant 1$, or $-\tfrac{1}{2} < x \leqslant \tfrac{1}{2}$

$$\ln(1-3x) = (-3x) - \frac{(-3x)^2}{2} + \frac{(-3x)^3}{3} - \dots, \; -1 < -3x \leqslant 1$$

$$= -3x - \tfrac{9}{2}x^2 - 9x^3 - \dots \qquad -\tfrac{1}{3} \leqslant x < \tfrac{1}{3}$$

Substitute $-3x$ for x in the expansion of $\ln(1+x)0$

$$\text{So } \ln\frac{\sqrt{1+2x}}{1-3x} = (x - x^2 + \tfrac{4}{3}x^3 - \dots)$$

$$- (-3x - \tfrac{9}{2}x^2 - 9x^3 - \dots), \, -\tfrac{1}{3} \leqslant x < \tfrac{1}{3}$$

$$= 4x + \tfrac{7}{2}x^2 + \tfrac{31}{3}x^3 + \dots, \qquad -\tfrac{1}{3} \leqslant x < \tfrac{1}{3}$$

You need both intervals to be satisfied. This is the case for $-\tfrac{1}{3} \leqslant x < \tfrac{1}{3}$

Example 8

Given that terms in x^n with $n > 4$ may be neglected (i.e. deliberately ignored), use the series expansions for e^x and $\sin x$ to show that

$$e^{\sin x} \approx 1 + x + \frac{x^2}{2} - \frac{x^4}{8}$$

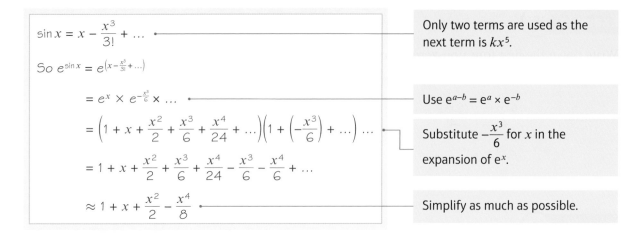

$$\sin x = x - \frac{x^3}{3!} + \ldots$$ ————————————— Only two terms are used as the next term is kx^5.

So $e^{\sin x} = e^{\left(x - \frac{x^3}{3!} + \ldots\right)}$

$$= e^x \times e^{-\frac{x^3}{6}} \times \ldots$$ ————————————— Use $e^{a-b} = e^a \times e^{-b}$

$$= \left(1 + x + \frac{x^2}{2} + \frac{x^3}{6} + \frac{x^4}{24} + \ldots\right)\left(1 + \left(-\frac{x^3}{6}\right) + \ldots\right) \ldots$$ ————————————— Substitute $-\frac{x^3}{6}$ for x in the expansion of e^x.

$$= 1 + x + \frac{x^2}{2} + \frac{x^3}{6} + \frac{x^4}{24} - \frac{x^3}{6} - \frac{x^4}{6} + \ldots$$

$$\approx 1 + x + \frac{x^2}{2} - \frac{x^4}{8}$$ ————————————— Simplify as much as possible.

Exercise 7C

(P) **1** Use the series expansions of e^x, $\ln(1+x)$ and $\sin x$ to expand the following functions as far as the fourth non-zero term. In each case state the values of x for which the expansion is valid.

a $\dfrac{1}{e^x}$

b $\dfrac{e^{2x} \times e^{3x}}{e^x}$

c e^{1+x}

d $\ln(1-x)$

e $\sin\left(\dfrac{x}{2}\right)$

f $\ln(2+3x)$

Hint For part **f**, write $2 + 3x$ as $2\left(1 + \dfrac{3x}{2}\right)$

(E/P) **2 a** Using the Maclaurin series of $\ln(1+x)$, show that

$$\ln\left(\frac{1+x}{1-x}\right) = 2\left(x + \frac{x^3}{3} + \frac{x^5}{5} + \ldots\right), \quad -1 < x < 1$$ **(4 marks)**

b Deduce the series expansion for $\ln\sqrt{\dfrac{1+x}{1-x}}$, $-1 < x < 1$ **(2 marks)**

c By choosing a suitable value of x, and using only the first three terms of the series from part **a**, find an approximation for $\ln\left(\frac{2}{3}\right)$, giving your answer to 4 decimal places. **(2 marks)**

d Show that the first three terms of your series from part **b**, with $x = \frac{3}{5}$, give an approximation for $\ln 2$, which is correct to 2 decimal places. **(2 marks)**

(E/P) **3** Show that, for small values of x, $e^{2x} - e^{-x} \approx 3x + \frac{3}{2}x^2$ **(4 marks)**

(E/P) **4 a** Show that $3x\sin 2x - \cos 3x = -1 + \frac{21}{2}x^2 - \frac{59}{8}x^4 - \ldots$ **(5 marks)**

b Hence find the $\lim_{x \to 0}\left(\dfrac{3x\sin 2x - \cos 3x + 1}{x^2}\right)$ **(1 mark)**

(P) **5** Find the series expansions, up to and including the term in x^4, of:

a $\ln(1 + x - 2x^2)$

Notation Factorise the quadratic first.

b $\ln(9 + 6x + x^2)$

and in each case give the range of values of x for which the expansion is valid.

(E/P) **6 a** Write down the series expansion of $\cos 2x$ in ascending powers of x, up to and
 including the term in x^8.   **(3 marks)**

   b Hence, or otherwise, find the first four non-zero terms in the series expansion
   for $\sin^2 x$.   **(3 marks)**

(E/P) **7** Show that the first two non-zero terms of the series expansion, in ascending powers of x,
 of $\ln(1 + x) + (x - 1)(e^x - 1)$ are px^3 and qx^4, where p and q are constants to be found.
    (6 marks)

(E/P) **8 a** By considering the product of the series expansions of $\sin x$ and $(1 - x)^{-2}$,

   expand $\dfrac{\sin x}{(1 - x)^2}$ in ascending powers of x as far as the term in x^4.   **(6 marks)**

   b Deduce the **gradient** of the **tangent**, at the **origin**, to the curve with

   equation $y = \dfrac{\sin x}{(1 - x)^2}$ **(3 marks)**

(P) **9** Use the Maclaurin series, together with a suitable substitution, to show that:

   a $(1 - 3x)\ln(1 + 2x) = 2x - 8x^2 + \dfrac{26}{3}x^3 - 12x^4 + \ldots$

   b $e^{2x}\sin x = x + 2x^2 + \dfrac{11}{6}x^3 + x^4 + \ldots$

   c $\sqrt{1 + x^2}\,e^{-x} = 1 - x + x^2 - \dfrac{2}{3}x^3 + \dfrac{1}{6}x^4 + \ldots$

(E/P) **10 a** Write down the first five non-zero terms in the series expansions of $e^{-\frac{x^2}{2}}$ **(3 marks)**

   b Using your result from part **a**, find an **approximate** value for $\displaystyle\int_{-1}^{1} e^{-\frac{x^2}{2}}\,dx$, giving your answer to
   3 decimal places.   **(3 marks)**

(E/P) **11 a** Show that $e^{px}\sin 3x = 3x + 3px^2 + \dfrac{3(p^2 - 3)}{2}x^3 + \ldots$ where p is a constant.   **(5 marks)**

   b Given that the first non-zero term in the expansion, in ascending powers of x,
   of $e^{px}\sin 3x + \ln(1 + qx) - x$ is kx^3, where k is a constant, find the values of
   p, q and k.   **(4 marks)**

(E/P) **12** $f(x) = e^{x - \ln x}\sin x, \; x > 0$

   a Show that, if x is sufficiently small and x^4 and higher powers of x are neglected,

   $$f(x) \approx 1 + x + \frac{x^2}{3}$$ **(5 marks)**

   b Show that using $x = 0.1$ in the result from part **a** gives an approximation for $f(0.1)$
   which is correct to 6 significant figures.   **(2 marks)**

(E/P) **13** $y = \sin 2x - \cos 2x$

   a Show that $\dfrac{d^4 y}{dx^4} = 16y$ **(4 marks)**

   b Find the first five terms of the Maclaurin series for y, giving each coefficient in
   its simplest form.   **(4 marks)**

Challenge

The Lorentz factor of a moving object, γ, is given by the formula

$$\gamma = \frac{1}{\sqrt{1 - \beta^2}}$$

where $\beta = \frac{v}{c}$ is the ratio of v, the speed of the object, to c, the speed of light (3×10^8 m s^{-1}).

a Find the Maclaurin series expansion of $\gamma = \dfrac{1}{\sqrt{1 - \beta^2}}$ in ascending powers of β up to the term in β^4.

The theory of special relativity predicts that a period of time observed as T within a stationary frame of reference will be observed as a period of time $\dfrac{T}{\gamma}$ in a moving frame of reference.

A spaceship travels from Earth to a planet 4.2 light years away. To an observer on Earth, the journey appears to take 20 years.

b Use your answer to part **a** to estimate the observed journey time for a person on the spaceship.

c Calculate the percentage error in your estimate.

d Comment on whether your approximation would be more or less accurate if the spaceship was travelling at three times the speed.

> **Notation** A light year is the distance light travels in one year.

7.4 Taylor series

Earlier in this chapter you used Maclaurin series expansions to write a function of x as an infinite series in ascending powers of x. However, the conditions of the Maclaurin series expansion mean that some functions, such as $\ln x$, cannot be expanded in this way.

> **Links** The Maclaurin series expansion requires that $f^{(n)}(0)$ exists and is finite for all $n \in \mathbb{N}$.
> If $f(x) = \ln x$ then $f'(x) = \dfrac{1}{x}$ so $f'(0)$ is undefined.
> ← **Further Pure 2 Section 7.2**

The construction of the Maclaurin series expansion focuses on $x = 0$ and, for a value of x very close to 0, a few terms of the series may well give a good approximation of the function.

For values of x further away from 0, even if they are in the interval of validity, more and more terms of the series are required to give a good degree of accuracy.

> **Notation** An extreme example of this is in using $x = 1$ in the series for $\ln(1 + x)$ to find $\ln 2$; thousands of terms of the series are required to reach 4 significant figure accuracy.

To overcome these problems, a series expansion focusing on $x = a$ can be derived.

This series expansion, called a **Taylor series**, is a more general form of the Maclaurin series.

Consider the functions f and g, where $f(x + a) \equiv g(x)$.

> **Notation** For example,
> $f(x) = \ln x$, $g(x) = \ln(x + 1)$

Then $f^{(r)}(x + a) = g^{(r)}(x)$, $r = 1, 2, 3, \ldots, a \neq 0$

In particular, $f^{(r)}(a) = g^{(r)}(0)$, $r = 1, 2, 3, \ldots$

So the Maclaurin series expansion for g,

$$g(x) = g(0) + g'(0)x + \frac{g''(0)}{2!}x^2 + \frac{g'''(0)}{3!}x^3 + \ldots + \frac{g^{(r)}(0)}{r!}x^r + \ldots$$

becomes

■ $f(x + a) = f(a) + f'(a)x + \dfrac{f''(a)}{2!}x^2 + \dfrac{f'''(a)}{3!}x^3 + \ldots + \dfrac{f^{(r)}(a)}{r!}x^r + \ldots$ (A)

Replacing x by $x - a$, gives a second useful form:

■ $f(x) = f(a) + f'(a)(x - a) + \dfrac{f''(a)}{2!}(x - a)^2 + \dfrac{f'''(a)}{3!}(x - a)^3 + \ldots + \dfrac{f^{(r)}(a)}{r!}(x - a)^r + \ldots$ (B)

> **Notation** The Taylor series allows you to approximate the value of $f(x)$ close to $x = a$.

The expansions (A) and (B) given above are known as Taylor series expansions of $f(x)$ at (or about) the point $x = a$.

The Taylor series expansion is valid only if $f^{(n)}(a)$ exists and is finite for all $n \in \mathbb{N}$, and for values of x for which the infinite series converges.

Example 9

Find the Taylor series expansion of e^{-x} in powers of $(x + 4)$ up to and including the term in $(x + 4)^3$.

Let $f(x) = e^{-x}$ and $a = -4$.

$f(x) = f(-4) + f'(-4)(x + 4) + \dfrac{f''(-4)}{2!}(x + 4)^2 + \dfrac{f'''(-4)}{3!}(x + 4)^3 + \ldots$

> Use the Taylor series expansion **(B)**.

$f(x) = e^{-x} \Rightarrow f(-4) = e^4$

$f'(x) = -e^{-x} \Rightarrow f'(-4) = -e^4$

$f''(x) = e^{-x} \Rightarrow f''(-4) = e^4$

$f'''(x) = -e^{-x} \Rightarrow f'''(-4) = -e^4$

> You need to find $f(-4)$, $f'(-4)$, $f''(-4)$ and $f'''(-4)$.

Substituting the values in the series expansion gives

$e^{-x} = e^4 - e^4(x + 4) + \dfrac{e^4}{2!}(x + 4)^2 - \dfrac{e^4}{3!}(x + 4)^3 + \ldots$

$e^{-x} = e^4\left(1 - (x + 4) + \tfrac{1}{2}(x + 4)^2 - \tfrac{1}{6}(x + 4)^3 + \ldots\right)$

> Take a factor of e^4 out of each term on the right-hand side.

Example 10

Express $\tan\left(x + \dfrac{\pi}{4}\right)$ as a series in ascending powers of x up to and including the term x^3.

Let $f(x) = \tan x$, then $\tan\left(x + \dfrac{\pi}{4}\right) = f\left(x + \dfrac{\pi}{4}\right)$.

$f(x) = \tan x \Rightarrow f\left(\dfrac{\pi}{4}\right) = 1$

$f'(x) = \sec^2 x \Rightarrow f'\left(\dfrac{\pi}{4}\right) = 2$

> You need to use the Taylor series expansion **(A)** with $f(x) = \tan x$ and $a = \dfrac{\pi}{4}$

$f''(x) = 2 \times \sec x \times (\sec x \tan x)$

$\qquad = 2 \times \sec^2 x \times \tan x \Rightarrow f''\left(\dfrac{\pi}{4}\right) = 2 \times 2 \times 1 = 4$

$f'''(x) = 2 \times \sec^2 x \times \sec^2 x + 2 \times \tan x \,(2 \times \sec^2 x \tan x)$

$\qquad \Rightarrow f'''\left(\dfrac{\pi}{4}\right) = 2 \times 2 \times 2 + 2 \times 4 = 16$

Using $f(x + a) = f(a) + f'(a)x + \dfrac{f''(a)}{2!}x^2 + \dfrac{f'''(a)}{3!}x^3 + \ldots$

$\tan\left(x + \dfrac{\pi}{4}\right) = 1 + 2x + \dfrac{4}{2!}x^2 + \dfrac{16}{3!}x^3 + \ldots$

$\qquad = 1 + 2x + 2x^2 + \dfrac{8}{3}x^3 + \ldots$

Online Explore the Taylor series expansion of $f(x) = \tan x$ using GeoGebra.

Watch out Make sure you simplify your coefficients as much as possible.

Example 11

a Show that the Taylor series about $\dfrac{\pi}{6}$ of $\sin x$ in ascending powers of $\left(x - \dfrac{\pi}{6}\right)$ up to and including the term $\left(x - \dfrac{\pi}{6}\right)^2$ is $\sin x = \dfrac{1}{2} + \dfrac{\sqrt{3}}{2}\left(x - \dfrac{\pi}{6}\right) - \dfrac{1}{4}\left(x - \dfrac{\pi}{6}\right)^2$

b Using the series in part **a** find, in terms of π, an approximation for $\sin 40°$.

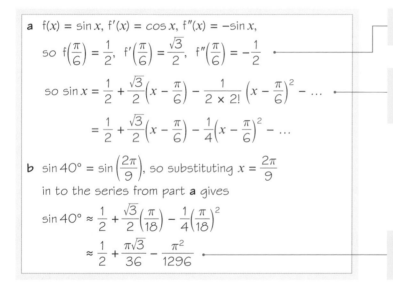

a $f(x) = \sin x$, $f'(x) = \cos x$, $f''(x) = -\sin x$,

so $f\left(\dfrac{\pi}{6}\right) = \dfrac{1}{2}$, $f'\left(\dfrac{\pi}{6}\right) = \dfrac{\sqrt{3}}{2}$, $f''\left(\dfrac{\pi}{6}\right) = -\dfrac{1}{2}$

so $\sin x = \dfrac{1}{2} + \dfrac{\sqrt{3}}{2}\left(x - \dfrac{\pi}{6}\right) - \dfrac{1}{2 \times 2!}\left(x - \dfrac{\pi}{6}\right)^2 - \ldots$

$\qquad = \dfrac{1}{2} + \dfrac{\sqrt{3}}{2}\left(x - \dfrac{\pi}{6}\right) - \dfrac{1}{4}\left(x - \dfrac{\pi}{6}\right)^2 - \ldots$

b $\sin 40° = \sin\left(\dfrac{2\pi}{9}\right)$, so substituting $x = \dfrac{2\pi}{9}$

in to the series from part **a** gives

$\sin 40° \approx \dfrac{1}{2} + \dfrac{\sqrt{3}}{2}\left(\dfrac{\pi}{18}\right) - \dfrac{1}{4}\left(\dfrac{\pi}{18}\right)^2$

$\qquad \approx \dfrac{1}{2} + \dfrac{\pi\sqrt{3}}{36} - \dfrac{\pi^2}{1296}$

Find $f(a)$, $f'(a)$ and $f''(a)$ where $a = \dfrac{\pi}{6}$

Substitute into Taylor series expansion **(B)** with $a = \dfrac{\pi}{6}$

The percentage error in this approximation is about 0.1%.

Exercise 7D

1 a Find the Taylor series expansion of $\sqrt{x}$ in ascending powers of $(x - 1)$ as far as the term in $(x - 1)^4$.

 b Use your answer in **a** to obtain an estimate for $\sqrt{1.2}$, giving your answer to 3 decimal places.

2 Use a Taylor series expansion to express each function as a series in ascending powers of $(x - a)$ as far as the term in $(x - a)^k$, for the given values of a and k.

 a $\ln x$ $(a = e, k = 2)$ **b** $\tan x\left(a = \dfrac{\pi}{3}, k = 3\right)$ **c** $\cos x\,(a = 1, k = 4)$

3   **a**   Use a Taylor series expansion to express each function as a series in ascending powers of x as far as the term in x^4.

     i $\cos\left(x + \dfrac{\pi}{4}\right)$ **ii** $\ln(x + 5)$ **iii** $\sin\left(x - \dfrac{\pi}{3}\right)$

   b   Use your result in **ii** to find an approximation for $\ln 5.2$, giving your answer to 4 significant figures.

(E)   **4**   Given that $y = xe^x$

     a   show that $\dfrac{d^n y}{dx^n} = (n + x)e^x$ **(3 marks)**

     b   find the Taylor series expansion of xe^x in ascending powers of $(x + 1)$ up to and including the term in $(x + 1)^4$ **(3 marks)**

(E)   **5**   **a**   Find the Taylor series for $x^3 \ln x$ in ascending powers of $(x - 1)$ up to and including the term in $(x - 1)^4$ **(4 marks)**

     b   Using your series from **a**, find an approximation for $\ln 1.5$, giving your answer to 4 decimal places.   **(2 marks)**

(E)   **6**   Find the Taylor series expansion of $\tan(x - \alpha)$ about 0, where $\alpha = \arctan\left(\dfrac{3}{4}\right)$, in ascending powers of x up to and including the term in x^2.   **(4 marks)**

(E)   **7**   Find the Taylor series expansion of $\sin 2x$ about $\dfrac{\pi}{6}$ in ascending powers of $\left(x - \dfrac{\pi}{6}\right)$ up to and including the term in $\left(x - \dfrac{\pi}{6}\right)^4$ **(4 marks)**

(E)   **8**   Given that $y = \dfrac{1}{\sqrt{(1 + x)}}$

     a   find the values of $\dfrac{dy}{dx}$ and $\dfrac{d^2y}{dx^2}$ when $x = 3$ **(3 marks)**

     b   find the Taylor series of $\dfrac{1}{\sqrt{(1 + x)}}$, in ascending powers of $(x - 3)$ up to and including the term in $(x - 3)^2$ **(4 marks)**

(E/P)   **9**   Show that the Taylor series of $\ln x$ in powers of $(x - 2)$ is
$$\ln 2 + \sum_{n=1}^{\infty} (-1)^{n-1} \frac{(x - 2)^n}{n \, 2^n}$$
         (6 marks)

Challenge

   a   Find the Taylor series expansion of $\ln(\cos 2x)$ about π in ascending powers of $(x - \pi)$ up to and including the term in $(x - \pi)^4$

   b   Hence obtain an estimate for $\ln\left(\dfrac{\sqrt{3}}{2}\right)$

7.5   Series solutions of differential equations

You can use Taylor series to find **series solutions** of differential equations that can't be solved using other techniques. This can allow you to find useful approximate solutions, and to find solutions that cannot be expressed using elementary functions.

> **Links**   You can use integrating factors or auxiliary equations to solve some first and second-order differential equations directly.
>
> ← **Further Pure 2 Sections 5.2, 6.1**

Suppose you have a first-order differential equation of the form $\dfrac{dy}{dx} = f(x, y)$ and know the initial condition that at $x = x_0$, $y = y_0$, then you can calculate $\left.\dfrac{dy}{dx}\right|_{x_0}$ by substituting x_0 and y_0 into the original differential equation.

> **Watch out** $f(x, y)$ denotes a function of both x and y, such as $x^2y + 1$, or e^{xy}. Such functions cannot always be written as a product of functions $g(x)h(y)$.

By successive differentiation of the original differential equation, the values of $\left.\dfrac{d^2y}{dx^2}\right|_{x_0}$, $\left.\dfrac{d^3y}{dx^3}\right|_{x_0}$ and so on can be found by substituting previous results into the derived equations.

> **Notation** $\left.\dfrac{dy}{dx}\right|_{x_0}$ is used to denote the value of $\dfrac{dy}{dx}$ when $x = x_0$

- The series solution to the differential equation $\dfrac{dy}{dx} = f(x, y)$ is found using the Taylor series expansion in the form

$$y = y_0 + (x - x_0)\left.\frac{dy}{dx}\right|_{x_0} + \frac{(x - x_0)^2}{2!}\left.\frac{d^2y}{dx^2}\right|_{x_0} + \frac{(x - x_0)^3}{3!}\left.\frac{d^3y}{dx^3}\right|_{x_0} + \dots \qquad \text{(C)}$$

- In the situation where $x_0 = 0$, this reduces to the Maclaurin series

$$y = y_0 + x\left.\frac{dy}{dx}\right|_{0} + \frac{x^2}{2!}\left.\frac{d^2y}{dx^2}\right|_{0} + \frac{x^3}{3!}\left.\frac{d^3y}{dx^3}\right|_{0} + \dots \qquad \text{(D)}$$

Second-order and higher differential equations can be solved in the same manner.

Example 12

Use the Taylor series method to find a series solution, in ascending powers of x up to and including the term in x^3, of

$$\frac{d^2y}{dx^2} = y - \sin x$$

given that when $x = 0$, $y = 1$ and $\dfrac{dy}{dx} = 2$.

The given conditions are $x_0 = 0$, $y_0 = 1$, $\left.\dfrac{dy}{dx}\right|_0 = 2$

Substituting $x_0 = 0$ and $y_0 = 1$, into $\dfrac{d^2y}{dx^2} = y - \sin x$

gives $\left.\dfrac{d^2y}{dx^2}\right|_0 = 1 - \sin 0 = 1$

$\dfrac{d^3y}{dx^3} = \dfrac{dy}{dx} - \cos x$ **(1)**

First find $\left.\dfrac{d^2y}{dx^2}\right|_0$

Differentiate the given differential equation with respect to x.

Substituting $x_0 = 0$ and $\left.\dfrac{dy}{dx}\right|_0 = 2$ into **(1)**

gives $\left.\dfrac{d^3y}{dx^3}\right|_0 = 2 - \cos 0 = 1.$

Find $\left.\dfrac{d^3y}{dx^3}\right|_0$

Substituting the results into

$$y = y_0 + x\left.\dfrac{dy}{dx}\right|_0 + \dfrac{x^2}{2!}\left.\dfrac{d^2y}{dx^2}\right|_0 + \dfrac{x^3}{3!}\left.\dfrac{d^3y}{dx^3}\right|_0 + \dots$$

Then use the Taylor series expansion **(D)**.

gives $y = 1 + x \times 2 + \dfrac{x^2}{2!} \times 1 + \dfrac{x^3}{3!} \times 1 + \dots$

$$= 1 + 2x + \dfrac{x^2}{2} + \dfrac{x^3}{6} + \dots$$

Example 13

Given that $\dfrac{d^2y}{dx^2} + 2\dfrac{dy}{dx} = xy$ and that $y = 1$ and $\dfrac{dy}{dx} = 2$ at $x = 1$, express y as a series in ascending powers of $(x - 1)$ up to and including the term in $(x - 1)^4$

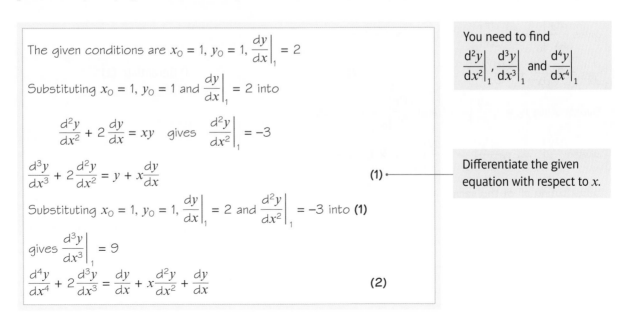

The given conditions are $x_0 = 1$, $y_0 = 1$, $\left.\dfrac{dy}{dx}\right|_1 = 2$

Substituting $x_0 = 1$, $y_0 = 1$ and $\left.\dfrac{dy}{dx}\right|_1 = 2$ into

$\dfrac{d^2y}{dx^2} + 2\dfrac{dy}{dx} = xy$ gives $\left.\dfrac{d^2y}{dx^2}\right|_1 = -3$

$\dfrac{d^3y}{dx^3} + 2\dfrac{d^2y}{dx^2} = y + x\dfrac{dy}{dx}$ **(1)**

Substituting $x_0 = 1$, $y_0 = 1$, $\left.\dfrac{dy}{dx}\right|_1 = 2$ and $\left.\dfrac{d^2y}{dx^2}\right|_1 = -3$ into **(1)**

gives $\left.\dfrac{d^3y}{dx^3}\right|_1 = 9$

$\dfrac{d^4y}{dx^4} + 2\dfrac{d^3y}{dx^3} = \dfrac{dy}{dx} + x\dfrac{d^2y}{dx^2} + \dfrac{dy}{dx}$ **(2)**

You need to find
$\left.\dfrac{d^2y}{dx^2}\right|_1$, $\left.\dfrac{d^3y}{dx^3}\right|_1$ and $\left.\dfrac{d^4y}{dx^4}\right|_1$

Differentiate the given equation with respect to x.

Substituting $x_0 = 1$, $\left.\dfrac{dy}{dx}\right|_1 = 2$, $\left.\dfrac{d^2y}{dx^2}\right|_1 = -3$ and $\left.\dfrac{d^3y}{dx^3}\right|_1 = 9$

into **(2)** gives $\left.\dfrac{d^4y}{dx^4}\right|_1 = -17$

Substituting all the values into

$$y = y_0 + (x - x_0)\left.\frac{dy}{dx}\right|_1 + \frac{(x - x_0)^2}{2!}\left.\frac{d^2y}{dx^2}\right|_1 + \frac{(x - x_0)^3}{3!}\left.\frac{d^3y}{dx^3}\right|_1 + \ldots$$

gives $y = 1 + 2(x - 1) + \dfrac{-3}{2!}(x - 1)^2 + \dfrac{9}{3!}(x - 1)^3 + \dfrac{-17}{4!}(x - 1)^4 + \ldots$

$$y = 1 + 2(x - 1) - \tfrac{3}{2}(x - 1)^2 + \tfrac{3}{2}(x - 1)^3 - \tfrac{17}{24}(x - 1)^4 + \ldots$$

Watch out The initial conditions are given at $x_0 = 1$ so you need to make sure you expand about this point in order to use the series solution.

Then use the Taylor series expansion **(C)**.

Example 14

Given that y satisfies the differential equation $\dfrac{dy}{dx} = y^2 - x$ and that $y = 1$ at $x = 0$, find a series solution for y in ascending powers of x up to and including the term in x^3.

The given conditions are $x_0 = 0$, $y_0 = 1$.

Substituting $x_0 = 0$ and $y_0 = 1$ into $\dfrac{dy}{dx} = y^2 - x$

gives $\left.\dfrac{dy}{dx}\right|_0 = 1^2 - 0 = 1$

$$\frac{d^2y}{dx^2} = 2y\frac{dy}{dx} - 1 \qquad (1)$$

Substituting $y_0 = 1$ and $\left.\dfrac{dy}{dx}\right|_0 = 1$ into **(1)**

gives $\left.\dfrac{d^2y}{dx^2}\right|_0 = 2y_0\left.\dfrac{dy}{dx}\right|_0 - 1 = 2 \times 1 \times 1 - 1 = 1$

$$\frac{d^3y}{dx^3} = 2y\frac{d^2y}{dx^2} + 2\left(\frac{dy}{dx}\right)^2 \qquad (2)$$

Substituting $y_0 = 1$, $\left.\dfrac{dy}{dx}\right|_0 = 1$ and $\left.\dfrac{d^2y}{dx^2}\right|_0 = 1$ into **(2)**

gives $\left.\dfrac{d^3y}{dx^3}\right|_0 = 2y_0\left.\dfrac{d^2y}{dx^2}\right|_0 + 2\left.\dfrac{dy}{dx}\right|_0^2 = 2 \times 1 \times 1 + 2 \times 1^2 = 4$

Substituting all of the values into

$$y = y_0 + x\left.\frac{dy}{dx}\right|_0 + \frac{x^2}{2!}\left.\frac{d^2y}{dx^2}\right|_0 + \frac{x^3}{3!}\left.\frac{d^3y}{dx^3}\right|_0 + \ldots$$

gives $y = 1 + x + \tfrac{1}{2}x^2 + \tfrac{2}{3}x^3 + \ldots$

You need to find $\left.\dfrac{d^2y}{dx^2}\right|_1$, $\left.\dfrac{d^3y}{dx^3}\right|_1$ and $\left.\dfrac{d^4y}{dx^4}\right|_1$

Differentiate the given equation with respect to x.

Differentiate **(1)**.

Use Taylor series expansion **(D)**.

Exercise 7E

(E) **1** Find a series solution, in ascending powers of x up to and including the term in x^4, for the differential equation $\dfrac{d^2y}{dx^2} = x + 2y$, given that at $x = 0$, $y = 1$ and $\dfrac{dy}{dx} = \dfrac{1}{2}$ **(8 marks)**

(E) **2** The variable y satisfies $(1 + x^2)\dfrac{d^2y}{dx^2} + x\dfrac{dy}{dx} = 0$ and at $x = 0$, $y = 0$ and $\dfrac{dy}{dx} = 1$

Use the Taylor series method to find a series expansion for y in powers of x up to and including the term in x^3.   **(8 marks)**

(E) **3** Given that y satisfies the differential equation $\dfrac{dy}{dx} + y - e^x = 0$, and that $y = 2$ at $x = 0$, find a series solution for y in ascending powers of x up to and including the term in x^3.   **(6 marks)**

(E) **4** Use the Taylor series method to find a series solution for $\dfrac{d^2y}{dx^2} + x\dfrac{dy}{dx} + y = 0$, given that at $x = 0$, $y = 1$ and $\dfrac{dy}{dx} = 2$, giving your answer in ascending powers of x up to and including the term in x^4.   **(8 marks)**

(E) **5** The variable y satisfies the differential equation $\dfrac{d^2y}{dx^2} + 2\dfrac{dy}{dx} = 3xy$, and $y = 1$ and $\dfrac{dy}{dx} = -1$ at $x = 1$.

Express y as a series in powers of $(x - 1)$ up to and including the term in $(x - 1)^3$ **(8 marks)**

(E) **6** Find a series solution, in ascending powers of x up to and including the term x^4, to the differential equation $\dfrac{d^2y}{dx^2} + 2y\dfrac{dy}{dx} + y^3 = 1 + x$, given that at $x = 0$, $y = 1$ and $\dfrac{dy}{dx} = 1$ **(8 marks)**

(E/P) **7** $(1 + 2x)\dfrac{dy}{dx} = x + 2y^2$

a Show that $(1 + 2x)\dfrac{d^3y}{dx^3} + 4(1 - y)\dfrac{d^2y}{dx^2} = 4\left(\dfrac{dy}{dx}\right)^2$ **(4 marks)**

b Given that $y = 1$ at $x = 0$, find a series solution of $(1 + 2x)\dfrac{dy}{dx} = x + 2y^2$, in ascending powers of x up to and including the term in x^3.   **(4 marks)**

(E/P) **8** Find the series solution in ascending powers of $\left(x - \dfrac{\pi}{4}\right)$ up to and including the term in $\left(x - \dfrac{\pi}{4}\right)^2$ for the differential equation $\sin x\dfrac{dy}{dx} + y\cos x = y^2$ given that $y = \sqrt{2}$ at $x = \dfrac{\pi}{4}$ **(6 marks)**

9 The variable y satisfies the differential equation $\dfrac{dy}{dx} - x^2 - y^2 = 0$

   a Show that:

   i $\dfrac{d^2y}{dx^2} - 2y\dfrac{dy}{dx} - 2x = 0$ **(2 marks)**

   ii $\dfrac{d^3y}{dx^3} - 2y\dfrac{d^2y}{dx^2} - 2\left(\dfrac{dy}{dx}\right)^2 = 2$ **(2 marks)**

   b Derive a similar equation involving $\dfrac{d^4y}{dx^4}, \dfrac{d^3y}{dx^3}, \dfrac{d^2y}{dx^2}, \dfrac{dy}{dx}$ and y. **(3 marks)**

   c Given also that $y = 1$ at $x = 0$, express y as a series in ascending powers of x in powers of x up to and including the term in x^4 **(4 marks)**

10 Given that $\cos x \dfrac{dy}{dx} + y\sin x + 2y^3 = 0$, and that $y = 1$ at $x = 0$, use the Taylor series method to show that, close to $x = 0$, $y \approx 1 - 2x + \dfrac{11}{2}x^2 - \dfrac{56}{3}x^3$ **(6 marks)**

11 $\dfrac{d^2y}{dx^2} = 4x\dfrac{dy}{dx} - 2y$ **(1)**

   a Show that
   $$\dfrac{d^5y}{dx^5} = px\dfrac{d^4y}{dx^4} + q\dfrac{d^3y}{dx^3},$$
   where p and q are integers to be determined. **(4 marks)**

   b Hence find a series solution, in ascending powers of $(x - 1)$ up to the term in x^5 of differential equation **(1)**, given that $y = \dfrac{dy}{dx} = 2$ when $x = 1$. **(5 marks)**

Chapter review 7

1 a Given that $y = e^{1-2x}$, find an expression, in terms of y, for $\dfrac{d^ny}{dx^n}$

   b Hence show that $\dfrac{d^8y}{dx^8}$ at $x = \ln 32$ is $\dfrac{e}{4}$

2 a For the function $f(x) = \ln(1 + e^x)$, find the values of $f'(0)$ and $f''(0)$.

   b Show that $f'''(0) = 0$.

   c Find the series expansion of $\ln(1 + e^x)$, in ascending powers of x up to and including the term in x^2.

3 a Write down the Maclaurin series of $\cos 4x$ in ascending powers of x, up to and including the term in x^6. **(3 marks)**

   b Hence, or otherwise, show that the first three non-zero terms in the series expansion of $\sin^2 2x$ are $4x^2 - \dfrac{16}{3}x^4 + \dfrac{128}{45}x^6$ **(3 marks)**

4 Given that terms in x^5 and higher powers may be neglected, use the Maclaurin series for e^x and $\cos x$ to show that $e^{\cos x} \approx e\left(1 - \dfrac{x^2}{2} + \dfrac{x^4}{6}\right)$ **(5 marks)**

5 Using Taylor series, show that the first three terms in the series expansion of $\left(x - \frac{\pi}{4}\right)\cot x$, in powers of $\left(x - \frac{\pi}{4}\right)$, are $\left(x - \frac{\pi}{4}\right) - 2\left(x - \frac{\pi}{4}\right)^2 + 2\left(x - \frac{\pi}{4}\right)^3$

(E/P) 6 Given that $|2x| < 1$, find the first two non-zero terms in the series expansion of $\ln\left((1 + x)^2(1 - 2x)\right)$ in ascending powers of x.   **(5 marks)**

(E/P) 7 Use differentiation and Maclaurin series to express $\ln(\sec x + \tan x)$ as a series in ascending powers of x up to and including the term in x^3.   **(5 marks)**

(P) 8 Show that the results of differentiating the standard series expansions of e^x, $\sin x$ and $\cos x$ agree with

     a $\frac{d}{dx}(e^x) = e^x$ **b** $\frac{d}{dx}(\sin x) = \cos x$ **c** $\frac{d}{dx}(\cos x) = -\sin x$

(E) 9 **a** Given that $\cos x = 1 - \frac{x^2}{2!} + \frac{x^4}{4!} - \ldots$, show that $\sec x = 1 + \frac{x^2}{2} + \frac{5}{24}x^4 + \ldots$ **(4 marks)**

     b Using the result found in part **a**, and given that $\sin x = x - \frac{x^3}{3!} + \frac{x^5}{5!} - \ldots$, find the first three non-zero terms in the series expansion, in ascending powers of x, for $\tan x$.   **(4 marks)**

(E/P) 10 By using the series expansions of e^x and $\cos x$, or otherwise, find the expansion of $e^x \cos 3x$ in ascending powers of x up to and including the term in x^3.   **(5 marks)**

(E/P) 11 Find the first three derivatives of $(1 + x)^2 \ln(1 + x)$. Hence, or otherwise, find the expansion of $(1 + x)^2 \ln(1 + x)$ in ascending powers of x up to and including the term in x^3.   **(5 marks)**

(E/P) 12 **a** Expand $\ln(1 + \sin x)$ in ascending powers of x up to and including the term in x^4.   **(4 marks)**

     b Hence find an approximation for $\int_0^{\frac{\pi}{6}} \ln(1 + \sin x)\,dx$ giving your answer to 3 decimal places.   **(3 marks)**

(E/P) 13 **a** Using the first two terms, $x + \frac{x^3}{3}$, in the expansion of $\tan x$, show that
$$e^{\tan x} = 1 + x + \frac{x^2}{2} + \frac{x^3}{2} + \ldots$$ **(3 marks)**

     b Deduce the first four terms in the series expansion of $e^{-\tan x}$, in ascending powers of x.   **(3 marks)**

(P) 14 **a** Using Maclaurin series and differentiation, show that $\ln\cos x = -\frac{x^2}{2} - \frac{x^4}{12} + \ldots$

     b Using $\cos x = 2\cos^2\left(\frac{x}{2}\right) - 1$ and the result in part **a**, show that
$$\ln(1 + \cos x) = \ln 2 - \frac{x^2}{4} - \frac{x^4}{96} + \ldots$$

(E/P) 15 $y = e^{3x} - e^{-3x}$

     a Show that $\frac{d^4y}{dx^4} = 81y$ **(4 marks)**

     b Find the first three non-zero terms of the Maclaurin series for y, giving each coefficient in its simplest form.   **(3 marks)**

     c Find an expression for the nth non-zero term of the Maclaurin series for y.   **(2 marks)**

16 a For the function $f(x) = \ln(1 + e^x)$, find the values of $f'(0)$ and $f''(0)$.

b Show that $f'''(0) = 0$.

c Find the Taylor series expansion of $\ln(1 + e^x)$, in ascending powers of x up to and including the term in x^2.

17 a Write down the Taylor series for $\cos 4x$ in ascending powers of x, up to and including the term in x^6.

b Hence, or otherwise, show that the first three non-zero terms in the series expansion of $\sin^2 2x$ are $4x^2 - \frac{16}{3}x^4 + \frac{128}{45}x^6$.

(P) 18 Given that terms in x^5 and higher powers may be neglected, use the Taylor series for e^x and $\cos x$, to show that $e^{\cos x} \approx e\left(1 - \frac{x^2}{2} + \frac{x^4}{6}\right)$

(E) 19 $\frac{dy}{dx} = 2 + x + \sin y$

a Given that $y = 0$, when $x = 0$, use the Taylor series method to obtain y as a series in ascending powers of x up to and including the term in x^3. **(5 marks)**

b Hence obtain an approximate value for y at $x = 0.1$ **(1 mark)**

(E) 20 Given that $|2x| < 1$, find the first two non-zero terms in the Taylor series expansion of $\ln((1 + x)^2(1 - 2x))$ in ascending powers of x. **(5 marks)**

(E) 21 Find the series solution, in ascending powers of x up to and including the term in x^3, of the differential equation $\frac{d^2y}{dx^2} - (x + 2)\frac{dy}{dx} + 3y = 0$, given that at $x = 0$, $y = 2$ and $\frac{dy}{dx} = 4$ **(5 marks)**

(E/P) 22 a Use differentiation and Maclaurin series expansion to express $\ln(\sec x + \tan x)$ as a series in ascending powers of x up to and including the term in x^3. **(4 marks)**

b Hence find $\lim\limits_{x \to 0} \dfrac{\sin x - \ln(\sec x + \tan x)}{x(\cos x - 1)}$ **(4 marks)**

23 Show that the results of differentiating the series expansions

$$e^x = 1 + x + \frac{x^2}{2!} + \frac{x^3}{3!} + \ldots + \frac{x^r}{r!} + \ldots$$

$$\sin x = x - \frac{x^3}{3!} + \frac{x^5}{5!} - \frac{x^7}{7!} + \ldots + \frac{(-1)^r x^{2r+1}}{(2r+1)!} + \ldots$$

$$\cos x = 1 - \frac{x^2}{2!} + \frac{x^4}{4!} - \frac{x^6}{6!} + \ldots + (-1)^r \frac{x^{2r}}{(2r)!} + \ldots$$

agree with the results

a $\dfrac{d}{dx}(e^x) = e^x$ **b** $\dfrac{d}{dx}(\sin x) = \cos x$ **c** $\dfrac{d}{dx}(\cos x) = -\sin x$

(E) 24 $\dfrac{d^2y}{dx^2} + y\dfrac{dy}{dx} = x$, and at $x = 1$, $y = 0$ and $\dfrac{dy}{dx} = 2$

Find a series solution of the differential equation, in ascending powers of $(x - 1)$ up to and including the term in $(x - 1)^3$ **(8 marks)**

(E) **25 a** Given that $\cos x = 1 - \dfrac{x^2}{2!} + \dfrac{x^4}{4!} - \ldots$, show that $\sec x = 1 + \dfrac{x^2}{2} + \dfrac{5}{24}x^4 + \ldots$ **(4 marks)**

　　 b Using the result found in part **a**, and given that $\sin x = x - \dfrac{x^3}{3!} + \dfrac{x^5}{5!} - \ldots$, find the first three non-zero terms in the series expansion, in ascending powers of x, for $\tan x$. **(4 marks)**

(E/P) **26** By using the Taylor series expansions of e^x and $\cos x$, or otherwise, find the expansion of $e^x \cos 3x$ in ascending powers of x up to and including the term in x^3. **(4 marks)**

(E) **27** $\dfrac{d^2y}{dx^2} + x^2\dfrac{dy}{dx} + y = 0$ with $y = 2$ at $x = 0$ and $\dfrac{dy}{dx} = 1$ at $x = 0$.

　　 a Use the Taylor series method to express y as a polynomial in x up to and including the term in x^3. **(4 marks)**

　　 b Show that at $x = 0$, $\dfrac{d^4y}{dx^4} = 0$ **(3 marks)**

(E) **28 a** Find the first three derivatives of $(1 + x)^2 \ln(1 + x)$ **(4 marks)**

　　 b Hence, or otherwise, find the Taylor series expansion of $(1 + x)^2 \ln(1 + x)$ in ascending powers of x up to and including the term in x^3. **(4 marks)**

(E) **29 a** Expand $\ln(1 + \sin x)$ in ascending powers of x up to and including the term in x^4. **(6 marks)**

　　 b Hence find an approximation for $\displaystyle\int_0^{\frac{\pi}{6}} \ln(1 + \sin x)\, dx$ giving your answer to 3 decimal places. **(3 marks)**

(E/P) **30 a** Using the first two terms, $x + \dfrac{x^3}{3}$, in the Taylor series of $\tan x$, show that
$$e^{\tan x} = 1 + x + \dfrac{x^2}{2} + \dfrac{x^3}{2} + \ldots$$ **(4 marks)**

　　 b Deduce the first four terms in the Taylor series of $e^{-\tan x}$, in ascending powers of x. **(2 marks)**

(E/P) **31** $y\dfrac{d^2y}{dx^2} + \left(\dfrac{dy}{dx}\right)^2 + y = 0$

　　 a Find an expression for $\dfrac{d^3y}{dx^3}$ **(5 marks)**

　　 Given that $y = 1$ and $\dfrac{dy}{dx} = 1$ at $x = 0$,

　　 b find the series solution for y, in ascending powers of x, up to an including the term in x^3. **(5 marks)**

　　 c Comment on whether it would be sensible to use your series solution from part **b** to give estimates for y at $x = 0.2$ and at $x = 50$. **(2 marks)**

(P) **32 a** Using Maclaurin series, and differentiation, show that $\ln \cos x = -\dfrac{x^2}{2} - \dfrac{x^4}{12} + \ldots$

　　 b Using $\cos x = 2\cos^2\left(\dfrac{x}{2}\right) - 1$, and the result in part **a**, show that
$$\ln(1 + \cos x) = \ln 2 - \dfrac{x^2}{4} - \dfrac{x^4}{96} + \ldots$$

(P) **33 a** By writing $3^x = e^{x \ln 3}$, find the first four terms in the Taylor series of 3^x.

　　 b Using your answer from part **a**, with a suitable value of x, find an approximation for $\sqrt{3}$, giving your answer to 3 significant figures.

(E/P) **34** **a** Given that $f(x) = \ln\left(1 + 2\cos\left(\frac{\pi x}{2}\right)\right)$, find f' and f''.   **(4 marks)**

     b Hence, using Taylor series, show that the first two non-zero terms, in ascending powers of $(x-1)$, of $\ln\left(1 + 2\cos\left(\frac{\pi x}{2}\right)\right)$ are $-\pi(x-1) - \frac{\pi^2}{2}(x-1)^2$ **(2 marks)**

Challenge

a Use induction to prove that the nth derivative of $\ln x$ is given by

$$\frac{d^n}{dx^n}\ln x = (-1)^{n+1}\frac{(n-1)!}{x^n}$$

b Hence write down the Taylor series expansion about $x = a$ of $\ln(x)$, where $a > 0$.

Summary of key points

1 The **Maclaurin series** of a function $f(x)$ is given by

$$f(x) = f(0) + f'(0)x + \frac{f''(0)}{2!}x^2 + \ldots + \frac{f^{(r)}(0)}{r!}x^r + \ldots$$

The series is valid provided that $f(0), f'(0), f''(0), \ldots, f^{(r)}(0), \ldots$ all have finite values.

2 The following Maclaurin series are given in the formulae booklet:

$$e^x = 1 + x + \frac{x^2}{2!} + \ldots + \frac{x^r}{r!} + \ldots \qquad \text{for all } x$$

$$\ln(1 + x) = x - \frac{x^2}{2} + \frac{x^3}{3} - \ldots + (-1)^{r+1}\frac{x^r}{r} + \ldots \qquad -1 < x < 1$$

$$\sin x = x - \frac{x^3}{3!} + \frac{x^5}{5!} - \ldots + (-1)^r\frac{x^{2r+1}}{(2r+1)!} + \ldots \qquad \text{for all } x$$

$$\cos x = 1 - \frac{x^3}{3!} + \frac{x^5}{5!} - \ldots + (-1)^r\frac{x^{2r}}{(2r+1)!} + \ldots \qquad \text{for all } x$$

$$\arctan x = x - \frac{x^3}{3} + \frac{x^5}{5} - \ldots + (-1)^r\frac{x^{2r+1}}{2r+1} + \ldots \qquad -1 \leqslant x \leqslant 1$$

3 $f(x + a) = f(a) + f'(a)x + \frac{f''(a)}{2!}x^2 + \frac{f'''(a)}{3!}x^3 + \ldots + \frac{f^{(r)}(a)}{r!}x^r + \ldots$ **(A)**

    $f(x) = f(a) + f'(a)(x - a) + \frac{f''(a)}{2!}(x - a)^2 + \frac{f'''(a)}{3!}(x - a)^3 + \ldots + \frac{f^{(r)}(a)}{r!}(x - a)^r + \ldots$ **(B)**

The expansions **(A)** and **(B)** given above are known as **Taylor series** expansions of $f(x)$ at (or about) the point $x = a$.

The Taylor series expansion is valid only if $f^{(n)}(a)$ exists and is finite for all $n \in \mathbb{N}$, and for values of x for which the infinite series converges.

4 • The series solution to the differential equation $\frac{dy}{dx} = f(x, y)$ is found using the Taylor series expansion in the form

$$y = y_0 + (x - x_0)\frac{dy}{dx}\bigg|_{x_0} + \frac{(x - x_0)^2}{2!}\frac{d^2y}{dx^2}\bigg|_{x_0} + \frac{(x - x_0)^3}{3!}\frac{d^3y}{dx^3}\bigg|_{x_0} + \ldots \quad \textbf{(C)}$$

• In the situation where $x_0 = 0$, this reduces to the Maclaurin series

$$y = y_0 + x\frac{dy}{dx}\bigg|_0 + \frac{x^2}{2!}\frac{d^2y}{dx^2}\bigg|_0 + \frac{x^3}{3!}\frac{d^3y}{dx^3}\bigg|_0 + \ldots \quad \textbf{(D)}$$

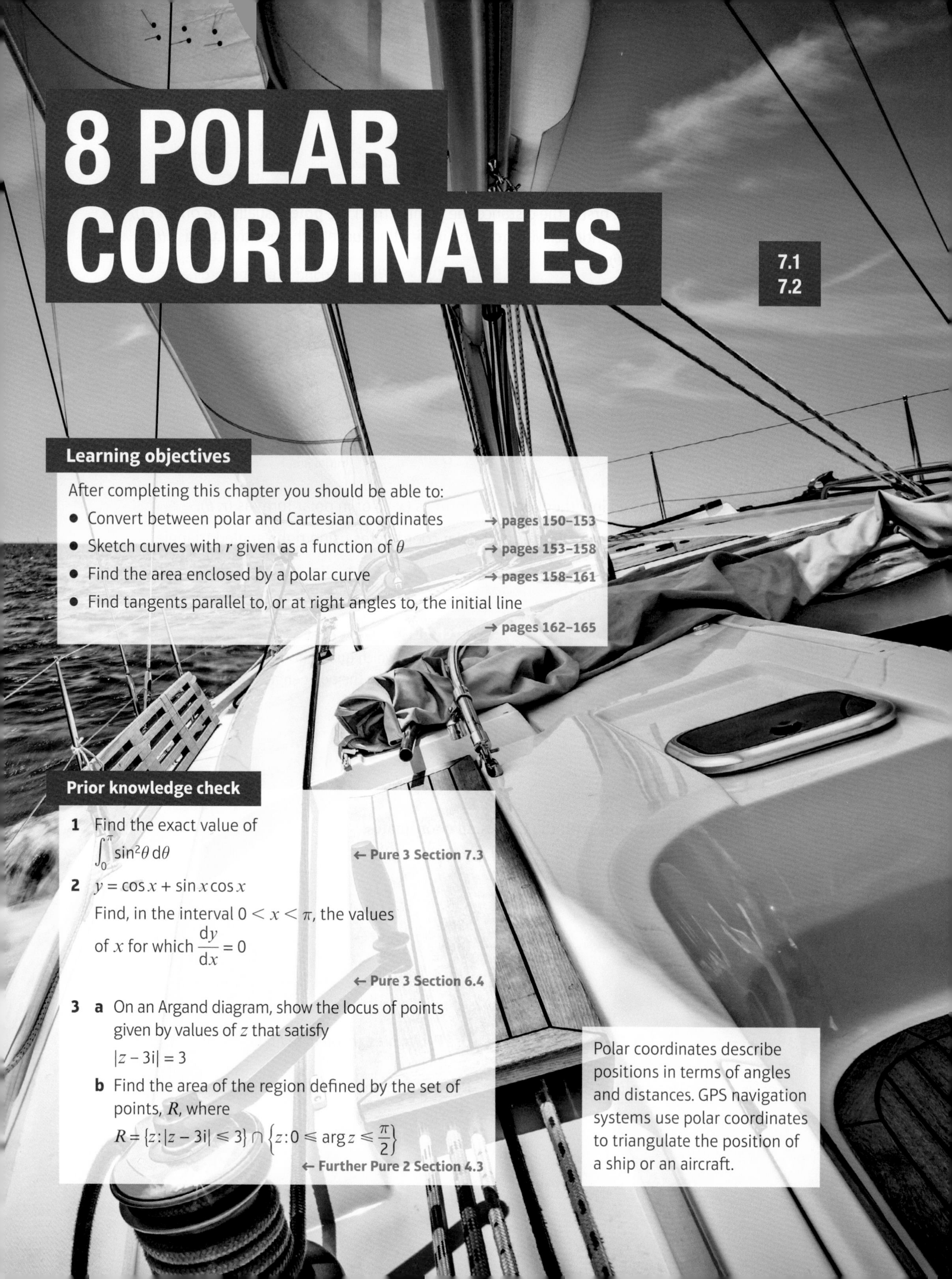

8 POLAR COORDINATES

Learning objectives

After completing this chapter you should be able to:

* Convert between polar and Cartesian coordinates → pages 150–153
* Sketch curves with r given as a function of θ → pages 153–158
* Find the area enclosed by a polar curve → pages 158–161
* Find tangents parallel to, or at right angles to, the initial line → pages 162–165

Prior knowledge check

1 Find the exact value of
$\int_0^\pi \sin^2\theta \, d\theta$ ← Pure 3 Section 7.3

2 $y = \cos x + \sin x \cos x$

Find, in the interval $0 < x < \pi$, the values
of x for which $\dfrac{dy}{dx} = 0$

← Pure 3 Section 6.4

3 **a** On an Argand diagram, show the locus of points
given by values of z that satisfy

$|z - 3i| = 3$

b Find the area of the region defined by the set of
points, R, where

$R = \{z : |z - 3i| \leqslant 3\} \cap \left\{z : 0 \leqslant \arg z \leqslant \dfrac{\pi}{2}\right\}$

← Further Pure 2 Section 4.3

Polar coordinates describe
positions in terms of angles
and distances. GPS navigation
systems use polar coordinates
to triangulate the position of
a ship or an aircraft.

8.1 Polar coordinates and equations

Polar coordinates are an alternative way of describing the position of a point P in two-dimensional space. You need two measurements: firstly, the distance the point is from the **pole** (usually the origin O), r, and secondly, the angle measured anticlockwise from the **initial line** (usually the positive x-axis), θ. Polar coordinates are written as (r, θ).

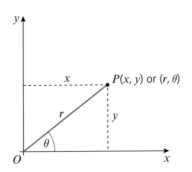

> **Notation**   When working in polar coordinates the axes might also be labelled like this:
>
>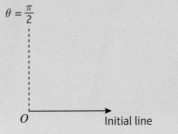

The coordinates of P can be written in either Cartesian form as (x, y) or in polar form as (r, θ).

You can convert between **Cartesian coordinates** and polar coordinates using right-angled triangle trigonometry.

From the diagram above you can see that:

- $r\cos\theta = x$
  $r\sin\theta = y$

- $r^2 = x^2 + y^2$

  $\theta = \arctan\left(\dfrac{y}{x}\right)$

> **Watch out**   Always draw a sketch diagram to check in which quadrant the point lies, and always measure the polar angle from the positive x-axis.

Example 1

Find polar coordinates of the points with the Cartesian coordinates:

a $(3, 4)$ **b** $(5, -12)$ **c** $(-\sqrt{3}, -1)$

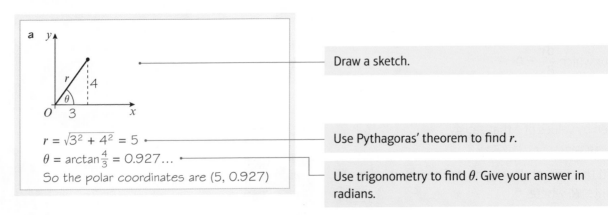

Draw a sketch.

$r = \sqrt{3^2 + 4^2} = 5$ Use Pythagoras' theorem to find r.

$\theta = \arctan\dfrac{4}{3} = 0.927\ldots$ Use trigonometry to find θ. Give your answer in radians.

So the polar coordinates are $(5, 0.927)$

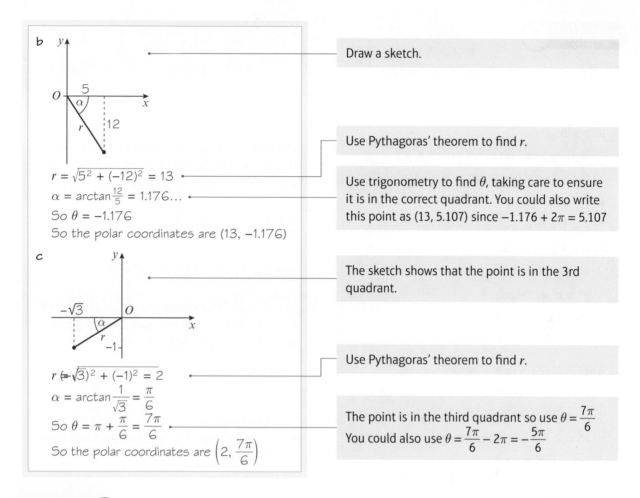

b

Draw a sketch.

Use Pythagoras' theorem to find r.

$r = \sqrt{5^2 + (-12)^2} = 13$

$\alpha = \arctan\frac{12}{5} = 1.176\ldots$

So $\theta = -1.176$

So the polar coordinates are $(13, -1.176)$

Use trigonometry to find θ, taking care to ensure it is in the correct quadrant. You could also write this point as $(13, 5.107)$ since $-1.176 + 2\pi = 5.107$

c

The sketch shows that the point is in the 3rd quadrant.

Use Pythagoras' theorem to find r.

$r = \sqrt{(-\sqrt{3})^2 + (-1)^2} = 2$

$\alpha = \arctan\frac{1}{\sqrt{3}} = \frac{\pi}{6}$

So $\theta = \pi + \frac{\pi}{6} = \frac{7\pi}{6}$

So the polar coordinates are $\left(2, \frac{7\pi}{6}\right)$

The point is in the third quadrant so use $\theta = \frac{7\pi}{6}$
You could also use $\theta = \frac{7\pi}{6} - 2\pi = -\frac{5\pi}{6}$

Example   **2**

Convert the polar coordinates into Cartesian form. The angles are measured in radians.

a $\left(10, \frac{4\pi}{3}\right)$ **b** $\left(8, \frac{2\pi}{3}\right)$

a $x = r\cos\theta = 10\cos\frac{4\pi}{3} = -5$

$y = r\sin\theta = 10\sin\frac{4\pi}{3} = -5\sqrt{3}$

So the Cartesian coordinates are $(-5, -5\sqrt{3})$

b $x = r\cos\theta = 8\cos\frac{2\pi}{3} = -4$

$y = r\sin\theta = 8\sin\frac{2\pi}{3} = 4\sqrt{3}$

So the Cartesian coordinates are $(-4, 4\sqrt{3})$

Polar equations of curves are usually given in the form $r = f(\theta)$. For example,

$r = 2\cos\theta$

$r = 1 + 2\theta$

$r = 3$ In this example r is constant.

You can convert between polar equations of curves and their Cartesian forms.

Example 3

Find Cartesian equations of the curves:

a $r = 5$ **b** $r = 2 + \cos 2\theta$ **c** $r^2 = \sin 2\theta, \quad 0 < \theta \leqslant \dfrac{\pi}{2}$

---

a $r = 5$

Square both sides to get $r^2 = 25$

So a Cartesian equation is $x^2 + y^2 = 25$

> You need to replace r with an equation in x and y. Use $r^2 = x^2 + y^2$. So the equation $r = 5$ represents a circle with centre O and radius 5.

b $r = 2 + \cos 2\theta$

$r = 1 + (1 + \cos 2\theta)$

$r = 1 + 2\cos^2\theta$

> You need an equation in x and y, so use $x = r\cos\theta$. This means first writing $\cos 2\theta$ in terms of $\cos\theta$.

Multiply by r^2:

$r^3 = r^2 + 2r^2\cos^2\theta$

$(x^2 + y^2)^{\frac{3}{2}} = x^2 + y^2 + 2x^2$

Or $(x^2 + y^2)^{\frac{3}{2}} = 3x^2 + y^2$

> Now use $x = r\cos\theta$ and $r^2 = x^2 + y^2$

> **Watch out** Polar coordinates often give rise to complicated Cartesian equations, which cannot be written easily in the form $y = \ldots$

c $r^2 = \sin 2\theta, \quad 0 < \theta \leqslant \dfrac{\pi}{2}$

$r^2 = 2\sin\theta\cos\theta$

Multiply by r^2:

$r^4 = 2 \times r\sin\theta \times r\cos\theta$

$(x^2 + y^2)^2 = 2xy$

> **Problem-solving**
> You need to use the substitutions $x = r\cos\theta$ and $y = r\sin\theta$. Use $\sin 2\theta \equiv 2\sin\theta\cos\theta$ and then multiply by r^2.

Example 4

Find polar equations for:

a $y^2 = 4x$ **b** $x^2 - y^2 = 5$ **c** $y\sqrt{3} = x + 4$

---

a $y^2 = 4x$

$r^2\sin^2\theta = 4r\cos\theta$

$r\sin^2\theta = 4\cos\theta$

$r = \dfrac{4\cos\theta}{\sin^2\theta} = 4\cot\theta\,\mathrm{cosec}\,\theta$

So a polar equation is $r = 4\cot\theta\,\mathrm{cosec}\,\theta$

> Substitute $x = r\cos\theta$ and $y = r\sin\theta$

> Divide by r and simplify.

b $x^2 - y^2 = 5$

$r^2\cos^2\theta - r^2\sin^2\theta = 5$

$r^2(\cos^2\theta - \sin^2\theta) = 5$

$r^2\cos 2\theta = 5$

So a polar equation is $r^2 = 5\sec 2\theta$

> Substitute $x = r\cos\theta$ and $y = r\sin\theta$

> Use $\cos 2\theta \equiv \cos^2\theta - \sin^2\theta$

c $y\sqrt{3} = x + 4$

$r\sqrt{3}\sin\theta = r\cos\theta + 4$

$r(\sqrt{3}\sin\theta - \cos\theta) = 4$

$r\left(\dfrac{\sqrt{3}}{2}\sin\theta - \dfrac{1}{2}\cos\theta\right) = \dfrac{4}{2}$

$r\sin\left(\theta - \dfrac{\pi}{6}\right) = 2$

So a polar equation is $r = 2\cosec\left(\theta - \dfrac{\pi}{6}\right)$

Substitute $x = r\cos\theta$ and $y = r\sin\theta$ and then try to simplify the trigonometric expression.

Use the $\sin(A - B)$ formula.

Exercise 8A

1 Find polar coordinates of the points with the Cartesian coordinates:
a $(5,12)$ **b** $(-5, 12)$ **c** $(-5, -12)$
d $(2, -3)$ **e** $(\sqrt{3}, -1)$

2 Convert the polar coordinates into Cartesian form.
a $\left(6, \dfrac{\pi}{6}\right)$ **b** $\left(6, -\dfrac{\pi}{6}\right)$ **c** $\left(6, \dfrac{3\pi}{4}\right)$
d $\left(10, \dfrac{5\pi}{4}\right)$ **e** $(2, \pi)$

3 Find Cartesian equations for the curves, where a is a positive constant.
a $r = 2$ **b** $r = 3\sec\theta$ **c** $r = 5\cosec\theta$
d $r = 4a\tan\theta\sec\theta$ **e** $r = 2a\cos\theta$ **f** $r = 3a\sin\theta$
g $r = 4(1 - \cos 2\theta)$ **h** $r = 2\cos^2\theta$ **i** $r^2 = 1 + \tan^2\theta$

4 Find polar equations for the curves.
a $x^2 + y^2 = 16$ **b** $xy = 4$ **c** $(x^2 + y^2)^2 = 2xy$
d $x^2 + y^2 - 2x = 0$ **e** $(x + y)^2 = 4$ **f** $x - y = 3$
g $y = 2x$ **h** $y = -\sqrt{3}x + a$ **i** $y = x(x - a)$

Challenge

Show that the distance, d, between the two points (r_1, θ_1) and (r_2, θ_2) in polar coordinates is
$d = \sqrt{r_1^2 + r_2^2 - 2r_1 r_2 \cos(\theta_1 - \theta_2)}$

8.2 Sketching curves

You can sketch curves given in polar form by learning the shapes of some standard curves.
- $r = a$ is a circle with centre O and radius a.
- $\theta = \alpha$ is a half-line through O and making an angle α with the initial line.
- $r = a\theta$ is a spiral starting at O.

Example 5

Sketch the curves

a $r = 5$ **b** $\theta = \dfrac{3\pi}{4}$ **c** $r = a\theta$

where a is a positive constant.

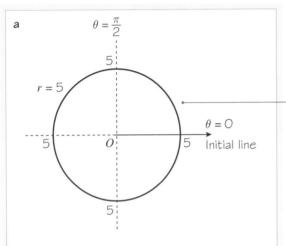

This is a standard curve: a circle with centre O and radius 5.

This is another standard graph: a half-line. Notice it is only 'half' of the line $y = -x$. The other half of the line would have equation $\theta = -\dfrac{\pi}{4}$ or $\theta = \dfrac{7\pi}{4}$

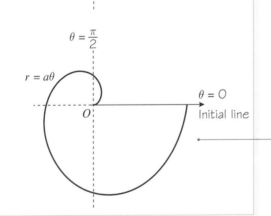

This is another standard curve: a spiral. It crosses the horizontal axis at $-a\pi$, 0 and $2a\pi$ and the vertical axis at $\dfrac{a\pi}{2}$ and $-\dfrac{3a\pi}{2}$. The curve here drawn for values of θ in the range $0 \leqslant \theta \leqslant 2\pi$.

You can also sketch curves by drawing up a table of values of r for particular values of θ.
It is common to choose only values of θ that give positive values of r.

Watch out Some graph-drawing programs and graphical calculators will sketch polar curves for negative values of r so take care when using these tools to help you.

Example (**6**)

Sketch the curves.

a $r = a(1 + \cos\theta)$ **b** $r = a\sin 3\theta$ **c** $r^2 = a^2\cos 2\theta$

a $r = a(1 + \cos\theta)$

θ	0	$\frac{\pi}{2}$	π	$\frac{3\pi}{2}$	2π
r	$2a$	a	0	a	$2a$

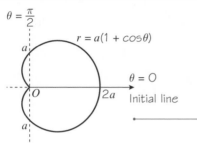

b $r = a\sin 3\theta$

Need to consider

$0 \leqslant \theta \leqslant \dfrac{\pi}{3}, \dfrac{2\pi}{3} \leqslant \theta \leqslant \pi$ and $\dfrac{4\pi}{3} \leqslant \theta \leqslant \dfrac{5\pi}{3}$

θ	0	$\frac{\pi}{6}$	$\frac{\pi}{3}$
r	0	a	0

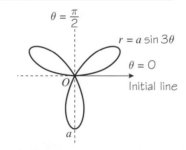

c $r^2 = a^2\cos 2\theta$

You need values of θ in the ranges

$-\dfrac{\pi}{4} \leqslant \theta \leqslant \dfrac{\pi}{4}$ and $\dfrac{3\pi}{4} \leqslant \theta \leqslant \dfrac{5\pi}{4}$

θ	$-\frac{\pi}{4}$	0	$\frac{\pi}{4}$	$\frac{3\pi}{4}$	π	$\frac{5\pi}{4}$
r	0	a	0	0	a	0

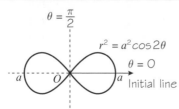

Problem-solving

When sketching polar curves it is useful to plot points for key values of θ. Make a table of values for θ at multiples of $\dfrac{\pi}{2}$ to determine the points at which the curve meets or intersects the coordinate axes.

This curve is 'heart' shaped and is known as a **cardioid**.

Since we only draw the curve when $r \geqslant 0$ you need to determine the values of θ required.

Choose values of θ which give exact values of r. The values shown here define the first loop of the curve. The values of r will be the same in the other two loops.

Problem-solving

The curve given by $r = a\sin 3\theta$ is typical of the patterns that arise in polar curves for equations of the form $r = a\cos n\theta$ or $r = a\sin n\theta$. They will have n loops symmetrically arranged around O.

Establish the values of θ for which the curve exists.

Draw up a table of values and sketch the curve.

Online   Explore curves given in polar form using GeoGebra.

Curves with equations of the form $r = a(p + q\cos\theta)$ are defined for all values of θ if $p \geqslant q$. An example of this, when $p = q$, was the cardioid seen in Example 6a. These curves fall into two types, those that are 'egg' shaped (i.e. a convex curve) and those with a 'dimple' (i.e. the curve is concave at $\theta = \pi$). The conditions for each type are given below:

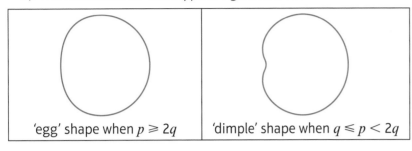

'egg' shape when $p \geqslant 2q$ 'dimple' shape when $q \leqslant p < 2q$

Links You can prove these conditions by considering the number of tangents to the curve that are **perpendicular** to the initial line.

Example 7

Sketch the curves.

a $r = a(5 + 2\cos\theta)$ **b** $r = a(3 + 2\cos\theta)$

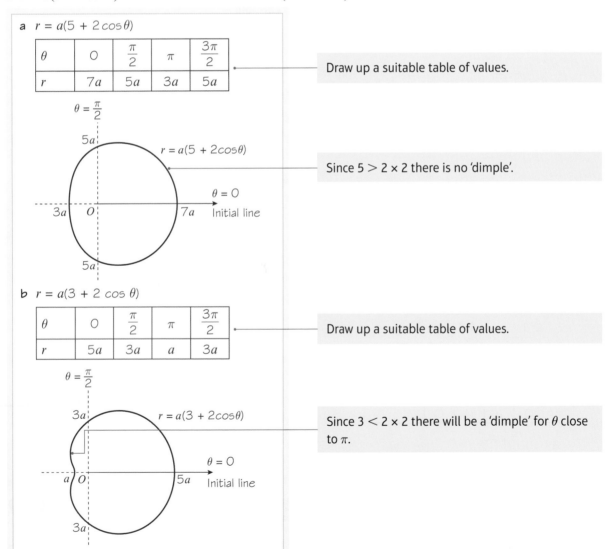

a $r = a(5 + 2\cos\theta)$

θ	O	$\dfrac{\pi}{2}$	π	$\dfrac{3\pi}{2}$
r	$7a$	$5a$	$3a$	$5a$

Draw up a suitable table of values.

Since $5 > 2 \times 2$ there is no 'dimple'.

b $r = a(3 + 2\cos\theta)$

θ	O	$\dfrac{\pi}{2}$	π	$\dfrac{3\pi}{2}$
r	$5a$	$3a$	a	$3a$

Draw up a suitable table of values.

Since $3 < 2 \times 2$ there will be a 'dimple' for θ close to π.

You may also need to find a polar curve to represent a locus of points on an Argand diagram.

> **Links**   If the pole is taken as the origin, and the initial line is taken as the positive real axis, then the point (r, θ) will represent the complex number $re^{i\theta}$ ← **Further Pure 2 Section 8.1**

Example 8

a Show on an Argand diagram the locus of points given by the values of z satisfying
$$|z - 3 - 4i| = 5$$

b Show that this locus of points can be represented by the polar curve $r = 6\cos\theta + 8\sin\theta$

a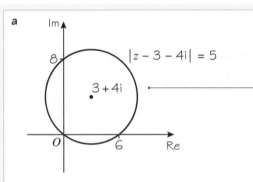

This locus is a circle with centre $3 + 4i$ and radius 5.

b In Cartesian form, $(x - 3)^2 + (y - 4)^2 = 25$
$(r\cos\theta - 3)^2 + (r\sin\theta - 4)^2 = 25$

Substitute for x and y in polar form.

$r^2\cos^2\theta - 6r\cos\theta + 9 + r^2\sin^2\theta$
$\qquad - 8r\sin\theta + 16 = 25$
$r^2(\cos^2\theta + \sin^2\theta) - 6r\cos\theta - 8r\sin\theta = 0$
$r^2 = 6r\cos\theta + 8r\sin\theta$
$r = 6\cos\theta + 8\sin\theta$

Exercise 8B

1 Sketch the curves.

   a $r = 6$ **b** $\theta = \dfrac{5\pi}{4}$ **c** $\theta = -\dfrac{\pi}{4}$

   d $r = 2\sec\theta$ **e** $r = 3\operatorname{cosec}\theta$ **f** $r = 2\sec\left(\theta - \dfrac{\pi}{3}\right)$

   g $r = a\sin\theta$ **h** $r = a(1 - \cos\theta)$ **i** $r = a\cos 3\theta$

   j $r = a(2 + \cos\theta)$ **k** $r = a(6 + \cos\theta)$ **l** $r = a(4 + 3\cos\theta)$

   m $r = a(2 + \sin\theta)$ **n** $r = a(6 + \sin\theta)$ **o** $r = a(4 + 3\sin\theta)$

   p $r = 2\theta$ **q** $r^2 = a^2\sin\theta$ **r** $r^2 = a^2\sin 2\theta$

(E) **2** Sketch the graph with polar equation
$$r = k\sec\left(\frac{\pi}{4} - \theta\right)$$
where k is a positive constant, giving the coordinates of any points of intersection with the coordinate axes in terms of k.   **(4 marks)**

E **3 a** Show on an Argand diagram the locus of points given by the values of z satisfying

$|z - 12 - 5i| = 13$ **(2 marks)**

b Show that this locus of points can be represented by the polar curve

$r = 24\cos\theta + 10\sin\theta$ **(4 marks)**

E **4 a** Show on an Argand diagram the locus of points given by the values of z satisfying

$|z + 4 + 3i| = 5$ **(2 marks)**

b Show that this locus of points can be represented by the polar curve

$r = -8\cos\theta - 6\sin\theta$ **(4 marks)**

8.3 Area enclosed by a polar curve

You can find areas enclosed by a polar curve using integration.

- The area of a sector bounded by a polar curve and the half-lines $\theta = \alpha$ and $\theta = \beta$, where θ is in radians, is given by the formula

$$\text{Area} = \tfrac{1}{2}\int_{\alpha}^{\beta} r^2 \, d\theta$$

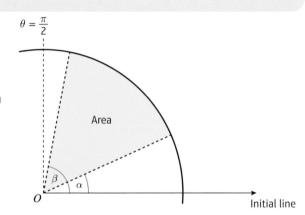

Example 9

Find the area enclosed by the cardioid with equation $r = a(1 + \cos\theta)$

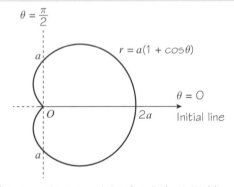

The curve is symmetric about the initial line and so finding the area above this line and doubling it gives:

$\text{Area} = 2 \times \dfrac{a^2}{2} \displaystyle\int_0^{\pi} (1 + \cos\theta)^2 \, d\theta$

$= a^2 \displaystyle\int_0^{\pi} (1 + 2\cos\theta + \cos^2\theta) \, d\theta$

$= a^2 \displaystyle\int_0^{\pi} \left(\tfrac{3}{2} + 2\cos\theta + \tfrac{1}{2}\cos 2\theta\right) d\theta$

$= a^2 \left[\tfrac{3}{2}\theta + 2\sin\theta + \tfrac{1}{4}\sin 2\theta\right]_0^{\pi}$

$= a^2 \left(\left(\tfrac{3}{2}\pi + 0 + 0\right) - 0\right)$

$= \dfrac{3a^2\pi}{2}$

Problem-solving

Start by sketching the curve. You can simplify your calculation by using the fact that the curve is **symmetric** about the initial line. Hence you can integrate from 0 to π and then double your answer.

Use the formula for area. Remember to square the expression for r.

You can use trigonometric identities for $\cos 2\theta$ to integrate terms in $\cos^2\theta$ or $\sin^2\theta$:

$$\cos^2\theta \equiv \dfrac{1 + \cos 2\theta}{2} \qquad \leftarrow \textbf{Pure 3 Section 4.3}$$

Watch out Unlike Cartesian integration, areas in the third and fourth quadrants do not produce negative integrals. You could obtain the same result by integrating between 0 and 2π:

$$\tfrac{1}{2}\int_0^{2\pi} a^2 (1 + \cos\theta)^2 \, d\theta = \dfrac{3a^2\pi}{2}$$

Example 10

Find the area of one loop of the curve with polar equation $r = a\sin 4\theta$

$r = a\sin 4\theta$ will have one loop for

$0 \leqslant \theta \leqslant \dfrac{\pi}{4}$.

$\text{Area} = \dfrac{1}{2}\displaystyle\int_0^{\frac{\pi}{4}} r^2\,d\theta = \dfrac{a^2}{2}\displaystyle\int_0^{\frac{\pi}{4}} \sin^2 4\theta\,d\theta$

$= \dfrac{a^2}{4}\displaystyle\int_0^{\frac{\pi}{4}} (1 - \cos 8\theta)\,d\theta$

$= \dfrac{a^2}{4}\left[\theta - \dfrac{\sin 8\theta}{8}\right]_0^{\frac{\pi}{4}}$

$= \dfrac{a^2}{4}\left(\dfrac{\pi}{4} - \dfrac{\sin 2\pi}{8}\right) - 0$

$= \dfrac{a^2\pi}{16}$

Find the values of θ which will give the beginning and end of a loop by solving $r = 0$.

Use the area formula.

Use the trigonometric identity for $\cos 2\theta$. In this case, $\sin^2 4\theta \equiv \dfrac{1 - \cos 8\theta}{2}$

Remember $\sin 2\pi = 0$.

Online Explore the area enclosed by a loop of the polar curve with the form $r = a\sin\theta$ using GeoGebra.

Watch out $r = \sin n\theta$ has n loops and so a simple way of finding the area of one loop would appear to be to find $\dfrac{1}{2}\displaystyle\int_0^{2\pi} r^2\,d\theta$ and divide by n. This would give $\dfrac{a^2\pi}{8}$

The reason why this is not the correct answer is because when you take r^2 in the integral you are also including the n loops given by $r < 0$. You need to choose your limits carefully so that $r \geqslant 0$ for all values within the range of the integral.

Example 11

a On the same diagram, sketch the curves with equations $r = 2 + \cos\theta$ and $r = 5\cos\theta$

b Find the polar coordinates of the points of intersection of these two curves.

c Find the exact area of the region which lies within both curves.

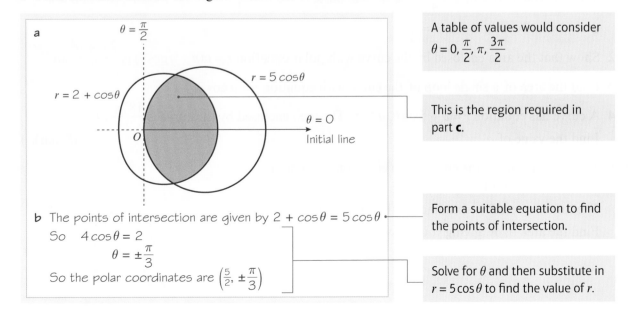

A table of values would consider $\theta = 0, \dfrac{\pi}{2}, \pi, \dfrac{3\pi}{2}$

This is the region required in part **c**.

b The points of intersection are given by $2 + \cos\theta = 5\cos\theta$

So $4\cos\theta = 2$

$\theta = \pm\dfrac{\pi}{3}$

So the polar coordinates are $\left(\dfrac{5}{2}, \pm\dfrac{\pi}{3}\right)$

Form a suitable equation to find the points of intersection.

Solve for θ and then substitute in $r = 5\cos\theta$ to find the value of r.

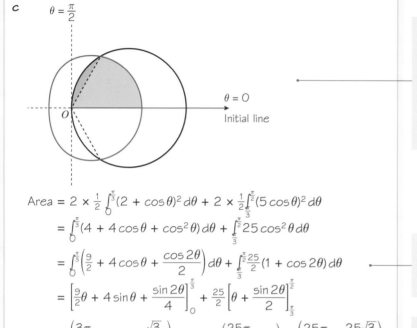

Remember that the area formula gives areas of *sectors*. So you need the sector formed by the red curve and the sector formed by the blue curve. Again you can use symmetry about the initial line.

$$\text{Area} = 2 \times \tfrac{1}{2}\int_0^{\frac{\pi}{3}}(2 + \cos\theta)^2\,d\theta + 2 \times \tfrac{1}{2}\int_{\frac{\pi}{3}}^{\frac{\pi}{2}}(5\cos\theta)^2\,d\theta$$

$$= \int_0^{\frac{\pi}{3}}(4 + 4\cos\theta + \cos^2\theta)\,d\theta + \int_{\frac{\pi}{3}}^{\frac{\pi}{2}}25\cos^2\theta\,d\theta$$

$$= \int_0^{\frac{\pi}{3}}\left(\tfrac{9}{2} + 4\cos\theta + \tfrac{\cos 2\theta}{2}\right)d\theta + \int_{\frac{\pi}{3}}^{\frac{\pi}{2}}\tfrac{25}{2}(1 + \cos 2\theta)\,d\theta$$

$$= \left[\tfrac{9}{2}\theta + 4\sin\theta + \tfrac{\sin 2\theta}{4}\right]_0^{\frac{\pi}{3}} + \tfrac{25}{2}\left[\theta + \tfrac{\sin 2\theta}{2}\right]_{\frac{\pi}{3}}^{\frac{\pi}{2}}$$

$$= \left(\tfrac{3\pi}{2} + 2\sqrt{3} + \tfrac{\sqrt{3}}{8}\right) - (0) + \left(\tfrac{25\pi}{4} + 0\right) - \left(\tfrac{25\pi}{6} + \tfrac{25\sqrt{3}}{8}\right)$$

$$= \tfrac{43\pi}{12} - \sqrt{3}$$

Square and use the trigonometric identity for $\cos 2\theta$.

Use the exact value of $\sin\dfrac{2\pi}{3}$

Exercise 8C

1 Find the area of the finite region bounded by the curve with the given polar equation and the half-lines $\theta = \alpha$ and $\theta = \beta$.

 a $r = a\cos\theta,\ \alpha = 0,\ \beta = \dfrac{\pi}{2}$ **b** $r = a(1 + \sin\theta),\ \alpha = -\dfrac{\pi}{2},\ \beta = \dfrac{\pi}{2}$ **c** $r = a\sin 3\theta,\ \alpha = \dfrac{\pi}{6},\ \beta = \dfrac{\pi}{4}$

 d $r^2 = a^2\cos 2\theta,\ \alpha = 0,\ \beta = \dfrac{\pi}{4}$ **e** $r^2 = a^2\tan\theta,\ \alpha = 0,\ \beta = \dfrac{\pi}{4}$ **f** $r = 2a\theta,\ \alpha = 0,\ \beta = \pi$

 g $r = a(3 + 2\cos\theta),\ \alpha = 0,\ \beta = \dfrac{\pi}{2}$

2 Show that the area enclosed by the curve with polar equation $r = a(p + q\cos\theta)$ is $\dfrac{2p^2 + q^2}{2}\pi a^2$

3 Find the area of a single loop of the curve with equation $r = a\cos 3\theta$

(E) 4 A curve has equation $r = a + 5\sin\theta,\ a > 5$. The area enclosed by the curve is $\dfrac{187\pi}{2}$
 Find the value of a. **(5 marks)**

(E/P) 5 The diagram shows the curves with equations $r = a\sin 4\theta$ and $r = a\sin 2\theta$ for $0 \le \theta \le \dfrac{\pi}{2}$
 The finite region R is contained within both curves.
 Find the area of R, giving your answer in terms of a. **(8 marks)**

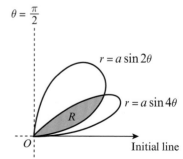

E/P   **6**   The diagram shows the curves with equations $r = 1 + \sin\theta$ and $r = 3\sin\theta$.

The finite region R is contained within both curves.

Find the area of R.   **(8 marks)**

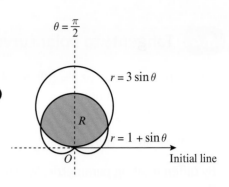

E/P   **7**   The set of points, A, is defined by

$$A = \left\{ z: -\frac{\pi}{4} \leqslant \arg z \leqslant 0 \right\} \cap \{ z: |z - 4 + 3i| \leqslant 5 \}$$

a   Sketch on an Argand diagram the set of points, A.   **(4 marks)**

Given that the locus of points given by the values of z satisfying $|z - 4 + 3i| = 5$ can be expressed in polar form using the equation $r = 8\cos\theta - 6\sin\theta$

b   find, correct to 3 significant figures, the area of the region defined by A.   **(8 marks)**

E/P   **8**   The set of points, A, is defined by

$$A = \left\{ z: \frac{\pi}{2} \leqslant \arg z \leqslant \pi \right\} \cap \{ z: |z + 12 - 5i| \leqslant 13 \}$$

a   Sketch on an Argand diagram the set of points, A.   **(4 marks)**

b   Find, correct to 3 significant figures, the area of the region defined by A.   **(8 marks)**

E/P   **9**   The diagram shows the curve C with polar equation

$$r = 1 + \cos 3\theta, \; 0 \leqslant \theta \leqslant \frac{\pi}{3}$$

At points A and B, the value of r is $\dfrac{2 + \sqrt{2}}{2}$

Point A lies on C and point B lies on the initial line.

Find, correct to 3 significant figures, the finite area bounded by the curve, the line segment AB and the initial line, shown shaded in the diagram.   **(9 marks)**

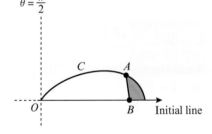

E/P   **10**   The diagram shows the curves $r = 1 + \sin\theta$ and $r = 3\sin\theta$.

Find the shaded area, giving your answer correct to 2 decimal places.   **(8 marks)**

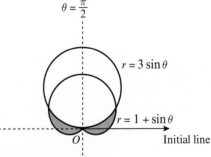

Challenge

The cross-section of a shell is modelled using the curve with polar equation $r = k\theta, \; 0 \leqslant \theta \leqslant 4\pi$, where k is a positive constant. The horizontal diameter of the shell, as shown in the diagram, is 3 cm.

a   Find the exact value of k.

b   Hence find the total shaded area of the cross-section.

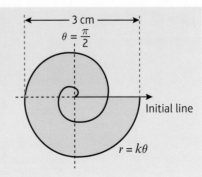

8.4 Tangents to polar curves

If you are given a curve $r = f(\theta)$ in polar form, you can write it as a parametric curve in Cartesian form, using θ as the parameter:

$$x = r\cos\theta = f(\theta)\cos\theta$$
$$y = r\sin\theta = f(\theta)\sin\theta$$

By differentiating parametrically, you can find the gradient of the curve at any point:

$$\frac{dy}{dx} = \frac{\dfrac{dy}{d\theta}}{\dfrac{dx}{d\theta}}$$

When $\dfrac{dy}{d\theta} = 0$, a tangent to the curve will be horizontal.

When $\dfrac{dx}{d\theta} = 0$, a tangent to the curve will be vertical.

You need to be able to find tangents to a polar curve that are **parallel** or **perpendicular** to the initial line.

- To find a tangent parallel to the initial line set $\dfrac{dy}{d\theta} = 0$
- To find a tangent perpendicular to the initial line set $\dfrac{dx}{d\theta} = 0$

Example 12

Find the coordinates of the points on $r = a(1 + \cos\theta)$ where the tangents are parallel to the initial line $\theta = 0$.

$$y = r\sin\theta = a(\sin\theta + \sin\theta\cos\theta)$$
$$\frac{dy}{d\theta} = a(\cos\theta + \cos^2\theta - \sin^2\theta)$$

Find an expression for y and then solve $\dfrac{dy}{d\theta} = 0$

So
$$0 = 2\cos^2\theta + \cos\theta - 1$$
$$0 = (2\cos\theta - 1)(\cos\theta + 1)$$

either $\cos\theta = \frac{1}{2} \Rightarrow \theta = \pm\frac{\pi}{3}$

Solve the equations to find θ and then substitute back to find r.

so $r = a(1 + \frac{1}{2}) = \frac{3a}{2}$

or $\cos\theta = -1 \Rightarrow \theta = \pi$, and so $r = 0$

So the tangents parallel to the initial line are at $\left(\frac{3a}{2}, \pm\frac{\pi}{3}\right)$ and $(0, \pi)$.

Problem-solving

You can see these tangents on a sketch of $y = a(1 + \cos\theta)$

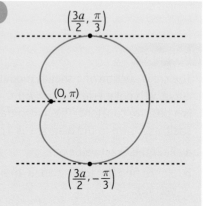

$\left(\frac{3a}{2}, \frac{\pi}{3}\right)$

$(0, \pi)$

$\left(\frac{3a}{2}, -\frac{\pi}{3}\right)$

Example 13

Find the equations and the points of contact of the tangents to the curve $r = a\sin 2\theta$, $0 \leqslant \theta \leqslant \dfrac{\pi}{2}$ that are:

a parallel to the initial line

b perpendicular to the initial line.

Give answers to 3 significant figures where appropriate.

a $y = r\sin\theta = a\sin\theta\sin 2\theta$

$\dfrac{dy}{d\theta} = a(\cos\theta\sin 2\theta + 2\cos 2\theta\sin\theta)$

$\qquad = 2a\sin\theta(\cos^2\theta + \cos^2\theta - \sin^2\theta)$

$\dfrac{dy}{d\theta} = 0 \Rightarrow \sin\theta = 0 \Rightarrow \theta = 0$

or $\quad 2\cos^2\theta = \sin^2\theta \Rightarrow \tan\theta = \pm\sqrt{2}$

$\qquad\qquad\qquad\qquad\qquad \Rightarrow \theta = 0.955$

So $\quad \theta = 0$ or 0.955

and $\quad r = 0$ or $r = 2a \times \dfrac{\sqrt{2}}{\sqrt{3}} \times \dfrac{1}{\sqrt{3}}$

So the points are $(0, 0)$ and $\left(\dfrac{2a\sqrt{2}}{3}, 0.955\right)$

The equation of the initial line is $\theta = 0$ and that is the tangent through $(0, 0)$.

The equation of the tangent through $\left(\dfrac{2a\sqrt{2}}{3}, 0.955\right)$

is $y = \dfrac{2a\sqrt{2}}{3} \times \sin\theta = \dfrac{2a\sqrt{2}}{3} \times \dfrac{\sqrt{2}}{\sqrt{3}} = \dfrac{4a}{3\sqrt{3}}$

So the equation of the tangent is

$r = \dfrac{4a}{3\sqrt{3}}\mathrm{cosec}\,\theta$

b $x = r\cos\theta = a\cos\theta\sin 2\theta$

$\dfrac{dx}{d\theta} = -a\sin\theta\sin 2\theta + 2a\cos\theta\cos 2\theta$

$\qquad = 2a\cos\theta\,(-\sin^2\theta + \cos^2\theta - \sin^2\theta)$

$\dfrac{dx}{d\theta} = 0 \Rightarrow \cos\theta = 0 \Rightarrow \theta = \dfrac{\pi}{2}$

So the y-axis is a tangent.

Or $\quad \cos^2\theta - 2\sin^2\theta = 0 \Rightarrow \tan\theta = \pm\dfrac{1}{\sqrt{2}}$

So $\quad \theta = 0.615$

and $r = 2a \times \dfrac{\sqrt{2}}{\sqrt{3}} \times \dfrac{1}{\sqrt{3}} = \dfrac{2a\sqrt{2}}{3}$

The tangent is at $\left(\dfrac{2a\sqrt{2}}{3}, 0.615\right)$

$x = \dfrac{2a\sqrt{2}}{3} \times \cos\alpha = \dfrac{2a\sqrt{2}}{3} \times \dfrac{\sqrt{2}}{\sqrt{3}} = \dfrac{4a}{3\sqrt{3}}$

So the equation of the tangent is:

$r = \dfrac{4a}{3\sqrt{3}}\sec\theta$

Form an expression for y and differentiate using the product rule.

Use $\sin 2\theta \equiv 2\sin\theta\cos\theta$ and then take out the common factor. Then use $\cos 2\theta \equiv \cos^2\theta - \sin^2\theta$

Choose values of θ within the range given in the question.

If $\tan\alpha = \sqrt{2}$ then drawing a triangle shows that $\sin\alpha = \dfrac{\sqrt{2}}{\sqrt{3}}$ and $\cos\alpha = \dfrac{1}{\sqrt{3}}$
Use $\sin 2A \equiv 2\sin A\cos A$ to find r.

Use $y = r\sin\theta$ to find the equation of the tangent and write it in polar form using $r = y\,\mathrm{cosec}\,\theta$.

Form an expression for x and differentiate using the product rule.

Use $\sin 2\theta = 2\sin\theta\cos\theta$ and then take out the common factor. Then use a formula for $\cos 2\theta$.

If $\tan\alpha = \dfrac{1}{\sqrt{2}}$ then drawing a triangle shows that $\cos\alpha = \dfrac{\sqrt{2}}{\sqrt{3}}$ and $\sin\alpha = \dfrac{1}{\sqrt{3}}$
Use $\sin 2A \equiv 2\sin A\cos A$ to find r.

Use $x = r\cos\theta$ to find the equation of the tangent in the form $r = x\sec\theta$

Example (14)

The curve C has equation $r = (p + q\cos\theta)$, where p and q are positive constants and $p > q$.
Prove that the curve is convex for $p \geqslant 2q$, and has a dimple for $p < 2q$.

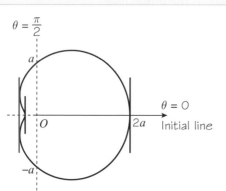

Problem-solving

If the curve is not convex then there will be more than two tangents to the curve that are perpendicular to the initial line.

$x = r\cos\theta = p\cos\theta + q\cos^2\theta$

$\dfrac{dx}{d\theta} = 0 \Rightarrow 0 = -p\sin\theta - 2q\cos\theta\sin\theta$

         $\Rightarrow 0 = -\sin\theta(p + 2q\cos\theta)$

Find an expression for x and differentiate.

This has solutions

$\sin\theta = 0$ when $\theta = 0$ or π

and $\cos\theta = -\dfrac{p}{2q}$

Solve the equation and consider all possible cases.

If $p < 2q$ then there will be two solutions to this equation in the second and third quadrants (the green tangents). In this case the curve is not convex and has a dimple.

The two tangents at the two points represented by these solutions have the same equation.

If $p = 2q$ then the solution is $\theta = \pi$ and so there are only two tangents (the blue ones). In this case the curve is convex.

If $p > 2q$ then there is no solution to this equation and only the two blue tangents are possible. In this case the curve is convex.

Hence the curve is convex for $p \geqslant 2q$, and has a dimple for $p < 2q$.

Exercise (8D)

1 Find the points on the cardioid $r = a(1 + \cos\theta)$ where the tangents are perpendicular to the initial line.

2 Find the points on the spiral $r = e^{2\theta}$, $0 \leqslant \theta \leqslant \pi$, where the tangents are:
   a perpendicular to the initial line   **b** parallel to the initial line.
   Give your answers to 3 significant figures.

3 a Find the points on the curve $r = a \cos 2\theta$, $-\dfrac{\pi}{4} \leqslant \theta \leqslant \dfrac{\pi}{4}$ where the tangents are parallel to the initial line, giving your answers to 3 significant figures where appropriate.

   b Find the equations of these tangents.

(E) **4** Find the points on the curve with equation $r = a(7 + 2 \cos \theta)$ where the tangents are parallel to the initial line. **(6 marks)**

(E) **5** Find the equations of the tangents to $r = 2 + \cos \theta$ that are perpendicular to the initial line. **(6 marks)**

(E) **6** Find the point on the curve with equation $r = a(1 + \tan \theta)$, $0 \leqslant \theta < \dfrac{\pi}{2}$, where the tangent is perpendicular to the initial line. **(6 marks)**

(E/P) **7** The curve C has polar equation
$$r = 1 + 3\cos\theta, \qquad 0 \leqslant \theta \leqslant \dfrac{\pi}{2}$$
The tangent to C at a point A on the curve is parallel to the initial line.
Point O is the pole.
Find the exact length of the line OA. **(7 marks)**

(E/P) **8** The diagram shows a cardioid with polar equation
$$r = 2(1 + \cos\theta)$$
The shaded area is enclosed by the curve and the vertical line segment which is tangent to the curve and perpendicular to the initial line.

Find the shaded area, correct to 3 significant figures. **(8 marks)**

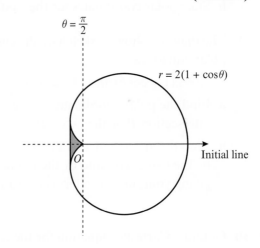

Chapter review 8

(E) **1** Determine the area enclosed by the curve with equation
$$r = a(1 + \tfrac{1}{2}\sin\theta), \quad a > 0, \quad 0 \leqslant \theta < 2\pi,$$
giving your answer in terms of a and π. **(6 marks)**

(E/P) **2 a** Sketch the curve with equation $r = a(1 + \cos\theta)$ for $0 \leqslant \theta \leqslant 2\pi$, where $a > 0$. **(2 marks)**

    b Sketch also the line with equation $r = 2a\sec\theta$ for $-\dfrac{\pi}{2} < \theta < \dfrac{\pi}{2}$, on the same diagram. **(2 marks)**

    c The half-line with equation $\theta = \alpha$, $0 < \alpha < \dfrac{\pi}{2}$, meets the curve at A and the line with equation $r = 2a\sec\theta$ at B. If O is the pole, find the value of $\cos\alpha$ for which $OB = 2OA$. **(5 marks)**

(E/P) **3** Sketch, in the same diagram, the curves with equations $r = 3\cos\theta$ and $r = 1 + \cos\theta$ and find the area of the region lying inside both curves. **(9 marks)**

(E)　4　Find the polar coordinates of the points on $r^2 = a^2 \sin 2\theta$ where the tangent is perpendicular to the initial line.　　　**(7 marks)**

(E/P)　5　a　Shade the region R for which the polar coordinates r, θ satisfy

$r \leqslant 4\cos 2\theta$　for　$-\dfrac{\pi}{4} \leqslant \theta \leqslant \dfrac{\pi}{4}$　　　**(2 marks)**

　　b　Find the area of R.　　　**(5 marks)**

(E)　6　Sketch the curve with polar equation $r = a(1 - \cos\theta)$, where $a > 0$, stating the polar coordinates of the point on the curve at which r has its maximum value.　　　**(5 marks)**

(E/P)　7　a　On the same diagram, sketch the curve C_1 with polar equation

$r = 2\cos 2\theta, \quad -\dfrac{\pi}{4} < \theta \leqslant \dfrac{\pi}{4}$

and the curve C_2 with polar equation $\theta = \dfrac{\pi}{12}$　　　**(3 marks)**

　　b　Find the area of the smaller region bounded by C_1 and C_2.　　　**(6 marks)**

(E)　8　a　Sketch on the same diagram the circle with polar equation $r = 4\cos\theta$ and the line with polar equation $r = 2\sec\theta$　　　**(4 marks)**

　　b　State polar coordinates for their points of intersection.　　　**(4 marks)**

(E/P)　9　The diagram shows a sketch of the curves with polar equations

$r = a(1 + \cos\theta)$ and $r = 3a\cos\theta, a > 0$

　　a　Find the polar coordinates of the point of intersection P of the two curves.　　**(4 marks)**

　　b　Find the area, shaded in the figure, bounded by the two curves and by the initial line $\theta = 0$, giving your answer in terms of a and π.

　　(7 marks)

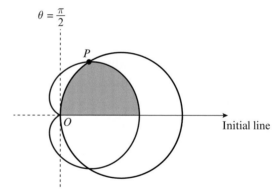

(E/P)　10　Obtain a Cartesian equation for the curve with polar equation

　　a　$r^2 = \sec 2\theta$　　　**(4 marks)**

　　b　$r^2 = \operatorname{cosec} 2\theta$　　　**(4 marks)**

(E/P)　11　a　Show on an Argand diagram the locus of points given by the values of z satisfying

$|z - 1 - \mathrm{i}| = \sqrt{2}$　　　**(2 marks)**

　　b　Show that this locus of points can be represented by the polar curve

$r = 2\cos\theta + 2\sin\theta$　　　**(4 marks)**

The set of points, A, is defined by

$A = \left\{ z : \dfrac{\pi}{6} \leqslant \arg z \leqslant \dfrac{\pi}{2} \right\} \cap \left\{ z : |z - 1 - \mathrm{i}| \leqslant \sqrt{2} \right\}$

　　c　Show, by sketching on your Argand diagram, the set of points, A.　　　**(2 marks)**

　　d　Find, correct to 3 significant figures, the area of the region defined by A.　　　**(5 marks)**

(E) **12** The diagram shows the curve C with polar equation

$$r = 4\cos 2\theta, \qquad 0 \leqslant \theta \leqslant \frac{\pi}{4}$$

At point A the value of r is 2. Point A lies on C and point B lies on the initial line vertically below A.

Find, correct to 3 significant figures, the area of the finite region bounded by the curve, the line segment AB and the initial line, shown shaded in the diagram. **(9 marks)**

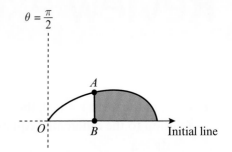

(E/P) **13** The diagram shows the curve with polar equation

$$r = 4\sin 2\theta, \qquad 0 \leqslant \theta \leqslant \frac{\pi}{2}$$

The shaded region is bounded by the curve, the initial line and the tangent to the curve which is perpendicular to the initial line.

Find, correct to 2 decimal places, the area of the shaded region. **(8 marks)**

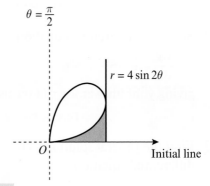

Challenge

The curve C has polar equation $r = \sqrt{2}\theta$

Show that an equation for the tangent to the curve at the point where

$\theta = \frac{\pi}{4}$ is $2(\pi - 4)y + 2(\pi + 4)x = \pi^2$

Summary of key points

1 For a point P with polar coordinates (r, θ) and Cartesian coordinates (x, y),

$r\cos\theta = x$ and $r\sin\theta = y$

$r^2 = x^2 + y^2$, $\theta = \arctan\left(\dfrac{y}{x}\right)$

Care must be taken to ensure that θ is in the correct quadrant.

2 • $r = a$ is a circle with centre O and radius a.

• $\theta = \alpha$ is a half-line through O and making an angle α with the initial line.

• $r = a\theta$ is a spiral starting at O.

3 The **area of a sector** bounded by a polar curve and the half-lines $\theta = \alpha$ and $\theta = \beta$, where θ is in radians, is given by the formula

$$\textbf{Area} = \tfrac{1}{2}\int_{\alpha}^{\beta} r^2 \, \mathbf{d\theta}$$

4 • To find a tangent parallel to the initial line set $\dfrac{dy}{d\theta} = 0$

• To find a tangent perpendicular to the initial line set $\dfrac{dx}{d\theta} = 0$

Review exercise

(E) 1 Find, in the form $y = f(x)$, the general solution to the differential equation

$$\frac{dy}{dx} + \frac{4}{x}y = 6x - 5, \ x > 0 \qquad \textbf{(5)}$$

← **Further Pure 2 Section 5.2**

(E) 2 Solve the differential equation

$$\frac{dy}{dx} - \frac{y}{x} = x^2, \ x > 0$$

giving your answer for y in terms of x. **(5)**

← **Further Pure 2 Section 5.2**

(E) 3 Find the general solution to the differential equation

$$(x + 1)\frac{dy}{dx} + 2y = \frac{1}{x}, \ x > 0$$

giving your answer in the form $y = f(x)$. **(5)**

← **Further Pure 2 Section 5.2**

(E) 4 Obtain the solution to

$$\frac{dy}{dx} + y\tan x = e^{2x}\cos x, \ 0 \le x < \frac{\pi}{2}$$

for which $y = 2$ at $x = 0$, giving your answer in the form $y = f(x)$. **(6)**

← **Further Pure 2 Section 5.2**

(E) 5 Find the general solution to the differential equation

$$\frac{dy}{dx} + 2y\cot 2x = \sin x, \ 0 < x < \frac{\pi}{2}$$

giving your answer in the form $y = f(x)$. **(5)**

← **Further Pure 2 Section 5.2**

(E) 6 Solve the differential equation

$$(1 + x)\frac{dy}{dx} - xy = xe^{-x}$$

given that $y = 1$ at $x = 0$. **(6)**

← **Further Pure 2 Section 5.2**

(E) 7 a Find the general solution to the differential equation

$$\cos x \frac{dy}{dx} + (\sin x)y = \cos^3 x \qquad \textbf{(5)}$$

b Show that, for $0 \le x \le 2\pi$, there are two points on the x-axis through which all the solution curves for this differential equation pass. **(4)**

c Sketch the graph, $0 \le x \le 2\pi$, of the particular solution for which $y = 0$ at $x = 0$. **(3)**

← **Further Pure 2 Section 5.2**

(E) 8 a Find the general solution to the differential equation

$$\frac{dy}{dx} + 2y = x \qquad \textbf{(5)}$$

Given that $y = 1$ at $x = 0$,

b find the exact values of the coordinates of the minimum point of the particular solution curve, **(3)**

c draw a sketch of the particular solution curve. **(2)**

← **Further Pure 2 Section 5.2**

(E/P) 9 Given that θ satisfies the differential equation

$$\frac{d^2\theta}{dt^2} + 4\frac{d\theta}{dt} + 5\theta = 0$$

and that, when $t = 0$, $\theta = 3$ and $\frac{d\theta}{dt} = -6$, express θ in terms of t. **(8)**

← **Further Pure 2 Sections 6.1, 6.3**

(E/P) 10 Given that $3x\sin 2x$ is a particular integral of the differential equation

$$\frac{d^2y}{dx^2} + 4y = k\cos 2x$$

where k is a constant,

a calculate the value of k **(3)**

b find the particular solution of the differential equation for which at $x = 0$, $y = 2$, and for which at $x = \frac{\pi}{4}$, $y = \frac{\pi}{2}$ **(8)**

← Further Pure 2 Sections 6.2, 6.3

(E/P) **11** Given that $a + bx$ is a particular integral of the differential equation

$$\frac{d^2y}{dx^2} - 4\frac{dy}{dx} + 4y = 16 + 4x$$

a find the values of the constants a and b **(3)**

b find the particular solution to this differential equation for which $y = 8$ and $\frac{dy}{dx} = 9$ at $x = 0$. **(8)**

← Further Pure 2 Sections 6.2, 6.3

(E/P) **12** $\frac{d^2y}{dx^2} + 4\frac{dy}{dx} + 5y = 65 \sin 2x$, $x > 0$

a Find the general solution to the differential equation. **(8)**

b Show that for large values of x this general solution may be approximated by a sine function and find this sine function. **(2)**

← Further Pure 2 Section 6.2

(E/P) **13 a** Find the general solution to the differential equation

$$\frac{d^2y}{dt^2} + 2\frac{dy}{dt} + 2y = 2e^{-t}$$ **(8)**

b Find the particular solution to this differential equation for which $y = 1$ and $\frac{dy}{dt} = 1$ at $t = 0$. **(2)**

←Further Pure 2 Sections 6.2, 6.3

(E/P) **14 a** Find the general solution to the differential equation

$$\frac{d^2x}{dt^2} + 2\frac{dx}{dt} + 5x = 0$$ **(8)**

b Given that $x = 1$ and $\frac{dx}{dt} = 1$ at $t = 0$, find the particular solution to the differential equation, giving your answer in the form $x = f(t)$. **(2)**

c Sketch the curve with equation $x = f(t)$, $0 \le t \le \pi$, showing the coordinates, as multiples of π, of the points where the curve cuts the t-axis. **(2)**

← Further Pure 2 Sections 6.2, 6.3

(E/P) **15 a** Find the general solution to the differential equation

$$2\frac{d^2y}{dt^2} + 7\frac{dy}{dt} + 3y = 3t^2 + 11t$$ **(8)**

b Find the particular solution to this differential equation for which $y = 1$ and $\frac{dy}{dt} = 1$ when $t = 0$. **(2)**

c For this particular solution, calculate the value of y when $t = 1$. **(2)**

← Further Pure 2 Sections 6.2, 6.3

(E/P) **16 a** Find the value of λ for which $\lambda x \cos 3x$ is a particular integral of the differential equation

$$\frac{d^2y}{dx^2} + 9y = -12 \sin 3x$$ **(3)**

b Hence find the general solution to this differential equation. **(6)**

The particular solution of the differential equation for which $y = 1$ and $\frac{dy}{dx} = 2$ at $x = 0$, is $y = g(x)$.

c Find g(x). **(2)**

d Sketch the graph of $y = $ g(x), $0 \le x \le \pi$. **(2)**

← Further Pure 2 Sections 6.2, 6.3

(E) **17** $\frac{d^2y}{dt^2} - 6\frac{dy}{dt} + 9y = 4e^{3t}$, $t \ge 0$

a Show that Kt^2e^{3t} is a particular integral of the differential equation, where K is a constant to be found. **(3)**

b Find the general solution to the differential equation. **(6)**

Given that a particular solution satisfies

$$y = 3 \text{ and } \frac{dy}{dt} = 1 \text{ when } t = 0,$$

c find this solution. **(2)**

Another particular solution which satisfies $y = 1$ and $\dfrac{dy}{dt} = 0$ when $t = 0$, has equation $y = (1 - 3t + 2t^2)e^{3t}$

d For this particular solution, draw a sketch graph of y against t, showing where the graph crosses the t-axis. Determine also the coordinates of the minimum point on the sketch graph. **(4)**

← **Further Pure 2 Sections 6.2, 6.3**

(E/P) **18 a** Find the general solution to the differential equation

$$2\frac{d^2x}{dt^2} + 5\frac{dx}{dt} + 2x = 2t + 9 \quad \textbf{(8)}$$

b Find the particular solution of this differential equation for which $x = 3$ and $\dfrac{dx}{dt} = -1$ when $t = 0$. **(2)**

← **Further Pure 2 Sections 6.2, 6.3**

19 Given that $x = At^2e^{-t}$ satisfies the differential equation

$$\frac{d^2x}{dt^2} + 2\frac{dx}{dt} + x = e^{-t},$$

a find the value of A. **(3)**

b Hence find the solution to the differential equation for which $x = 1$ and $\dfrac{dx}{dt} = 0$ at $t = 0$. **(7)**

c Use your solution to prove that for $t \geqslant 0$, $x \leqslant 1$. **(2)**

← **Further Pure 2 Sections 6.2, 6.3**

(E) **20** Given that $y = kx$ is a particular solution of the differential equation

$$\frac{d^2y}{dx^2} + y = 3x,$$

a find the value of the constant k. **(3)**

b Find the most general solution to this differential equation for which $y = 0$ at $x = 0$. **(6)**

c Prove that all curves given by this solution pass through the point $(\pi, 3\pi)$ and that they all have equal gradients when $x = \dfrac{\pi}{2}$ **(3)**

d Find the particular solution to the differential equation for which $y = 0$ at $x = 0$ and at $x = \dfrac{\pi}{2}$ **(2)**

e Show that a local minimum value of the solution in part **d** is

$$3\arccos\!\left(\frac{2}{\pi}\right) - \frac{3}{2}\sqrt{\pi^2 - 4} \quad \textbf{(4)}$$

← **Further Pure 2 Sections 6.2, 6.3**

(E) **21 a** By using the substitution $y = \frac{1}{2}(u - x)$, or otherwise, find the general solution of the differential equation

$$\frac{dy}{dx} = x + 2y \quad \textbf{(4)}$$

Given that $y = 2$ at $x = 0$,

b express y in terms of x. **(3)**

← **Further Pure 2 Section 5.3**

(E) **22 a** Use the substitution $y = vx$ to transform the equation

$$\frac{dy}{dx} = \frac{(4x + y)(x + y)}{x^2}, \, x > 0 \quad \textbf{(1)}$$

into the equation

$$x\frac{dv}{dx} = (2 + v)^2 \quad \textbf{(2) (4)}$$

b Solve differential equation **(2)** to find v in terms of x. **(4)**

c Hence show that $y = -2x - \dfrac{x}{\ln x + c}$, where c is an arbitrary constant, is the general solution to differential equation **(1)**. **(3)**

← **Further Pure 2 Section 5.3**

(E) **23 a** Show that the substitution $y = vx$ transforms the differential equation

$$\frac{dy}{dx} = \frac{3x - 4y}{4x + 3y} \quad \textbf{(1)}$$

into the differential equation

$$x\frac{dv}{dx} = -\frac{3v^2 + 8v - 3}{3v + 4} \quad \textbf{(2) (4)}$$

b Find the general solution of differential equation **(2)**. **(4)**

c Given that $y = 7$ at $x = 1$, show that the particular solution to differential equation **(1)** can be written as

$$(3y - x)(y + 3x) = 200 \quad \textbf{(3)}$$

← **Further Pure 2 Section 5.3**

(E) 24 a Use the substitution $\mu = y^{-2}$ to transform the differential equation
$$\frac{dy}{dx} + 2xy = xe^{-x^2}y^3 \quad \textbf{(1)}$$
into the differential equation
$$\frac{d\mu}{dx} - 4x\mu = -2xe^{-x^2} \quad \textbf{(2)} \quad \textbf{(4)}$$

b Find the general solution to differential equation **(2)**. **(4)**

c Hence obtain the solution to differential equation **(1)** for which $y = 1$ at $x = 0$. **(3)**

← Further Pure 2 Section 5.3

(E) 25 a Show that the transformation $y = xv$ transforms the equation
$$x^2\frac{d^2y}{dx^2} - 2x\frac{dy}{dx} + (2 + 9x^2)y = x^5 \quad \textbf{(1)}$$
into the equation
$$\frac{d^2v}{dx^2} + 9v = x^2 \quad \textbf{(2)}$$
$$\textbf{(6)}$$

b Solve differential equation **(2)** to find v as a function of x. **(4)**

c Hence state the general solution to differential equation **(1)**. **(2)**

← Further Pure 2 Section 6.4

(E) 26 Given that $x = t^{\frac{1}{2}}$, $x > 0$, $t > 0$, and that y is a function of x,

a find $\frac{dy}{dx}$ in terms of $\frac{dy}{dt}$ and t. **(2)**

Assuming that $\frac{d^2y}{dx^2} = 4t\frac{d^2y}{dt^2} + 2\frac{dy}{dt}$

b show that the substitution $x = t^{\frac{1}{2}}$ transforms the differential equation
$$\frac{d^2y}{dx^2} + \left(6x - \frac{1}{x}\right)\frac{dy}{dx} - 16x^2y = 4x^2e^{2x^2}$$
$$\textbf{(1)}$$
into the differential equation
$$\frac{d^2y}{dt^2} + 3\frac{dy}{dt} - 4y = e^{2t} \quad \textbf{(2)} \quad \textbf{(6)}$$

c Hence find the general solution to **(1)** giving y in terms of x. **(6)**

← Further Pure 2 Section 6.4

(E) 27 Given that $x = \ln t$, $t > 0$, and that y is a function of x,

a find $\frac{dy}{dx}$ in terms of $\frac{dy}{dt}$ and t **(2)**

b show that $\frac{d^2y}{dx^2} = t^2\frac{d^2y}{dt^2} + t\frac{dy}{dt}$ **(4)**

c Show that the substitution $x = \ln t$ transforms the differential equation
$$\frac{d^2y}{dx^2} - (1 - 6e^x)\frac{dy}{dx} + 10ye^{2x}$$
$$= 5e^{2x}\sin 2e^x \quad \textbf{(1)}$$
into the differential equation
$$\frac{d^2y}{dt^2} + 6\frac{dy}{dt} + 10y = 5\sin 2t \quad \textbf{(2)} \quad \textbf{(6)}$$

d Hence find the general solution to **(1)**, giving your answer in the form $y = f(x)$. **(6)**

← Further Pure 2 Section 6.4

(E/P) 28 Given that x is so small that terms in x^3 and higher powers of x may be neglected, show that
$$11\sin x - 6\cos x + 5 = A + Bx + Cx^2$$
stating the values of the constants A, B and C. **(6)**

← Further Pure 2 Sections 7.2, 7.3

(E/P) 29 Show that for $x > 1$,
$$\ln(x^2 - x + 1) + \ln(x + 1) - 3\ln x$$
$$= \frac{1}{x^3} - \frac{1}{2x^6} + \dots + \frac{(-1)^{n-1}}{nx^{3n}} + \dots \quad \textbf{(6)}$$
← Further Pure 2 Sections 7.2, 7.3

(E/P) 30 Given that x is so small that terms in x^4 and higher powers of x may be neglected, find the values of the constants A, B, C and D for which
$$e^{-2x}\cos 5x = A + Bx + Cx^2 + Dx^3 \quad \textbf{(6)}$$
← Further Pure 2 Sections 7.2, 7.3

(E/P) 31 a Find the first four terms of the expansion, in ascending powers of x, of
$$(2x + 3)^{-1}, |x| < \frac{2}{3} \quad \textbf{(3)}$$

b Hence, or otherwise, find the first four non-zero terms of the expansion, in ascending powers of x, of

$$\frac{\sin 2x}{2x + 3}, \ |x| < \frac{2}{3} \qquad \textbf{(5)}$$

← Further Pure 2 Sections 7.2, 7.3

(E/P) **32 a** By using the Maclaurin series for $\cos x$ and $\ln(1 + x)$, find the series expansion for $\ln(\cos x)$ in ascending powers of x up to and including the term in x^4. **(6)**

b Hence, or otherwise, obtain the first two non-zero terms in the series expansion for $\ln(\sec x)$ in ascending powers of x. **(4)**

← Further Pure 2 Sections 7.2, 7.3

(E) **33** Given that
$$f(x) = \ln(1 + \cos 2x), \quad 0 \le x < \frac{\pi}{2}$$
Show that:

a $f'(x) = -2\tan x$ **(2)**

b $f'''(x) = -(f''(x)\, f'(x) - (f''(x)^2)$ **(5)**

c Find the Maclaurin series expansion of $f(x)$, in ascending powers of x, up to and including the term in x^4. **(4)**

← Further Pure 2 Sections 7.1, 7.2, 7.3

(E) **34 a** Find the Taylor series of $\cos 2x$ in ascending powers of $\left(x - \frac{\pi}{4}\right)$ up to and including the term in $\left(x - \frac{\pi}{4}\right)^5$ **(4)**

b Use your answer to part **a** to obtain an estimate of $\cos 2$, giving your answer to 6 decimal places. **(2)**

← Further Pure 2 Section 7.4

(E) **35 a** Find the Taylor series of $\ln(\sin x)$ in ascending powers of $\left(x - \frac{\pi}{6}\right)$ up to and including the term in $\left(x - \frac{\pi}{6}\right)^3$ **(4)**

b Use your answer to part **a** to obtain an estimate of $\ln(\sin 0.5)$, giving your answer to 6 decimal places. **(2)**

← Further Pure 2 Section 7.4

(E) **36** Given that $y = \tan x$,

a find $\dfrac{dy}{dx}, \dfrac{d^2y}{dx^2}$ and $\dfrac{d^3y}{dx^3}$ **(3)**

b Find the Taylor series of $\tan x$ in ascending powers of $\left(x - \frac{\pi}{4}\right)$ up to and including the term in $\left(x - \frac{\pi}{4}\right)^3$ **(4)**

c Hence show that
$$\tan\frac{3\pi}{10} \approx 1 + \frac{\pi}{10} + \frac{\pi^2}{200} + \frac{\pi^3}{3000} \qquad \textbf{(3)}$$

← Further Pure 2 Section 7.4

(E) **37** Find the Taylor series of $\ln x$ about $x = 1$. **(3)**

← Further Pure 2 Section 7.4

(E) **38** $(1 - x^2)\dfrac{d^2y}{dx^2} - x\dfrac{dy}{dx} + 2y = 0$

At $x = 0$, $y = 2$ and $\dfrac{dy}{dx} = -1$

a Find the value of $\dfrac{d^3y}{dx^3}$ at $x = 0$. **(4)**

b Express y as a series in ascending powers of x, up to and including the term in x^3. **(4)**

← Further Pure 2 Section 7.5

(E) **39** $(1 + 2x)\dfrac{dy}{dx} = x + 4y^2$

a Show that
$$(1 + 2x)\frac{d^2y}{dx^2} = 1 + 2\,(4y - 1)\frac{dy}{dx} \quad \textbf{(1)}$$
(4)

b Differentiate equation **(1)** with respect to x to obtain an equation involving $\dfrac{d^3y}{dx^3}, \dfrac{d^2y}{dx^2}, \dfrac{dy}{dx}$, x and y. **(4)**

Given that $y = \frac{1}{2}$ at $x = 0$,

c find a series solution for y, in ascending powers of x, up to and including the term in x^3. **(4)**

← Further Pure 2 Sections 6.1, 7.5

(E/P) **40** $\dfrac{dy}{dx} = y^2 + xy + x$, $y = 1$ at $x = 0$

a Use the Taylor series method to find y as a series in ascending powers of x, up to and including the term in x^3. **(6)**

b Use your series to find y at $x = 0.1$, giving your answer to 2 decimal places. **(4)**

← Further Pure 2 Section 7.5

41 $y\dfrac{dy}{dx} = \dfrac{x+3}{y+1}$

Given that $y = 1.5$ at $x = 0$,

a use the Taylor series method to find the series solution for y, in ascending powers of x, up to and including the term in x^3. **(6)**

b Use your result to part **a** to estimate, to 3 decimal places, the value of y at $x = 0.1$. **(4)**

← Further Pure 2 Section 7.5

(E/P) **42** $y\dfrac{d^2y}{dx^2} + \left(\dfrac{dy}{dx}\right)^2 + y = 0$

a Find an expression for $\dfrac{d^3y}{dx^3}$ **(4)**

Given that $y = 1$ and $\dfrac{dy}{dx} = 1$ at $x = 0$,

b find the series solution for y, in ascending powers of x, up to and including the term in x^3. **(4)**

c Comment on whether it would be sensible to use your series solution to give estimates for y at $x = 0.2$ and at $x = 50$. **(2)**

← Further Pure 2 Section 7.5

(E/P) **43** $\dfrac{d^2y}{dx^2} - 4\dfrac{dy}{dx} + 3y^2 = 6$,

with $y = 1$ and $\dfrac{dy}{dx} = 0$ at $x = 0$.

a Use the Taylor series method to obtain y as a series of ascending powers of x, up to and including the term in x^4. **(6)**

b Hence find the approximate value of y when $x = 0.2$. **(3)**

← Further Pure 2 Section 7.5

(E) **44** Relative to the origin O as pole and initial line $\theta = 0$, find an equation in polar coordinate form for:

a a circle, centre O and radius 2 **(1)**

b a line perpendicular to the initial line and passing through the point with polar coordinates $(3, 0)$ **(2)**

c a straight line through the points with polar coordinates $(4, 0)$ and $\left(4, \dfrac{\pi}{3}\right)$. **(2)**

← Further Pure 2 Section 8.2

(E) **45 a** Sketch the curve with polar equation $r = a\cos 3\theta, 0 \leqslant \theta < 2\pi$ **(2)**

b Find the area enclosed by one loop of this curve. **(6)**

← Further Pure 2 Sections 8.2, 8.3

(E/P) **46 a** Sketch the curve with polar equation $r = 3\cos 2\theta, -\dfrac{\pi}{4} \leqslant \theta < \dfrac{\pi}{4}$ **(2)**

b Find the area of the smaller finite region enclosed between the curve and the half-line $\theta = \dfrac{\pi}{6}$ **(6)**

c Find the exact distance between the two tangents which are parallel to the initial line. **(6)**

← Further Pure 2 Sections 8.2, 8.3, 8.4

(E/P) **47 a** Sketch, on the same diagram, the curves defined by the polar equations $r = a$ and $r = a(1 + \cos\theta)$, where a is a positive constant and $-\pi < \theta \leqslant \pi$. **(4)**

b By considering the stationary values of $r\sin\theta$, or otherwise, find equations of the tangents to the curve $r = a(1 + \cos\theta)$ which are parallel to the initial line. **(6)**

c Show that the area of the region for which $a < r < a(1 + \cos\theta)$ is $\dfrac{(\pi + 8)a^2}{4}$ **(6)**

← Further Pure 2 Sections 8.2, 8.3, 8.4

(E/P) **48** The curve C has polar equation $r = 3a\cos\theta, -\dfrac{\pi}{2} \leqslant \theta < \dfrac{\pi}{2}$. The curve D has polar equation $r = a(1 + \cos\theta), -\pi \leqslant \theta < \pi$. Given that a is positive,

a sketch, on the same diagram, the graphs of C and D, indicating where each curve cuts the initial line. **(4)**

The graphs of C and D intersect at the pole O and at the points P and Q.

b Find the polar coordinates of P and Q. **(3)**

c Use integration to find the exact value of the area enclosed by the curve D and the lines $\theta = 0$ and $\theta = \frac{\pi}{3}$ **(6)**

The region R contains all points which lie outside D and inside C.

Given that the value of the smaller area enclosed by the curve C and the line $\theta = \frac{\pi}{3}$ is

$$\frac{3a^2}{16}(2\pi - 3\sqrt{3})$$

d show that the area of R is πa^2. **(6)**

← Further Pure 2 Sections 8.2, 8.3, 8.4

E **49 a** Show on an Argand diagram the locus of points given by the values of z satisfying

$$|z - 3 + 4i| = 5 \quad \textbf{(2)}$$

b Show that this locus of points can be represented by the polar curve $r = 6\cos\theta - 8\sin\theta$. **(4)**

The set of points A is defined by
$$A = \left\{z : -\frac{\pi}{2} \leqslant \arg z \leqslant 0\right\} \cap \{z : |z - 3 + 4i| \leqslant 5\}$$

c Find, correct to 3 significant figures, the area of the region defined by A. **(4)**

← Further Pure 2 Sections 8.2, 8.3

E/P **50 a** Sketch the curve with polar equation

$$r = \cos 2\theta, -\frac{\pi}{4} \leqslant \theta \leqslant \frac{\pi}{4} \quad \textbf{(2)}$$

At the distinct points A and B on this curve, the tangents to the curve are parallel to the initial line, $\theta = 0$.

b Determine the polar coordinates of A and B, giving your answers to 3 significant figures. **(6)**

← Further Pure 2 Sections 8.2, 8.3

E/P **51 a** Sketch the curve with polar equation

$$r = \sin 2\theta, 0 \leqslant \theta \leqslant \frac{\pi}{2} \quad \textbf{(2)}$$

At the point A, where A is distinct from O, on this curve, the tangent to the curve is parallel to $\theta = \frac{\pi}{2}$

b Determine the polar coordinates of the point A, giving your answer to 3 significant figures. **(6)**

← Further Pure 2 Sections 8.2, 8.4

E **52** The curve C has polar equation

$$r = 6\cos\theta, -\frac{\pi}{2} \leqslant \theta < \frac{\pi}{2}$$

and the line D has polar equation

$$r = 3\sec\left(\frac{\pi}{3} - \theta\right), -\frac{\pi}{6} \leqslant \theta < \frac{5\pi}{6}$$

a Find a Cartesian equation of C and a Cartesian equation of D. **(4)**

b Sketch on the same diagram the graphs of C and D, indicating where each cuts the initial line. **(4)**

The graphs of C and D intersect at the points P and Q.

c Find the polar coordinates of P and Q. **(3)**

← Further Pure 2 Sections 8.1, 8.2

E **53**

The figure shows a sketch of the curve C with polar equation

$$r^2 = a^2 \sin 2\theta, 0 \leqslant \theta \leqslant \frac{\pi}{2},$$

where a is a constant.

Find the area of the shaded region enclosed by C. **(6)**

← Further Pure 2 Section 8.2

E/P **54**

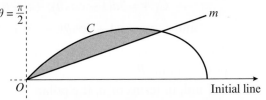

The figure shows a curve C with polar equation $r = 4a \cos 2\theta$, $0 \leqslant \theta \leqslant \frac{\pi}{4}$, and a line m with polar equation $\theta = \frac{\pi}{8}$. The shaded region, shown in the figure, is bounded by C and m. Use calculus to show that the area of the shaded region is $\frac{1}{2}a^2(\pi - 2)$ (6)

← Further Pure 2 Section 8.3

E/P **55**

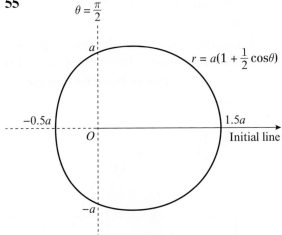

The curve shown in the figure has polar equation
$$r = a\left(1 + \frac{1}{2}\cos\theta\right), a > 0, 0 < \theta \leqslant 2\pi.$$
Determine the area enclosed by the curve, giving your answer in terms of a and π. (6)

← Further Pure 2 Section 8.3

E/P **56**

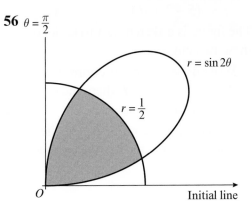

The figure show the half-lines $\theta = 0$, $\theta = \frac{\pi}{2}$ and the curves with polar equations
$$r = \frac{1}{2}, 0 \leqslant \theta \leqslant \frac{\pi}{2}, \text{ and}$$
$$r = \sin 2\theta, 0 \leqslant \theta \leqslant \frac{\pi}{2}$$

a Find the exact values of θ at the two points where the curves cross. (4)

b Find by integration the area of the shaded region, shown in the figure, which is bounded by both curves. (6)

← Further Pure 2 Sections 8.2, 8.3

E/P **57**

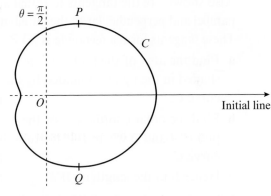

The curve C, shown in the figure, has polar equation
$$r = a(3 + \sqrt{5}\cos\theta), -\pi \leqslant \theta < \pi$$

a Find the polar coordinates of the points P and Q where the tangents to C are parallel to the initial line. (6)

The curve C represents the perimeter of the surface of a swimming pool. The direct distance from P to Q is 20 m.

b Calculate the value of a. (2)

c Find the area of the surface of the pool. (6)

← Further Pure 2 Sections 8.2, 8.3, 8.4

58

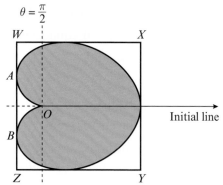

The figure shows a sketch of the cardioid C with equation $r = a(1 + \cos\theta)$, $-\pi < \theta \leqslant \pi$. Also shown are the tangents to C that are parallel and perpendicular to the initial line. These tangents form a rectangle $WXYZ$.

a Find the area of the finite region, shaded in the figure, bounded by the curve C. **(6)**

b Find the polar coordinates of the points A and B where WZ touches the curve C. **(6)**

c Hence find the length of WX. **(2)**

Given that the length of WZ is $\dfrac{3\sqrt{3}a}{2}$,

d find the area of the rectangle $WXYZ$. **(2)**

A heart-shape is modelled by the cardioid C, where $a = 10\,\text{cm}$. The heart shape is cut from the rectangular card $WXYZ$, shown in the figure.

e Find a numerical value for the area of card wasted in making this heart shape. **(3)**

← **Further Pure 2 Sections 8.3, 8.4**

E/P **59**

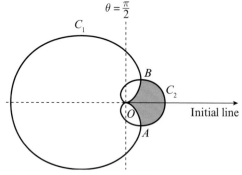

The figure is a sketch of two curves C_1 and C_2 with polar equations

$$C_1 : r = 3a(1 - \cos\theta), \ -\pi \leqslant \theta < \pi$$
$$\text{and } C_2 : r = a(1 + \cos\theta), \ -\pi \leqslant \theta < \pi$$

The curves meet at the pole O and at the points A and B.

a Find, in terms of a, the polar coordinates of the points A and B. **(2)**

b Show that the length of the line AB is $\dfrac{3\sqrt{3}}{2}a$. **(3)**

The region inside C_2 and outside C_1 is shaded in the figure.

c Find, in terms of a, the area of this region. **(6)**

A badge is designed which has the shape of the shaded region.

Given that the length of the line AB is $4.5\,\text{cm}$,

d calculate the area of this badge, giving your answer to 3 significant figures. **(3)**

← **Further Pure 2 Sections 8.2, 8.3**

E/P **60**

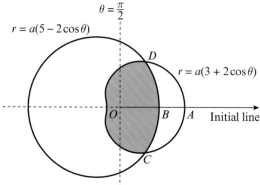

A logo is designed which consists of two overlapping closed curves.

The polar equations of these curves are

$$r = a(3 + 2\cos\theta), \ 0 \leqslant \theta < 2\pi \quad \text{and}$$
$$r = a(5 - 2\cos\theta), \ 0 \leqslant \theta < 2\pi$$

The figure is a sketch (not to scale) of these two curves.

a Write down the polar coordinates of the points A and B where the curves meet the initial line. **(2)**

b Find the polar coordinates of the points C and D where the two curves meet. **(4)**

c Show that the area of the overlapping region, which is shaded in the figure, is

$$\frac{a^2}{3}(49\pi - 48\sqrt{3})$$ **(6)**

← **Further Pure 2 Sections 8.2, 8.3**

Challenge

The diagram shows the curve C with polar equation $r = f(\theta)$. The line l is a tangent to the curve at the point $P(r, \theta)$, and α is the **acute angle** between l and the radial line at P.

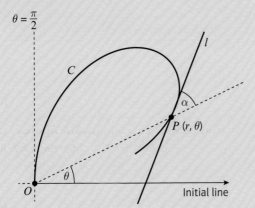

Show that $\tan \alpha = \dfrac{r}{\left(\dfrac{\mathrm{d}r}{\mathrm{d}\theta}\right)}$

← **Further Pure 2 Section 8.4**

Exam practice

Mathematics
International Advanced Subsidiary/
Advanced Level Further Pure 2

Time: 1 hour 30 minutes
You must have: Mathematical Formulae and Statistical Tables, Calculator
Answer ALL questions

....

1 Use algebra to find the set of values of x for which

$$\frac{1}{x+1} < \frac{x}{x+3}$$

(6)

2 Prove that

$$\sum_{r=1}^{n} \frac{1}{(r+2)(r+4)} = \frac{n(pn+q)}{24(n+3)(n+4)}$$

where p and q are constants to be found.

(5)

3 A complex number z has argument θ and modulus 1.

   a Show that $z^n - \dfrac{1}{z^n} = 2\mathrm{i}\sin n\theta,\ n \in \mathbb{Z}^+$

(2)

   b Hence, show that $8\sin^4\theta = \cos 4\theta - 4\cos 2\theta + 3$

(5)

4 **a** Show that the locus of points given by the values of z satisfying

    $|z + 12 + 5\mathrm{i}| = 13$

    can be represented by the polar curve with equation

    $r = -2(12\cos\theta + 5\sin\theta)$

(4)

   b Show on an Argand diagram the set of points A defined by

    $A = \left\{z : |z + 12 + 5\mathrm{i}| \leqslant 13\right\} \cap \left\{z : -\pi \leqslant \arg z \leqslant -\frac{3\pi}{4}\right\}$

(4)

   c Find, correct to 3 significant figures, the area of the region defined by A.

(5)

5 **a** Find the general solution to the differential equation

    $\cos x \dfrac{\mathrm{d}y}{\mathrm{d}x} + y \sin x = \cos^3 x$

(9)

   b Find the particular solution which satisfies the condition that $y = 3$ when $x = 0$.

(2)

6 a Show that the substitution $x = e^t$ transforms the differential equation

$$x^2 \frac{d^2y}{dx^2} + 8x \frac{dy}{dx} + 12y = 0, \qquad x > 0$$

into the differential equation

$$\frac{d^2y}{dt^2} + 7\frac{dy}{dt} + 12y = 0 \tag{8}$$

b Hence find the general solution of the original differential equation. **(5)**

7 $\dfrac{d^2y}{dx^2} + \left(\dfrac{dy}{dx}\right)^2 + 2y = 0$

Given that when $x = 0$, $y = \dfrac{dy}{dx} = 1$, find a series solution for y in ascending powers of x,

up to and including the term in x^3. **(9)**

8 The point P represents a complex number z in an Argand diagram. Given that

$$\sqrt{2}|z - i| = |z - 4|$$

a find a Cartesian equation for the locus of P, simplifying your answer **(3)**

b sketch the locus of P. **(2)**

c On your sketch from part **b**, shade the region for which

$$\sqrt{2}|z - i| < |z - 4| \qquad \text{and} \qquad |\arg(z + 1)| < \frac{\pi}{2} \tag{2}$$

d Find the complex numbers for which

$$\sqrt{2}|z - i| = |z - 4| \qquad \text{and} \qquad |\arg(z + 1)| = \frac{\pi}{2} \tag{4}$$

TOTAL FOR PAPER: 75 MARKS

GLOSSARY

acute (angle) **an angle less than 90°**

algebraic representing mathematical information with symbols (i.e. using letters and numbers)

alternating sequences **sequences** in which **successive** terms change repeatedly between being positive and negative

approximate not exact, but close enough to be used

approximation a number that is not exact

arbitrary something based on a random choice rather than a reason

arbitrary constant a **constant** to which various values may be assigned; it is unaffected by the changes in the values of the **variables** of the **equation**

arc a smooth curve joining two points

Argand diagram a diagram using Cartesian axes on which **complex numbers** are represented geometrically

argument the specific input of a **function**

argument of a complex number gives the angle between the positive real axis and the line joining the point to the **origin**

ascending increasing

asymptote a line that a curve approaches but never quite reaches

auxiliary equation an **equation** of the form $am^2 + bm + c = 0$ which is derived from a linear differential equation

axis (plural axes) either of the two lines by which the positions of points are measured in a graph

binomial an **algebraic expression** of the **sum** or difference of two terms. For example, $(a + b)^n$ is the general form of a binomial expression

binomial expansion the **algebraic expansion** of **powers** of a **binomial**

bound forming the edge of an area

boundary the line (real or imaginary) that marks the edge of an area

boundary conditions restrictions used to find a **particular solution** to a **second-order differential equation**

cardioid a curve that is heart-shaped

Cartesian coordinates a unique point in a **plane** specified by a pair of **numerical coordinates**

chain rule a formula used to **differentiate** composite **functions**, or functions of another function

circumference the **boundary** of a curved geometric shape

coefficient in $4x^3$, the coefficient of x^3 is 4

complementary function (C.F.) the general solution of a **homogeneous differential equation**

complex conjugate each of a pair of **complex numbers** having their real parts identical and their imaginary parts of equal magnitude but opposite sign. If $z = a + bi$, then $z^* = a - bi$, where $a, b \in \mathbb{R}$

complex number a number that can be expressed in the form $a + bi$ (where a and b are **real numbers** and i is a solution of the **equation** $x^2 = -1$); called an **imaginary number** because there is no real number that satisfies this equation

consecutive following one after another, without being interrupted

constant a term that does not include a **variable**. In the **expression** $x^2 + 3x - 6$, the constant term is -6

convention the way something is usually done

converge (of a **series**) approaching a limiting value as the number of terms increases

converse opposite

convert change

coordinates a set of values that show an exact position. In a two-dimensional grid, the first number represents a point on the x-axis and the second number represents a point on the y-axis

corresponding an equivalent; connected with what you have just mentioned

critical value a value that is important in the context of solving a problem

cubic a **polynomial** of **degree** 3

deduce to conclude from a known or assumed fact

degree the degree of a **polynomial** is equal to the highest **power** in that polynomial

de Moivre's theorem $(r(\cos\theta + i\sin\theta))^n = r^n(\cos n\theta + i\sin n\theta)$

denominator the bottom part of a fraction

derivative a way to represent the rate of change, in other words, $\frac{dy}{dx}$ is the first derivative, and $\frac{d^2y}{dx^2}$ is the second derivative

differentiate the process of finding the instantaneous rate of change of a function with respect to one of its **variables**

differentiation the instantaneous rate of change of a **function** with respect to one of its **variables**

distinct not equal

diverge to move away from a **limit** as the **argument** (input) of the **function** increases or decreases or as the number of terms of the **series** increases

enclosed surrounded on all sides

enlargement a **transformation** of a shape that involves increasing or decreasing the length of each side by a **scale factor**

equate to make equal

equation a statement where values of two mathematical **expressions** are equal. Solving an **equation** consists of determining the value(s) of the **variable**

Euler's relation $e^{i\theta} = \cos\theta + i\sin\theta$

exponential form involving exponents

expression any group of **algebraic** terms. For example, $2x + 6y + 3z$ is an algebraic expression

factorise to rewrite an **expression** using brackets. We factorise $x^2 + 3x + 2$ to get $(x + 1)(x + 2)$

finite having a fixed size; not **infinite**

finite series the **sum** of the values of a **finite sequence**

first-order differential equation an **equation** in which f(x, y) is a **function** of two **variables** defined on a region in the xy-plane. For example, the terms in the **sequence** $1, \frac{1}{2}, \frac{1}{4}, \frac{1}{8}, \frac{1}{16}, \frac{1}{32}, ..., \left(\frac{1}{2}\right)n - 1$ **converge** toward a value of zero as n tends toward infinity

fractional involving fractions

function the relationship between a set of inputs and a set of outputs, where each input is related to exactly one output

gradient the slope of a line

half-line a straight line extending **infinitely** in a single direction from a point

homogeneous differential equation a differential equation of the form $a\dfrac{d^2y}{dx^2} + b\dfrac{dy}{dx} + c = 0$

identity an equality that holds true without being affected by the values chosen for its **variables**

imaginary number a number that is expressed in terms of the square root of a negative number a, where $a \in \mathbb{R}$, and i $= \sqrt{-1}$, so i$^2 = -1$

infinite without **limit**; not **finite**

infinite series the sum of the values in an infinite **sequence**

initial line a line, usually the x-axis, that the angle θ is measured from when using in **polar coordinates**

integer a whole number. The symbol for integers is $\mathbb{Z}$

integrating factor a **function** that is used as a multiplier for another function in order to allow that function to be solved

intersection the point where two lines meet or cross over

intersects meets or crosses at a point

interval the range of a set of numbers. For example, 3, 4, 5, 6, 7 are the members of the set of numbers satisfied by the interval $2 < x < 8$, where x is an **integer**

invariant (point or line) a fixed point or line that does not move under a **transformation**

inverse operations that reverse each other. For example, the inverse of $y = x^2$ is $x = \sqrt{y}$

limit a value toward which an **expression converges** as one or more **variables** approach certain values

locus (of a set of points) the set of points that satisfies given conditions or a rule

loop a closed curve

Maclaurin series an expansion **series** of a **function**, where the **approximate** value of the function is determined as a **sum** of the **derivatives** of that function

major arc an **arc** of a circle having measure greater than or equal to 180° (π **radians**)

mapping a relationship such that each element of a given set (the domain of the function) is associated with an element of another set (the range of the function)

method of differences a way to calculate a **polynomial** using its values at several **consecutive** points

midpoint (of a line **segment**) a point on a line that divides it into two equal parts

minor arc an **arc** of a circle having measure less than 180° (π **radians**)

modulus (of a **complex number**) the distance of a point from the **origin**. For any complex number $z = a + bi$, $|z| = \sqrt{a^2 + b^2}$

modulus–argument form the modulus–argument form of a **complex number** is $z = r(\cos\theta + i\sin\theta)$, where $r = |z|$ and $\theta = \arg z$

non-homogeneous differential equation a differential equation of the form $a\dfrac{d^2y}{dx^2} + b\dfrac{dy}{dx} + c = $ f(x)

numerator the top part of a fraction

numerical relating to numbers

origin the point where the y-axis and x-axis **intersect** on a flat **coordinate plane**

parallel two lines side-by-side, the same distance apart at every point

parametric equation a set of **equations** that express a set of quantities as **functions** of a number of independent **variables**, known as parameters. For example, $x = ct, y = \dfrac{c}{t}, t \in \mathbb{R}$ are the parametric equations of a hyperbola

particular integral (P.I.) is a **function** that satisfies a differential equation

particular solution the exact solution to a differential equation

perpendicular one line meeting another at 90°

perpendicular bisector a perpendicular line that divides a line **segment** into two equal parts

plane a flat two-dimensional surface extending into infinity

polar coordinate (system) a two-dimensional **coordinate** system in which each point on a **plane** is determined by a distance from a reference point and an angle from a reference direction

pole the point, usually the **origin**, from which the distance of a point is measured

polynomial an **expression** of two or more **algebraic** terms with positive whole number indices. For example, $2x + 6x^2 + 7x^6$ is a polynomial with positive with **integer** exponents

power another name for an index number

product $2 \times 3 = 6$, so 6 is the product of 2 and 3

product rule a method for differentiating problems where one **function** is multiplied by another

proof by mathematical induction a special form of deductive reasoning (i.e. using the information you have to form an opinion). It is used to prove a fact about all the elements in an infinite set by performing a **finite** number of steps

quadrant the area when two-dimensional axes are divided into four quadrants

quadratic expressions such as $x^2 + 3x$ are quadratic, where the highest **power** of any variable is 2

radian describes an angle **subtended** by a circular arc as the length of the arc divided by the radius of the arc. One radian is the angle **subtended** at the centre of a circle by an arc that is equal in length to the radius of the circle

rational number a number that can be expressed as an **integer** or fraction

real number a value that can be represented along a number line and includes all rational and irrational numbers. The symbol for real numbers is $\mathbb{R}$

roots the set of all possible solutions. A quadratic **equation** has up to 2 roots

rotation a **transformation** of an object about its centre by a specified angle

scale factor a number which multiplies some quantity. The ratio of any two **corresponding** lengths in two similar geometric figures is called a scale factor

second-order differential equations differential equations contains second derivatives e.g. $\dfrac{d^2y}{dx^2}$

segment (i) part of a line connecting two points (ii) the area of a circle cut off by a chord

separating the variables a method used to solve certain types of differential equations

sequence a **series** of numbers following a set rule. 4, 9, 14, 19, … is an example of an arithmetic sequence

series the **sum** of terms in a **sequence**

series expansions a method for calculating a **function** that cannot be expressed more easily

series solution a solution to certain types of differential equations

subtended an angle subtended by an **arc**, line **segment**, or any other section of a curve is one whose two rays pass through the endpoints of the arc

successive coming or following on after the other

sum the addition of two or more numbers. For example, $2 + 3 = 5$, so 5 is the sum of 2 and 3

surd a number that cannot be simplified to remove a square root. For example, $\sqrt{2}$ is a surd because it is an irrational number, whereas $\sqrt{4} = \pm 2$ which is a rational number and not a surd

symmetrical when a shape looks the same following a **transformation** such as reflection or rotation

tangent (i) a trigonometric **function** that is equal to the ratio of the side opposite an **acute angle** (in a right-angled triangle) to the adjacent side
(ii) a line that touches a curve at a point without crossing over and matches the **gradient** of the curve at that point

Taylor series an expansion **series** of a **function**, where the **approximate** value of the function is determined as a **sum** of the **derivatives** of that function

transform to map linearly

transformation a linear **mapping** that is either a reflection, rotation or stretch

translation a **function** that moves an object a certain distance

nth root of unity the solutions to $z^n = 1$

valid true

variable a quantity that is able to be changed, i.e. not **constant**

vector an object that has both a magnitude and a direction. Geometrically, a vector is a directed line **segment**, whose length is the magnitude of the vector and with an arrow indicating the direction

verify show

vertex (plural vertices) where two lines meet at an angle, especially in a polygon

w-plane a geometric representation of the **complex numbers**, $w = u + vi$ where u is represented by the horizontal axis and vi is represented by the vertical axis

z-plane a geometric representation of the **complex numbers**, $z = x + yi$ where x is represented by the horizontal axis and yi is represented by the vertical axis

ANSWERS

CHAPTER 1

Prior knowledge check

1 a $x < -\frac{1}{3}$ or $x > 1$ **b** $-2 - \sqrt{6} < x < -2 + \sqrt{6}$

2 a $x > 2$ or $x < -\frac{4}{3}$ **b** $\frac{3}{2} < x < \frac{5}{2}$

Exercise 1A

1 a $-1 < x < 6$ **b** $x \leqslant -3$ or $x \geqslant 2$

   c $-1 < x < 1$ **d** $-\sqrt{3} < x < -1$ or $1 < x < \sqrt{3}$

   e $0 \leqslant x < 1$ or $x \geqslant \frac{3}{2}$ **f** $x < -1$ or $0 < x < 2$

   g $x < -2$ or $-1 < x < 1$ or $x > 2$

   h $-1 < x < 0$ or $0 < x < 2$

   i $x < 4$ or $x > \frac{14}{3}$

   j $-2 < x < 5$ or $x > \frac{17}{2}$

2 a $\{x : x > \frac{1}{3}\} \cup \{x : -5 < x < 0\}$

   b $\{x : x < 0\} \cup \{x : 2 < x < 5\}$

   c $\{x : x < -2\} \cup \{x : 0 < x < 1\}$

   d $\{x : x < -3\} \cup \{x : -1 < x < 1\}$

   e $\{x : -\frac{1}{3} < x < 0\} \cup \{x : 0 < x < \frac{1}{2}\}$

   f $\{x : -1 < x < -\frac{1}{3}\} \cup \{x : x > \frac{1}{2}\}$

3 $-5 < x < -4$ and $-1 - \sqrt{7} < x < -1 + \sqrt{7}$

4 $\{x : -\frac{1}{2} < x < \dfrac{5 - \sqrt{29}}{2}\} \cup \{x : 3 < x < \dfrac{5 + \sqrt{29}}{2}\}$

5 a The student did not square the denominators before cross-multiplying. Multiplying by negative values does not preserve the inequality.

   b $-\frac{4}{3} < x < -1$ or $0 < x < 4$

6 $\{x : -2 < x < -1\} \cup \{x : -\frac{1}{2} < x < 0\}$

Challenge

$x < \ln\frac{1}{2}$ or $x > \ln 1$

Exercise 1B

1 a
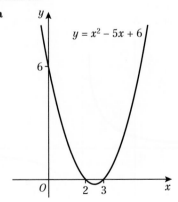

$y = x^2 - 5x + 6$

b
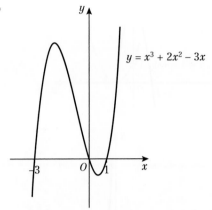

$y = x^3 + 2x^2 - 3x$

c
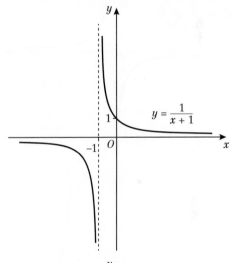

$y = \dfrac{1}{x + 1}$

d
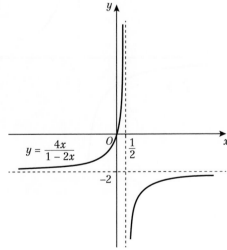

$y = \dfrac{4x}{1 - 2x}$

2 a

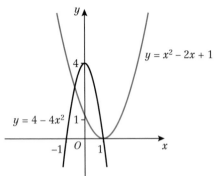

$y = x^2 - 2x + 1$

$y = 4 - 4x^2$

b

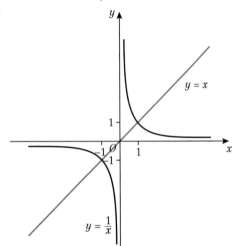

$y = x$

$y = \dfrac{1}{x}$

c

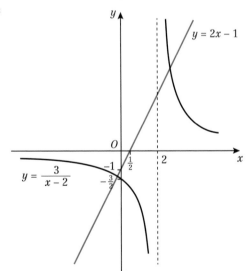

$y = 2x - 1$

$y = \dfrac{3}{x - 2}$

d

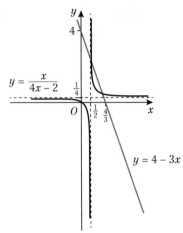

$y = \dfrac{x}{4x - 2}$

$y = 4 - 3x$

3 a $\left(7, \dfrac{1}{4}\right)$

  b $(4, 2)$ and $(-1, -3)$

  c $(-2, 0)$, $(0, -4)$, $(4, 12)$

4 a

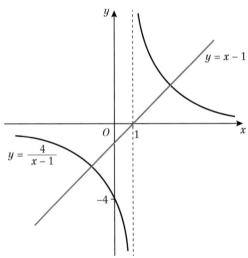

$y = x - 1$

$y = \dfrac{4}{x - 1}$

  b $(3, 2)$ and $(-1, -2)$

  c $-1 < x < 1$ or $x > 3$

5 a

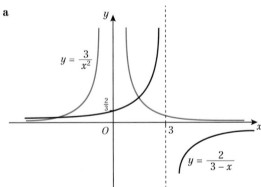

$y = \dfrac{3}{x^2}$

$y = \dfrac{2}{3 - x}$

  b $\left(-3, \dfrac{1}{3}\right)$ and $\left(\dfrac{3}{2}, \dfrac{4}{3}\right)$ **c** $-3 < x < \dfrac{3}{2}$ or $x > 3$

6 a

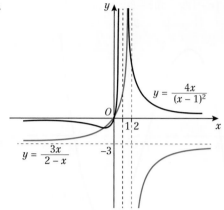

$y = \dfrac{4x}{(x-1)^2}$

$y = \dfrac{3x}{2-x}$

b $(0, 0)$, $(\frac{5}{3}, 15)$ and $(-1, -1)$
c $x \leqslant -1$ or $0 \leqslant x < 1$ or $1 < x \leqslant \frac{5}{3}$ or $2 < x$

7 a

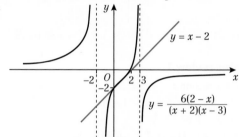

$y = x - 2$

$y = \dfrac{6(2-x)}{(x+2)(x-3)}$

b $(0, -2)$, $(1, -1)$ and $(2, 0)$
c $x < -2$ or $0 \leqslant x \leqslant 1$ or $2 \leqslant x < 3$

8 a

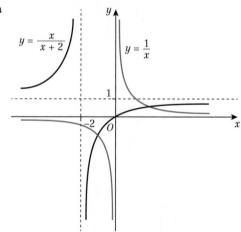

$y = \dfrac{x}{x+2}$ $\quad y = \dfrac{1}{x}$

b $(-1, -1)$ and $(2, \frac{1}{2})$
c $-2 < x < -1$ or $0 < x < 2$

Challenge

a

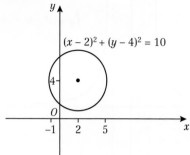

$(x-2)^2 + (y-4)^2 = 10$

b $(-1, 3)$, $(1, 1)$, $(3, 7)$, $(5, 5)$,

c

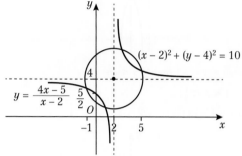

$(x-2)^2 + (y-4)^2 = 10$

$y = \dfrac{4x-5}{x-2}$

d $-1 < x < 1$ and $3 < x < 5$

Exercise 1C

1 a $x < \frac{6}{7}$
b $\frac{1}{2}(-\sqrt{13} - 1) < t < \frac{1}{2}(\sqrt{13} - 1)$
c $-7 < x < -2 - \sqrt{7}$ or $-2 + \sqrt{7} < x < 3$
d $x \geqslant 1$ or $x \leqslant -2$
e $x > 1$ or $x < -3$
f $x > 1$ or $x < -\frac{1}{3}$

2 a

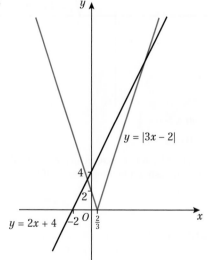

$y = |3x - 2|$

$y = 2x + 4$

b $\{x: -\frac{2}{5} \leqslant x \leqslant 6\}$

3 a

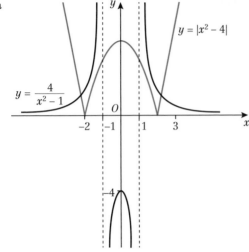

$$y = |x^2 - 4|$$
$$y = \frac{4}{x^2 - 1}$$

b $-\sqrt{5} \leqslant x < -1$ or $1 < x \leqslant \sqrt{5}$

4 $\{x: -1 < x < \frac{1}{3}\}$

5 $\{x:x < -1 - \sqrt{3}\} \cup \{x: -\sqrt{2} < x < \sqrt{3} - 1\}$

6 a

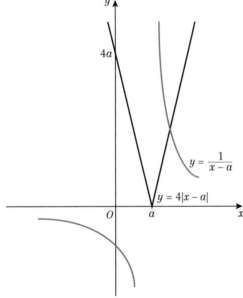

$$y = \frac{1}{x - a}$$
$$y = 4|x - a|$$

b $x < a$ or $x > a + \frac{1}{2}$

7 $-2 < x < 0$ or $x > 2$

8 a The student hasn't checked which critical values actually correspond to intersections of the graphs.

b $1 < x < 5$

Challenge

a $f(-1) = (-1)^3 + 3(-1)^2 - 13(-1) - 15 = -1 + 3 + 13 - 15 = 0$
So by the factor theorem $(x + 1)$ is a factor.

b $f(x) = (x + 1)(x + 5)(x - 3)$

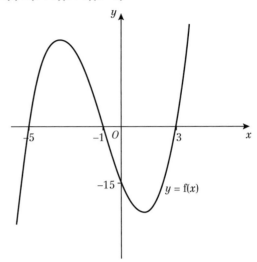

$$y = f(x)$$

c $x = -5, 1 - \sqrt{5} \leqslant x \leqslant 1 - \sqrt{3}, 1 + \sqrt{3} \leqslant x \leqslant 1 + \sqrt{5}$

Chapter review 1

1 $0 \leqslant x \leqslant 2$ or $x \geqslant 4$

2 $-2 < x < 1 - \sqrt{6}$ or $x > 1 + \sqrt{6}$

3 $0 < x < 2$ or $x > \frac{7}{2}$

4 $\{x:0 < x < \frac{3}{2}\} \cup \{x:3 < x < 4\}$

5 $\{x:x < -1\} \cup \{x:1 < x < 11\}$

6 a

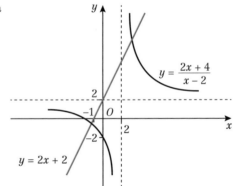

$$y = \frac{2x + 4}{x - 2}$$
$$y = 2x + 2$$

b $1 - \sqrt{5} < x < 2$ or $x > 1 + \sqrt{5}$

7 a

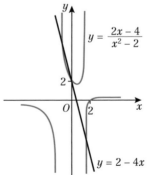

$$y = \frac{2x - 4}{x^2 - 2}$$
$$y = 2 - 4x$$

b $-\sqrt{2} < x < -1$ or $0 < x < \sqrt{2}$ or $x > \frac{3}{2}$

8 a

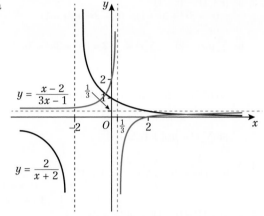

b $-2 < x < 3 - \sqrt{11}$ and $\frac{1}{3} < x < 3 + \sqrt{11}$

9 a

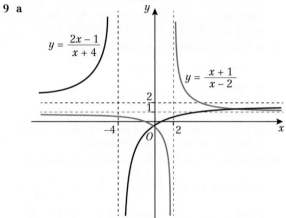

b $x < -4, 5 - 3\sqrt{3} < x < 2, 5 + 3\sqrt{3} < x$

10 $1 < x < 5$

11 $-3 < x < 3$

12 $x < \frac{2}{7}$

13 $x < \sqrt{3} - 1$ or $x > \sqrt{3} + 1$

14 a

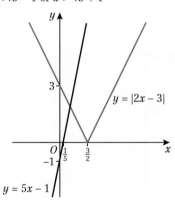

b $x > \frac{4}{7}$

15 a $x = -1 - \sqrt{7}, 0, 1, -1 + \sqrt{7}$

b

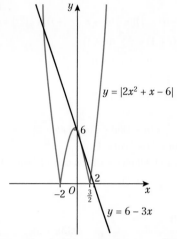

c $x < -1 - \sqrt{7}$ or $0 < x < 1$ or $x > -1 + \sqrt{7}$

16 a

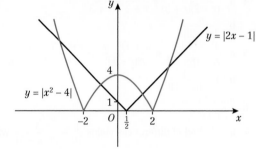

b $x = -1 - \sqrt{6}, -1, -1 + \sqrt{6}, 3$

c $x < -1 - \sqrt{6}$, or $-1 < x < -1 + \sqrt{6}$ or $x > 3$

Challenge

Solving $x^2 - 5x + 2 = x - 3$ and $x^2 - 5x + 2 = 3 - x$ we find that the critical values are $x = 2 - \sqrt{5}, 1, 2 + \sqrt{5}, 5$

Sketching the graphs we have

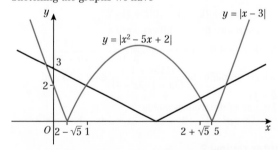

$\{x : x < 2 - \sqrt{5}\} \cup \{x : 1 < x < 2 + \sqrt{5}\} \cup \{x : x > 5\}$

CHAPTER 2

Prior knowledge check

1 a 1098   **b** 10761619.5

2 a Use the following:

$$\sum_{r=1}^{n} r^2 = \frac{n(n+1)(2n+1)}{6}$$

$$\sum_{r=1}^{n} r^2 = \frac{n(n+1)}{2}$$

and simplify to get the answer.

b 10073

Exercise 2A

1 a $\frac{1}{2}(r(r+1) - r(r-1)) = \frac{1}{2}(r^2 + r - r^2 + r) = \frac{1}{2}(2r) = r$

b $\sum_{r=1}^{n} r = \frac{1}{2}\sum_{r=1}^{n} r(r+1) - \frac{1}{2}\sum_{r=1}^{n} r(r-1)$

$r = 1$: $\frac{1}{2} \times 1 \times 2 - \frac{1}{2} \times 1 \times 0$

$r = 2$: $\frac{1}{2} \times 2 \times 3 - \frac{1}{2} \times 2 \times 1$

$r = 3$: $\frac{1}{2} \times 3 \times 4 - \frac{1}{2} \times 3 \times 2$

$\vdots$

$r = n-1$: $\frac{1}{2} \times (n-1)(n) - \frac{1}{2}(n-1)(n-2)$

$r = n$: $\frac{1}{2}n(n+1) - \frac{1}{2}n(n-1)$

When you add, all terms cancel except $\frac{1}{2}n(n+1)$

Hence $\sum_{r=1}^{n} r = \frac{1}{2}n(n+1)$

2 $\dfrac{n(n+3)}{4(n+1)(n+2)}$

3 a $\dfrac{1}{2r} - \dfrac{1}{2(r+2)}$ **b** $\dfrac{n(3n+5)}{4(n+1)(n+2)}$

4 a $\dfrac{1}{(r+2)(r+3)} \equiv \dfrac{1}{r+2} - \dfrac{1}{r+3}$

b $\dfrac{n}{3(n+3)}$

5 a $\dfrac{1}{r!} - \dfrac{1}{(r+1)!} \equiv \dfrac{(r+1)! - r!}{r!(r+1)!} \equiv \dfrac{r!(r+1-1)}{r!(r+1)!} \equiv \dfrac{r}{(r+1)!}$

b $1 - \dfrac{1}{(n+1)!}$

6 $\dfrac{n(n+2)}{(n+1)^2}$

7 a Method of differences yields $\dfrac{1}{10} - \dfrac{1}{2(2n+5)}$, which

simplifies to $\dfrac{n}{10n+25}$, so $a = 10$ and $b = 25$.

b For $n = 1$, $\dfrac{1}{5 \times 7} = \dfrac{1}{10+25}$. Assume true for $n = k$.

Let $n = k+1$, then

$\sum_{r=1}^{k+1} \dfrac{1}{(2r+3)(2r+5)} = \dfrac{k}{10k+25} + \dfrac{1}{(2k+5)(2k+7)}$

$= \dfrac{2k^2 + 7k + 5}{(2k+1)(2k+7)} = \dfrac{k+1}{10(k+1) + 25}$

Therefore true for all values of n.

8 Method of differences yields $\dfrac{4}{3}\left(\dfrac{1}{3r-2} - \dfrac{1}{3r+4}\right)$,

which simplifies to $\dfrac{n(15n+17)}{(3n+1)(3n+4)}$, so $a = 15$ and

$b = 17$.

9 Method of differences yields

$(n+1)^2 + n^2 - 1^2 - 0^2 = 2n^2 + 2n = 2n(n+1)$ so $a = 2$.

Chapter review 2

1 a $\dfrac{2}{(r+2)(r+4)} = \dfrac{1}{r+2} - \dfrac{1}{r+4}$

b $\sum_{r=1}^{n} \dfrac{2}{(r+2)(r+4)} = \sum_{r=1}^{n}\left(\dfrac{1}{r+2} - \dfrac{1}{r+4}\right)$

$= \dfrac{1}{3} + \dfrac{1}{4} - \dfrac{1}{n+3} - \dfrac{1}{n+4}$

$= \dfrac{7n^2 + 25n}{12(n+3)(n+4)}$

2 a $\dfrac{4}{(4r-1)(4r+3)} = \dfrac{1}{4r-1} - \dfrac{1}{4r+3}$

b $\sum_{r=1}^{n} \dfrac{4}{(4r-1)(4r+3)} = \dfrac{1}{3} - \dfrac{1}{4n+3} = \dfrac{4n+3-3}{3(4n+3)}$

$= \dfrac{4n}{3(4n+3)}$

c 0.00126

3 a $(r+1)^3 - (r-1)^3$

$= (r^3 + 3r^2 + 3r + 1) - (r^3 - 3r^2 + 3r - 1)$

$= 6r^2 + 2$

b $\sum_{r=1}^{n}(6r^2 + 2) = 6\sum_{r=1}^{n} r^2 + \sum_{r=1}^{n} 2 = 2n^3 + 3n^2 + 3n$

So $6\sum_{r=1}^{n} r^2 + \sum_{r=1}^{n} 2 = 6\sum_{r=1}^{n} r^2 + 2n = 2n^3 + 3n^2 + 3n$

So $6\sum_{r=1}^{n} r^2 = 2n^3 + 3n^2 + n = n(2n^2 + 3n + 1)$

$= n(n+1)(2n+1)$

So $\sum_{r=1}^{n} r^2 = \frac{1}{6}n(n+1)(2n+1)$

4 $\sum_{r=1}^{n} \dfrac{4}{(r+1)(r+3)} = \sum_{r=1}^{n}\left(\dfrac{2}{r+1} - \dfrac{2}{r+3}\right)$

$= \dfrac{2}{2} + \dfrac{2}{3} - \dfrac{2}{n+2} - \dfrac{2}{n+3} = \dfrac{n(5n+13)}{3(n+2)(n+3)}$

5 $\sum_{r=1}^{n}((r+1)^3 - (r-1)^3) = n(2n^2 + 3n + 3)$

Calculate

$(2n)(2(2n)^2 + 3(2n) + 3) - (n-1)(2(n-1)^2 + 3(n-1) + 3)$

which gives that $a = 14$, $b = 15$, $c = 3$, $d = 2$

6 a Method of differences yields $\dfrac{3n}{12n+16}$,

so $a = 3$, $b = 12$ and $c = 16$.

b Simplify: $\dfrac{6n}{24n+16} - \dfrac{3n-3}{12n+4}$

7 The general term $\dfrac{1}{r} + \dfrac{1}{r+1}$ is a um, not a difference,

so the terms will not cancel out, and the method of
differences cannot be used in this case.

8 Recognise this is $\sum_{r=1}^{n} \dfrac{1}{r(r+1)}$ and apply method of

differences. Simplify $\dfrac{1}{2} + \dfrac{1}{4} - \left(\dfrac{1}{2(n+1)} + \dfrac{1}{2(n+2)}\right)$ to

obtain $\dfrac{3}{4} - \dfrac{2n+3}{2(n+1)(n+2)}$, stating $a = 2$ and $b = 3$.

9 a $\dfrac{1}{2r+1} - \dfrac{1}{2r+5}$

b 0.0218

Challenge

a $k = 11$ **b** $a = 11$, $b = 48$, $c = 49$

CHAPTER 3

Prior knowledge check

1 a 8   **b** $\dfrac{\pi}{3}$ **c** 16

d $\dfrac{\pi}{2}$ **e** 4   **f** $\dfrac{\pi}{6}$

2

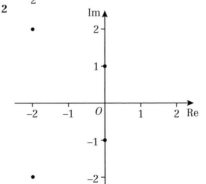

3 4032

Exercise 3A

1 a $3e^{\pi i}$ **b** $6e^{\frac{\pi i}{2}}$

  c $4e^{-\frac{5\pi i}{6}}$ **d** $\sqrt{65}\,e^{3.02i}$

  e $\sqrt{29}\,e^{-1.19i}$ **f** $2\sqrt{6}e^{\frac{3\pi i}{4}}$

  g $2\sqrt{2}e^{\frac{\pi i}{4}}$ **h** $8e^{-\frac{\pi i}{6}}$

  i $2e^{-\frac{\pi i}{5}}$

2 a $\frac{1}{2}+\frac{\sqrt{3}}{2}i$ **b** -4

  c $3+3i$ **d** $4\sqrt{3}+4i$

  e $-3i$ **f** $-\frac{\sqrt{3}}{2}+\frac{1}{2}i$

  g -1 **h** $-3-3i$

  i $-4+4i\sqrt{3}$

3 a $\cos\left(-\frac{10\pi}{13}\right)+i\sin\left(-\frac{10\pi}{13}\right)$

  b $4\left(\cos\left(-\frac{3\pi}{5}\right)+i\sin\left(-\frac{3\pi}{5}\right)\right)$

  c $5\left(\cos\left(\frac{7\pi}{8}\right)+i\sin\left(\frac{7\pi}{8}\right)\right)$

4 $e^{i\theta}=\cos\theta+i\sin\theta$ **(1)**

  $e^{-i\theta}=\cos(-\theta)+i\sin(-\theta)=\cos\theta-i\sin\theta$ **(2)**

  (1) – (2): $e^{i\theta}-e^{-i\theta}=2i\sin\theta$

  $\frac{1}{2i}(e^{i\theta}-e^{-i\theta})=\sin\theta$

  $\Rightarrow \sin\theta=\frac{1}{2i}(e^{i\theta}-e^{-i\theta})$ (as required)

Exercise 3B

1 a $\cos\frac{7\pi}{12}+i\sin\frac{7\pi}{12}$ **b** $3\sqrt{5}\cos4\theta+3i\sqrt{5}\sin4\theta$

  c $3i\sqrt{2}$

2 a $-\frac{1}{4}$ **b** $\frac{\sqrt{3}}{4}\cos\frac{5\pi}{7}+i\frac{\sqrt{3}}{4}\sin\frac{5\pi}{7}$

  c $-i$

3 a $e^{5i\theta}$ **b** $e^{\pi i}$ **c** $6e^{\frac{\pi i}{3}}$ **d** $3\sqrt{2}e^{\frac{\pi i}{4}}$

4 a $e^{3i\theta}$ **b** $2\sqrt{2}e^{\frac{\pi i}{4}}$ **c** $\frac{3}{4}e^{-\frac{\pi i}{2}}$

5 a $6\sqrt{3}e^{\frac{5\pi i}{6}}$ **b** $\sqrt{3}e^{\frac{7\pi i}{12}}$ **c** $18e^{-\frac{7\pi i}{12}}$ **d** $6e^{\frac{\pi i}{4}}$

6 $\frac{(\cos9\theta+i\sin9\theta)(\cos4\theta+i\sin4\theta)}{\cos7\theta+i\sin7\theta}=\frac{e^{9i\theta}e^{4i\theta}}{e^{7i\theta}}=e^{9i\theta+4i\theta-7i\theta}$

  $=e^{6i\theta}=\cos6\theta+i\sin6\theta$

7 $2e^{\frac{\pi}{6}i},\ 2e^{-\frac{5\pi i}{6}}$

8 a $2e^{\frac{\pi i}{2}}$

  b $n=1$: LHS $=(1+i)^1=1+i$

    RHS $=2^{\frac{1}{2}}e^{\frac{\pi i}{4}}=\sqrt{2}\left(\cos\frac{\pi}{4}+i\sin\frac{\pi}{4}\right)=\sqrt{2}\left(\frac{1}{\sqrt{2}}+i\frac{1}{\sqrt{2}}\right)$

    $=1+i$

    As LHS = RHS, the equation holds for $n=1$.

    Assume the equation holds for $n=k$, $k\in\mathbb{Z}^+$.

    i.e. $(1+i)^k=2^{\frac{k}{2}}e^{\frac{k\pi i}{4}}$

    With $n=k+1$, the equation becomes

    $(1+i)^{k+1}=(1+i)^k\times(1+i)=2^{\frac{k}{2}}e^{\frac{k\pi i}{4}}\times(1+i)$

    $=2^{\frac{k}{2}}e^{\frac{k\pi i}{4}}\times2^{\frac{1}{2}}e^{\frac{\pi i}{4}}$

    $=2^{\frac{k}{2}+\frac{1}{2}}e^{\frac{k\pi i}{4}+\frac{\pi i}{4}}=2^{\frac{k+1}{2}}e^{\frac{(k+1)\pi i}{4}}$

    Therefore, the equation holds when $n=k+1$.

    If the equation holds for $n=k$, then it has been shown to be true for $n=k+1$.

    As the equation holds for $n=1$, it is now also true for all $n\in\mathbb{Z}^+$ by mathematical induction.

  c 256

9 $e^{i\theta}=\cos\theta+i\sin\theta,\ e^{-i\theta}=\cos\theta-i\sin\theta$

  So $e^{i\theta}e^{-i\theta}=(\cos\theta+i\sin\theta)(\cos\theta-i\sin\theta)$

  LHS $=e^{i(\theta-\theta)}=e^0=1$

  RHS $=\cos^2\theta-i^2\sin^2\theta=\cos^2\theta+\sin^2\theta$

  Hence $\cos^2\theta+\sin^2\theta\equiv1$

Challenge

a $n=1$; LHS $=(re^{i\theta})^1=re^{i\theta}$

  RHS $=r^1e^{i\theta}=re^{i\theta}$

  As LHS = RHS, the equation holds for $n=1$.

  Assume the equation holds for $n=k$, $k\in\mathbb{Z}^+$.

  i.e. $(re^{i\theta})^k=r^ke^{ik\theta}$

  With $n=k+1$, the equation becomes

  $(re^{i\theta})^{k+1}=(re^{i\theta})^k\times re^{i\theta}=r^ke^{ik\theta}\times re^{i\theta}=r^{k+1}e^{i(k\theta+\theta)}=r^{k+1}e^{i(k+1)\theta}$

  Therefore, the equation holds when $n=k+1$.

  If the equation holds for $n=k$, then it has been shown to be true for $n=k+1$.

  As the equation holds for $n=1$, it is now also true for all $n\in\mathbb{Z}^+$ by mathematical induction.

b Given $n\in\mathbb{Z}^+$, we have: $(re^{i\theta})^{-n}=\frac{1}{(re^{i\theta})^n}=\frac{1}{r^ne^{in\theta}}=r^{-n}e^{-in\theta}$

Exercise 3C

1 a $\cos6\theta+i\sin6\theta$ **b** $\cos12\theta+i\sin12\theta$

  c $-\frac{\sqrt{3}}{2}+\frac{1}{2}i$ **d** $-\frac{1}{2}+\frac{\sqrt{3}}{2}i$

  e 1 **f** i

2 a $e^{i\theta}$ **b** $e^{2i\theta}$ **c** $e^{-6i\theta}$

  d $e^{-i\theta}$ **e** $e^{11i\theta}$ **f** $e^{5i\theta}$

3 a 1 **b** -1 **c** 1

4 a $(1+i)^5=-4-4i$ **b** $(-2+2i)^8=4096$

  c $(1-i)^6=8i$ **d** $(1-i\sqrt{3})^6=64$

  e $\left(\frac{3}{2}-\frac{1}{2}\sqrt{3}i\right)^9=81i\sqrt{3}$

  f $(-2\sqrt{3}-2i)^5=512\sqrt{3}-512i$

5 $(3+\sqrt{3}i)^5=-432+144i\sqrt{3}$

6 $-8+8i\sqrt{3}$

7 $-27i$

8 a $2e^{\frac{2\pi i}{3}}$ **b** 3

9 Write $a+bi$ and $a-bi$ as $r(\cos\theta+i\sin\theta)$ and $r(\cos\theta-i\sin\theta)$ respectively.

  Then by de Moivre's theorem,

  $(a+bi)^n+(a-bi)^n=r^n(\cos n\theta+i\sin n\theta)$

                  $+r^n(\cos n\theta-i\sin n\theta)$

                  $=2r^n\cos n\theta$

  which is always real.

Challenge

Given $n\in\mathbb{Z}^+$, we have:

$(r(\cos\theta+i\sin))^{-n}=\frac{1}{(r(\cos\theta+i\sin))^n}=\frac{1}{r^n(\cos n\theta+i\sin n\theta)}$

by de Moivre's theorem for positive integer exponents.

$=\frac{1}{r^n(\cos n\theta+i\sin n\theta)}\times\frac{\cos n\theta-i\sin n\theta}{\cos n\theta-i\sin n\theta}$

$=\frac{\cos n\theta-i\sin n\theta}{r^n(\cos^2 n\theta-i^2\sin^2 n\theta)}=\frac{\cos n\theta-i\sin n\theta}{r^n(\cos^2 n\theta+\sin^2 n\theta)}$

$=r^{-n}(\cos n\theta-i\sin n\theta)=r^{-n}(\cos(-n\theta)+i\sin(-n\theta))$

Exercise 3D

1 a $(\cos\theta + i\sin\theta)^3 = \cos3\theta + i\sin3\theta$

$= \cos^3\theta + 3i\cos^2\theta\sin\theta + 3i^2\cos\theta\sin^2\theta + i^3\sin^3\theta$

$= \cos^3\theta + 3i\cos^2\theta\sin\theta - 3\cos\theta\sin^2\theta - i\sin^3\theta$

$\Rightarrow \cos3\theta + i\sin3\theta = \cos^3\theta + 3i\cos^2\theta\sin\theta$
$\qquad\qquad - 3\cos\theta\sin^2\theta - i\sin^3\theta$

Equating the imaginary parts:

$\sin3\theta = 3\cos^2\theta\sin\theta - \sin^3\theta$

$\qquad = 3\sin\theta(1 - \sin^2\theta) - \sin^3\theta$

$\qquad = 3\sin\theta - 4\sin^3\theta$

b $(\cos\theta + i\sin\theta)^5 = \cos5\theta + i\sin5\theta$

$= \cos^5\theta + 5i\cos^4\theta\sin\theta + 10i^2\cos^3\theta\sin^2\theta$

$\qquad + 10i^3\cos^2\theta\sin^3\theta + 5i^4\cos\theta\sin^4\theta + i^5\sin^5\theta$

$\Rightarrow \cos5\theta + i\sin5\theta = \cos^5\theta + 5i\cos^4\theta\sin\theta$

$\qquad - 10\cos^3\theta\sin^2\theta - 10i\cos^2\theta\sin^3\theta$

$\qquad + 5\cos\theta\sin^4\theta + i\sin^5\theta$

Equating the imaginary parts:

$\sin5\theta = 5\cos^4\theta\sin\theta - 10\cos^2\theta\sin^3\theta + \sin^5\theta$

$\qquad = 5(1 - \sin^2\theta)^2\sin\theta - 10(1 - \sin^2\theta)\sin^3\theta + \sin^5\theta$

$\qquad = 16\sin^5\theta - 20\sin^3\theta + 5\sin\theta$

c $(\cos\theta + i\sin\theta)^7 = \cos7\theta + i\sin7\theta$

$= \cos^7\theta + 7i\cos^6\theta\sin\theta + 21i^2\cos^5\theta\sin^2\theta$

$\qquad + 35i^3\cos^4\theta\sin^3\theta + 35i^4\cos^3\theta\sin^4\theta$

$\qquad + 21i^5\cos^2\theta\sin^5\theta + 7i^6\cos\theta\sin^6\theta + i^7\sin^7\theta$

$\Rightarrow \cos7\theta + i\sin7\theta = \cos^7\theta + 7i\cos^6\theta\sin\theta$

$\qquad - 21\cos^5\theta\sin^2\theta - 35i\cos^4\theta\sin^3\theta + 35\cos^3\theta\sin^4\theta$

$\qquad + 21i\cos^2\theta\sin^5\theta - 7\cos\theta\sin^6\theta - i\sin^7\theta$

Equating the real parts:

$\cos7\theta = \cos^7\theta - 21\cos^5\theta\sin^2\theta + 35\cos^3\theta\sin^4\theta$

$\qquad - 7\cos\theta\sin^6\theta = \cos^7\theta - 21\cos^5\theta(1 - \cos^2\theta)$

$\qquad + 35\cos^3\theta(1 - \cos^2\theta)^2 - 7\cos\theta(1 - \cos^2\theta)^3$

$\qquad = 64\cos^7\theta - 112\cos^5\theta + 56\cos^3\theta - 7\cos\theta$

d Let $z = \cos\theta + i\sin\theta$

$\left(z + \frac{1}{z}\right)^4 = (2\cos\theta)^4 = 16\cos^4\theta$

$= z^4 + 4z^3\left(\frac{1}{z}\right) + 6z^2\left(\frac{1}{z^2}\right) + 4z\left(\frac{1}{z^3}\right) + \frac{1}{z^4}$

$= \left(z^4 + \frac{1}{z^4}\right) + 4\left(z^2 + \frac{1}{z^2}\right) + 6$

$= 2\cos4\theta + 4(2\cos2\theta) + 6$

$16\cos^4\theta = 2\cos4\theta + 4(2\cos2\theta) + 6$

$\qquad = 2(\cos4\theta + 4\cos2\theta + 3)$

$\Rightarrow \cos^4\theta = \frac{1}{8}(\cos4\theta + 4\cos2\theta + 3)$

e Let $z = \cos\theta + i\sin\theta$

$\left(z - \frac{1}{z}\right)^5 = (2i\sin\theta)^5 = 32i^5\sin^5\theta = 32i\sin^5\theta$

$= z^5 + 5z^4\left(-\frac{1}{z}\right) + 10z^3\left(-\frac{1}{z}\right)^2 + 10z^2\left(-\frac{1}{z}\right)^3$

$\qquad + 5z\left(-\frac{1}{z}\right)^4 + \left(-\frac{1}{z}\right)^5$

$= z^5 - 5z^3 + 10z - \frac{10}{z} + \frac{5}{z^3} - \frac{1}{z^5}$

$= \left(z^5 - \frac{1}{z^5}\right) - 5\left(z^3 - \frac{1}{z^3}\right) + 10\left(z - \frac{1}{z}\right)$

$= 2i\sin5\theta - 5(2i\sin3\theta) + 10(2i\sin\theta)$

$32i\sin^5\theta = 2i\sin5\theta - 10i\sin3\theta + 20i\sin\theta$

$\Rightarrow \sin^5\theta = \frac{1}{16}(\sin5\theta - 5\sin3\theta + 10\sin\theta)$

2 a $(\cos\theta + i\sin\theta)^5 = \cos5\theta + i\sin5\theta$

$= \cos^5\theta + {}^5C_1\cos^4\theta(i\sin\theta) + {}^5C_2\cos^3\theta(i\sin\theta)^2$

$\qquad + {}^5C_3\cos^2\theta(i\sin\theta)^3 + {}^5C_4\cos\theta(i\sin\theta)^4 + (i\sin\theta)^5$

$= \cos^5\theta + 5i\cos^4\theta\sin\theta - 10\cos^3\theta\sin^2\theta$

$\qquad - 10i\cos^2\theta\sin^3\theta + 5\cos\theta\sin^4\theta + i\sin^5\theta$

Equating the real parts gives

$\cos5\theta = \cos^5\theta - 10\cos^3\theta\sin^2\theta + 5\cos\theta\sin^4\theta$

$= \cos^5\theta - 10\cos^3\theta(1 - \cos^2\theta) + 5\cos\theta(1 - \cos^2\theta)^2$

$= \cos^5\theta - 10\cos^3\theta(1 - \cos^2\theta)$

$\qquad + 5\cos\theta(1 - 2\cos^2\theta + \cos^4\theta)$

$= 16\cos^5\theta - 20\cos^3\theta + 5\cos\theta$

b 0.475, 1.57, 2.67 (3 s.f.)

3 a Let $z = \cos\theta + i\sin\theta$, then $2\cos\theta = z + \frac{1}{z}$

$\left(z + \frac{1}{z}\right)^6 = (2\cos\theta)^6 = 64\cos^6\theta$

$= z^6 + 6z^5\left(\frac{1}{z}\right) + 15z^4\left(\frac{1}{z^2}\right) + 20z^3\left(\frac{1}{z^3}\right)$

$\qquad + 15z^2\left(\frac{1}{z^4}\right) + 6z\left(\frac{1}{z^5}\right) + \left(\frac{1}{z^6}\right)$

$= \left(z^6 + \frac{1}{z^6}\right) + 6\left(z^4 + \frac{1}{z^4}\right) + 15\left(z^2 + \frac{1}{z^2}\right) + 20$

$= 2\cos6\theta + 6(2\cos4\theta) + 15(2\cos2\theta) + 20$

$64\cos^6\theta = 2\cos6\theta + 6(2\cos4\theta) + 15(2\cos2\theta) + 20$

$32\cos^6\theta = \cos6\theta + 6\cos4\theta + 15\cos2\theta + 10$

b $\int_0^{\frac{\pi}{6}}\cos^6\theta\,d\theta = \frac{5\pi}{96} + \frac{9}{64}\sqrt{3}$

4 a If $z = \cos\theta + i\sin\theta$, then $2\cos\theta = z + \frac{1}{z}$ and

$2i\sin\theta = z - \frac{1}{z}$

So, $2^2\cos^2\theta \times (2i)^4\sin^4\theta = \left(z + \frac{1}{z}\right)^2\left(z - \frac{1}{z}\right)^4$

$= \left(\left(z + \frac{1}{z}\right)\left(z - \frac{1}{z}\right)\right)^2\left(z - \frac{1}{z}\right)^2 = \left(z^2 - \frac{1}{z^2}\right)^2\left(z - \frac{1}{z}\right)^2$

$= \left(z^4 - 2 + \frac{1}{z^4}\right)\left(z^2 - 2 + \frac{1}{z^2}\right)$

$= z^6 - 2z^4 - z^2 + 4 - \frac{1}{z^2} - \frac{2}{z^4} + \frac{1}{z^6}$

$= \left(z^6 + \frac{1}{z^6}\right) - 2\left(z^4 + \frac{1}{z^4}\right) - \left(z^2 + \frac{1}{z^2}\right) + 4$

$= 2\cos6\theta - 2(2\cos4\theta) - 2\cos2\theta + 4$

So, $64\cos^2\theta\sin^4\theta = 2\cos6\theta - 4\cos4\theta - 2\cos2\theta + 4$

$\Rightarrow 32\cos^2\theta\sin^4\theta = \cos6\theta - 2\cos4\theta - \cos2\theta + 2$

b $\frac{\pi}{48}$

5 a $\frac{5\pi}{32}$ **b** $\frac{\pi}{64} + \frac{1}{48}$ **c** $\frac{67}{6144}$

6 a $(\cos\theta + i\sin\theta)^6 = \cos6\theta + i\sin6\theta$

$= \cos^6\theta + {}^6C_1\cos^5\theta(i\sin\theta) + {}^6C_2\cos^4\theta(i\sin\theta)^2$

$\qquad + {}^6C_3\cos^3\theta(i\sin\theta)^3 + {}^6C_4\cos^2\theta(i\sin\theta)^4$

$\qquad + {}^6C_5\cos\theta(i\sin\theta)^5 + (i\sin\theta)^6$

$= \cos^6\theta + 6i\cos^5\theta\sin\theta - 15\cos^4\theta\sin^2\theta$

$\qquad - 20i\cos^3\theta\sin^3\theta + 15\cos^2\theta\sin^4\theta$

$\qquad + 6i\cos\theta\sin^5\theta - \sin^6\theta$

Equating the real parts gives

$\cos6\theta = \cos^6\theta - 15\cos^4\theta\sin^2\theta + 15\cos^2\theta\sin^4\theta - \sin^6\theta$

$= \cos^6\theta - 15\cos^4\theta(1 - \cos^2\theta) + 15\cos^2\theta(1 - \cos^2\theta)^2$

$\qquad - (1 - \cos^2\theta)^3$

$= \cos^6\theta - 15\cos^4\theta(1 - \cos^2\theta) + 15\cos^2\theta(1 - 2\cos^2\theta$

$\qquad + \cos^4\theta) - (1 - 3\cos^2\theta + 3\cos^4\theta - \cos^6\theta)$

$= 32\cos^6\theta - 48\cos^4\theta + 18\cos^2\theta - 1$

b $\cos\frac{\pi}{18} \approx 0.985$, $\cos\frac{5\pi}{18} \approx 0.643$, $\cos\frac{7\pi}{18} \approx 0.342$,

$\cos\frac{11\pi}{18} \approx -0.342$, $\cos\frac{13\pi}{18} \approx -0.643$, $\cos\frac{17\pi}{18} \approx -0.985$

7 a $\cos4\theta + i\sin4\theta = (\cos\theta + i\sin\theta)^4$

$= \cos^4\theta + 4i\cos^3\theta\sin\theta + 6i^2\cos^2\theta\sin^2\theta$

$\qquad + 4i^3\cos\theta\sin^3\theta + i^4\sin^4\theta$

$= \cos^4\theta + 4i\cos^3\theta\sin\theta - 6\cos^2\theta\sin^2\theta$

$\qquad - 4i\cos\theta\sin^3\theta + \sin^4\theta$

Equating the imaginary parts:

$\sin4\theta = 4\cos^3\theta\sin\theta - 4\cos\theta\sin^3\theta$

Online Worked solutions are available in SolutionBank.

b Equating the real parts:

$\cos 4\theta = \cos^4\theta - 6\cos^2\theta\sin^2\theta + \sin^4\theta$

$\tan 4\theta = \dfrac{\sin 4\theta}{\cos 4\theta} = \dfrac{4\cos^3\theta\sin\theta - 4\cos\theta\sin^3\theta}{\cos^4\theta - 6\cos^2\theta\sin^2\theta + \sin^4\theta}$

$= \dfrac{\left(\dfrac{1}{\cos^4\theta}\right)(4\cos^3\theta\sin\theta - 4\cos\theta\sin^3\theta)}{\left(\dfrac{1}{\cos^4\theta}\right)(\cos^4\theta - 6\cos^2\theta\sin^2\theta + \sin^4\theta)}$

$= \dfrac{4\tan\theta - 4\tan^3\theta}{1 - 6\tan^2\theta + \tan^4\theta}$

c $x = 0.20, 1.50, -5.03, -0.67$ (2 d.p.)

Exercise 3E

1 a $z = 1, i, -1, -i$

b $z = \dfrac{\sqrt{3}}{2} + \dfrac{1}{2}i, -\dfrac{\sqrt{3}}{2} + \dfrac{1}{2}i, -i$

c $z = 3, -\dfrac{3}{2} + \dfrac{3\sqrt{3}}{2}i, -\dfrac{3}{2} - \dfrac{3\sqrt{3}}{2}i$

d $z = 2 + 2i, -2 + 2i, 2 - 2i, -2 - 2i$

e $z = 1 + i, -1 + i, 1 - i, -1 - i$

f $z = \sqrt{3} - i, 2i, -\sqrt{3} - i$

2 a $z = \cos 0 + i\sin 0, \cos\dfrac{2\pi}{7} + i\sin\dfrac{2\pi}{7},$

$\cos\dfrac{4\pi}{7} + i\sin\dfrac{4\pi}{7}, \cos\dfrac{6\pi}{7} + i\sin\dfrac{6\pi}{7}$

$\cos\left(-\dfrac{2\pi}{7}\right) + i\sin\left(-\dfrac{2\pi}{7}\right), \cos\left(-\dfrac{4\pi}{7}\right) + i\sin\left(-\dfrac{4\pi}{7}\right),$

$\cos\left(-\dfrac{6\pi}{7}\right) + i\sin\left(-\dfrac{6\pi}{7}\right)$

b $z = 2\left(\cos\left(-\dfrac{\pi}{8}\right) + i\sin\left(-\dfrac{\pi}{8}\right)\right),$

$2\left(\cos\left(\dfrac{3\pi}{8}\right) + i\sin\left(\dfrac{3\pi}{8}\right)\right), 2\left(\cos\left(\dfrac{7\pi}{8}\right) + i\sin\left(\dfrac{7\pi}{8}\right)\right),$

$2\left(\cos\left(-\dfrac{5\pi}{8}\right) + i\sin\left(-\dfrac{5\pi}{8}\right)\right)$

c $z = 2\left(\cos\dfrac{\pi}{5} + i\sin\dfrac{\pi}{5}\right), 2\left(\cos\dfrac{3\pi}{5} + i\sin\dfrac{3\pi}{5}\right),$

$2(\cos\pi + i\sin\pi), 2\left(\cos\left(-\dfrac{\pi}{5}\right) + i\sin\left(-\dfrac{\pi}{5}\right)\right),$

$2\left(\cos\left(-\dfrac{3\pi}{5}\right) + i\sin\left(-\dfrac{3\pi}{5}\right)\right)$

d $z = \sqrt{2}\left(\cos\dfrac{\pi}{12} + i\sin\dfrac{\pi}{12}\right), \sqrt{2}\left(\cos\dfrac{3\pi}{4} + i\sin\dfrac{3\pi}{4}\right),$

$\sqrt{2}\left(\cos\left(-\dfrac{7\pi}{12}\right) + i\sin\left(\dfrac{-7\pi}{12}\right)\right)$

e $z = \sqrt{2}\left(\cos\left(-\dfrac{\pi}{12}\right) + i\sin\left(-\dfrac{\pi}{12}\right)\right),$

$\sqrt{2}\left(\cos\left(\dfrac{5\pi}{12}\right) + i\sin\left(\dfrac{5\pi}{12}\right)\right), \sqrt{2}\left(\cos\left(\dfrac{11\pi}{12}\right) + i\sin\left(\dfrac{11\pi}{12}\right)\right),$

$\sqrt{2}\left(\cos\left(-\dfrac{7\pi}{12}\right) + i\sin\left(-\dfrac{7\pi}{12}\right)\right)$

f $z = 4\left(\cos\left(-\dfrac{5\pi}{18}\right) + i\sin\left(-\dfrac{5\pi}{18}\right)\right),$

$4\left(\cos\left(\dfrac{7\pi}{18}\right) + i\sin\left(\dfrac{7\pi}{18}\right)\right), 4\left(\cos\left(-\dfrac{17\pi}{18}\right) + i\sin\left(-\dfrac{17\pi}{18}\right)\right)$

3 a $z = 5^{\frac{1}{4}}e^{0.23i}, 5^{\frac{1}{4}}e^{1.80i}, 5^{\frac{1}{4}}e^{-1.34i}, 5^{\frac{1}{4}}e^{-2.91i}$

b $z = \sqrt{3}e^{-0.29i}, \sqrt{3}e^{1.80i}, \sqrt{3}e^{-2.39i}$

c $z = \sqrt{2}e^{0.57i}, z = \sqrt{2}e^{2.14i}, z = \sqrt{2}e^{-1.00i}, z = \sqrt{2}e^{-2.57i}$

4 a $z = -\dfrac{1}{2} + \dfrac{\sqrt{3}}{2}i, -2, -\dfrac{1}{2} - \dfrac{\sqrt{3}}{2}i$

b

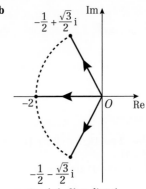

c centre $(-1, 0)$ radius 1

5 a $z = 1, \cos\left(\dfrac{2\pi}{5}\right) + i\sin\left(\dfrac{2\pi}{5}\right), \cos\left(\dfrac{4\pi}{5}\right) + i\sin\left(\dfrac{4\pi}{5}\right),$

$\cos\left(-\dfrac{2\pi}{5}\right) + i\sin\left(-\dfrac{2\pi}{5}\right), \cos\left(-\dfrac{4\pi}{5}\right) + i\sin\left(-\dfrac{4\pi}{5}\right)$

b $z_1 + z_2 + z_3 + z_4 + z_5 = 0$

$1 + \cos\dfrac{2\pi}{5} + i\sin\dfrac{2\pi}{5} + \cos\dfrac{4\pi}{5} + i\sin\dfrac{4\pi}{5} + \cos\left(-\dfrac{2\pi}{5}\right)$

$+ i\sin\left(-\dfrac{2\pi}{5}\right) + \cos\left(-\dfrac{4\pi}{5}\right) + i\sin\left(-\dfrac{4\pi}{5}\right) = 0$

$\Rightarrow 1 + \cos\dfrac{2\pi}{5} + i\sin\dfrac{2\pi}{5} + \cos\dfrac{4\pi}{5} + i\sin\dfrac{4\pi}{5}$

$+ \cos\left(\dfrac{2\pi}{5}\right) - i\sin\left(\dfrac{2\pi}{5}\right) + \cos\left(\dfrac{4\pi}{5}\right) - i\sin\left(\dfrac{4\pi}{5}\right) = 0$

$\Rightarrow 1 + 2\cos\dfrac{2\pi}{5} + 2\cos\dfrac{4\pi}{5} = 0$

$\cos\dfrac{2\pi}{5} + \cos\dfrac{4\pi}{5} = -\dfrac{1}{2}$

6 a $r = 4, \theta = -\dfrac{2\pi}{3}$

b $z = \sqrt{2}e^{-\frac{\pi i}{6}}, \sqrt{2}e^{\frac{\pi i}{3}}, \sqrt{2}e^{\frac{5\pi i}{6}}, \sqrt{2}e^{-\frac{2\pi i}{3}}$

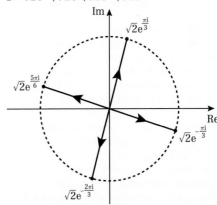

7 $\sqrt{2}e^{-\frac{7\pi i}{12}}, \sqrt{2}e^{-\frac{\pi i}{12}}, \sqrt{2}e^{\frac{5\pi i}{12}}, \sqrt{2}e^{\frac{11\pi i}{12}}$

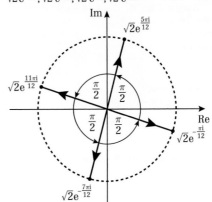

8 a $r = \sqrt{8}, \theta = \dfrac{\pi}{6}$

  b $w = 4\mathrm{e}^{\frac{2\pi i}{9}}, w = 4\mathrm{e}^{\frac{8\pi i}{9}}, w = 4\mathrm{e}^{-\frac{4\pi i}{9}}$

9 a $\mathrm{e}^{\frac{\pi i}{4}}, \mathrm{i}, \mathrm{e}^{\frac{3\pi i}{4}}, -1, \mathrm{e}^{\frac{5\pi i}{4}}, -\mathrm{i}, \mathrm{e}^{\frac{7\pi i}{4}}$

  b Expressing as a product of the linear factors:

  $(z + 1)(z - \mathrm{i})(z + \mathrm{i})\left(z - \dfrac{\sqrt{2}}{2} - \dfrac{\sqrt{2}}{2}\mathrm{i}\right)\left(z - \dfrac{\sqrt{2}}{2} + \dfrac{\sqrt{2}}{2}\mathrm{i}\right)$

  $\left(z + \dfrac{\sqrt{2}}{2} + \dfrac{\sqrt{2}}{2}\mathrm{i}\right)\left(z + \dfrac{\sqrt{2}}{2} - \dfrac{\sqrt{2}}{2}\mathrm{i}\right)$

  $= (z + 1)(z^2 + 1)(z^2 - \sqrt{2}\,z + 1)(z^2 + \sqrt{2}\,z + 1)$

  $= (z + 1)(z^2 + 1)(z^4 + 1)$

  Therefore $(z^2 + 1)$ and $(z^4 + 1)$ are factors.

Challenge

a $1, \mathrm{e}^{\frac{\pi i}{3}}, \mathrm{e}^{-\frac{\pi i}{3}}, \mathrm{e}^{\frac{2\pi i}{3}}, \mathrm{e}^{-\frac{2\pi i}{3}}, \mathrm{e}^{\pi i}$

b Rewrite the equation as $\left(1 + \dfrac{1}{z}\right)^6 = 1$.

  Then $1 + \dfrac{1}{z} = \mathrm{e}^{\frac{k\pi i}{3}}$ for some $k \in \mathbb{Z}$, by **a**.

  So, $\dfrac{1}{z} = \mathrm{e}^{\frac{k\pi i}{3}} - 1$

Chapter review 3

1 a $\mathrm{e}^{\mathrm{i}\theta} = \cos\theta + \mathrm{i}\sin\theta, \ \mathrm{e}^{-\mathrm{i}\theta} = \cos\theta - \mathrm{i}\sin\theta$

  $\mathrm{e}^{\mathrm{i}\theta} + \mathrm{e}^{-\mathrm{i}\theta} = 2\cos\theta$, so $\cos\theta = \frac{1}{2}(\mathrm{e}^{\mathrm{i}\theta} + \mathrm{e}^{-\mathrm{i}\theta})$

  b $\cos A \cos B = \frac{1}{2}(\mathrm{e}^{\mathrm{i}A} + \mathrm{e}^{-\mathrm{i}A}) \times \frac{1}{2}(\mathrm{e}^{\mathrm{i}B} + \mathrm{e}^{-\mathrm{i}B})$

  $= \frac{1}{4}(\mathrm{e}^{\mathrm{i}A} + \mathrm{e}^{-\mathrm{i}A})(\mathrm{e}^{\mathrm{i}B} + \mathrm{e}^{-\mathrm{i}B})$

  $= \frac{1}{4}(\mathrm{e}^{\mathrm{i}(A+B)} + \mathrm{e}^{\mathrm{i}(A-B)} + \mathrm{e}^{\mathrm{i}(B-A)} + \mathrm{e}^{-\mathrm{i}(A+B)})$

  $= \frac{1}{4}((\mathrm{e}^{\mathrm{i}(A+B)} + \mathrm{e}^{-\mathrm{i}(A+B)}) + (\mathrm{e}^{\mathrm{i}(A-B)} + \mathrm{e}^{-\mathrm{i}(A-B)}))$

  $= \frac{1}{4}(2\cos(A + B) + 2\cos(A - B))$

  $= \dfrac{\cos(A + B) + \cos(A - B)}{2}$

2 $n = 1$; LHS $= r(\cos\theta + \mathrm{i}\sin\theta)$

  RHS $= r^1(\cos\theta + \mathrm{i}\sin\theta) = r(\cos\theta + \mathrm{i}\sin\theta)$

  As LHS = RHS, the equation holds for $n = 1$.

  Assume the equation holds for $n = k, k \in \mathbb{Z}^+$.

  i.e. $z^k = r^k(\cos k\theta + \mathrm{i}\sin k\theta)$

  With $n = k + 1$, the equation becomes:

  $z^{k+1} = z^k \times z$

  $= r^k(\cos k\theta + \mathrm{i}\sin k\theta) \times r(\cos\theta + \mathrm{i}\sin\theta)$

  $= r^{k+1}((\cos k\theta\cos\theta - \sin k\theta\sin\theta) +$

  $\quad \mathrm{i}(\sin k\theta\cos\theta + \cos k\theta\sin\theta))$

  $= r^{k+1}(\cos(k + 1)\theta + \mathrm{i}\sin(k + 1)\theta)$

  by the addition formulae.

  Therefore, the equation holds when $n = k + 1$.

  b $\cot 3\theta = \dfrac{1 - 3\tan^2\theta}{3\tan\theta - \tan^3\theta} = \dfrac{1 - 3\cot^{-2}\theta}{3\cot^{-1}\theta - \cot^{-3}\theta}$

  $= \dfrac{\cot^3\theta - 3\cot\theta}{3\cot^2\theta - 1}$

3 $\cos 7x + \mathrm{i}\sin 7x$

4 a 16

  b 256

5 a Let $z = \cos\theta + \mathrm{i}\sin\theta$

  $z^n = (\cos\theta + \mathrm{i}\sin\theta)^n = \cos n\theta + \mathrm{i}\sin n\theta$

  $\dfrac{1}{z^n} = z^{-n} = (\cos\theta + \mathrm{i}\sin\theta)^{-n} = \cos(-n\theta) + \mathrm{i}\sin(-n\theta)$

  $= \cos n\theta - \mathrm{i}\sin n\theta$

  $\Rightarrow z^n + \dfrac{1}{z^n} = \cos n\theta + \mathrm{i}\sin n\theta + \cos n\theta - \mathrm{i}\sin n\theta = 2\cos n\theta$

b $\left(z^2 + \dfrac{1}{z^2}\right)^3 = 2\cos 6\theta + 6\cos 2\theta$

c $a = \frac{1}{4}, b = \frac{3}{4}$

d $\displaystyle\int_0^{\frac{\pi}{6}} \cos^3 2\theta\, \mathrm{d}\theta = \int_0^{\frac{\pi}{6}} \left(\tfrac{1}{4}\cos 6\theta + \tfrac{3}{4}\cos 2\theta\right)\mathrm{d}\theta$

  $= \left[\tfrac{1}{24}\sin 6\theta + \tfrac{3}{8}\sin 2\theta\right]_0^{\frac{\pi}{6}} = \tfrac{3}{16}\sqrt{3}$

6 a If $z = \cos\theta + \mathrm{i}\sin\theta$, then $2\cos\theta = z + \dfrac{1}{z}$

  So $2^5\cos^5\theta = \left(z + \dfrac{1}{z}\right)^5$

  $= z^5 + {}^5C_1 z^4\left(\dfrac{1}{z}\right) + {}^5C_2 z^3\left(\dfrac{1}{z^2}\right) + {}^5C_3 z^2\left(\dfrac{1}{z^3}\right) + {}^5C_4 z\left(\dfrac{1}{z^4}\right) + \dfrac{1}{z^5}$

  $= z^5 + 5z^3 + 10z + \dfrac{10}{z} + \dfrac{5}{z^3} + \dfrac{1}{z^5}$

  $= \left(z^5 + \dfrac{1}{z^5}\right) + 5\left(z^3 + \dfrac{1}{z^3}\right) + 10\left(z + \dfrac{1}{z}\right)$

  $= 2\cos 5\theta + 5(2\cos 3\theta) + 10(2\cos\theta)$

  So $32\cos^5\theta = 2\cos 5\theta + 10\cos 3\theta + 20\cos\theta$

  $\cos^5\theta = \tfrac{1}{16}(\cos 5\theta + 5\cos 3\theta + 10\cos\theta)$

  b $\dfrac{16}{15}$

7 a If $z = \cos\theta + \mathrm{i}\sin\theta$, then $2\mathrm{i}\sin\theta = z - \dfrac{1}{z}$

  So $(2\mathrm{i})^6\sin^6\theta = \left(z - \dfrac{1}{z}\right)^6$

  $= z^6 - {}^6C_1 z^5\left(\dfrac{1}{z}\right) + {}^6C_2 z^4\left(\dfrac{1}{z^2}\right) - {}^6C_3 z^3\left(\dfrac{1}{z^3}\right)$

  $\quad + {}^6C_4 z^2\left(\dfrac{1}{z^4}\right) - {}^6C_5 z\left(\dfrac{1}{z^5}\right) + \dfrac{1}{z^6}$

  $= z^6 - 6z^4 + 15z^2 - 20 + \dfrac{15}{z^2} - \dfrac{6}{z^4} + \dfrac{1}{z^6}$

  $= \left(z^6 + \dfrac{1}{z^6}\right) - 6\left(z^4 + \dfrac{1}{z^4}\right) + 15\left(z^2 + \dfrac{1}{z^2}\right) - 20$

  $= 2\cos 6\theta - 6(2\cos 4\theta) + 15(2\cos 2\theta) - 20$

  So, $-64\sin^6\theta = 2\cos 6\theta - 12\cos 4\theta + 30\cos 2\theta - 20$

  b $\cos^6\theta \equiv \tfrac{1}{32}(\cos 6\theta + 6\cos 4\theta + 15\cos 2\theta + 10)$

  c $\dfrac{\pi}{4}$

8 $(\cos\theta + \mathrm{i}\sin\theta)^6 = \cos 6\theta + \mathrm{i}\sin 6\theta$

  $= \cos^6\theta + {}^6C_1\cos^5\theta(\mathrm{i}\sin\theta) + {}^6C_2\cos^4\theta(\mathrm{i}\sin\theta)^2$

  $\quad + {}^6C_3\cos^3\theta(\mathrm{i}\sin\theta)^3 + {}^6C_4\cos^2\theta(\mathrm{i}\sin\theta)^4$

  $\quad + {}^6C_5\cos\theta(\mathrm{i}\sin\theta)^5 + (\mathrm{i}\sin\theta)^6$

  $= \cos^6\theta + 6\mathrm{i}\cos^5\theta\sin\theta - 15\cos^4\theta\sin^2\theta - 20\mathrm{i}\cos^3\theta\sin^3\theta$

  $\quad + 15\cos^2\theta\sin^4\theta + 6\mathrm{i}\cos\theta\sin^5\theta - \sin^6\theta$

  Equating imaginary parts gives

  $\sin 6\theta = 6\cos^5\theta\sin\theta - 20\cos^3\theta\sin^3\theta + 6\cos\theta\sin^5\theta$

  $= 2\sin\theta\cos\theta(3\cos^4\theta - 10\cos^2\theta\sin^2\theta + 3\sin^4\theta)$

  $= \sin 2\theta(3\cos^4\theta - 10\cos^2\theta(1 - \cos^2\theta) + 3(1 - \cos^2\theta)^2)$

  $= \sin 2\theta(3\cos^4\theta - 10\cos^2\theta(1 - \cos^2\theta) + 3(1 - 2\cos^2\theta +$

  $\quad \cos^4\theta))$

  $= \sin 2\theta(16\cos^4\theta - 16\cos^2\theta + 3)$

9 a $(\cos\theta + \mathrm{i}\sin\theta)^5 = \cos 5\theta + \mathrm{i}\sin 5\theta$

  $= \cos^5\theta + {}^5C_1\cos^4\theta(\mathrm{i}\sin\theta) + {}^5C_2\cos^3\theta(\mathrm{i}\sin\theta)^2$

  $\quad + {}^5C_3\cos^2\theta(\mathrm{i}\sin\theta)^3 + {}^5C_4\cos\theta(\mathrm{i}\sin\theta)^4 + (\mathrm{i}\sin\theta)^5$

  $= \cos^5\theta + 5\mathrm{i}\cos^4\theta\sin\theta - 10\cos^3\theta\sin^2\theta - 10\mathrm{i}\cos^2\theta\sin^3\theta$

  $\quad + 5\cos\theta\sin^4\theta + \mathrm{i}\sin^5\theta$

  Equating real parts gives

  $\cos 5\theta = \cos^5\theta - 10\cos^3\theta\sin^2\theta + 5\cos\theta\sin^4\theta$

  $= \cos^5\theta - 10\cos^3\theta(1 - \cos^2\theta) + 5\cos\theta(1 - \cos^2\theta)^2$

  $= \cos^5\theta - 10\cos^3\theta(1 - \cos^2\theta) + 5\cos\theta(1 - 2\cos^2\theta +$

  $\quad \cos^4\theta)$

  $= 16\cos^5\theta - 20\cos^3\theta + 5\cos\theta$

  b $-1, \frac{1}{4}(1 + \sqrt{5}) \approx 0.809, \frac{1}{4}(1 - \sqrt{5}) \approx -0.309$

10 a Let $z = \cos\theta + i\sin\theta$

$$\left(z - \frac{1}{z}\right)^5 = (2i\sin\theta)^5 = 32i^5\sin^5\theta = 32i\sin^5\theta$$

$$= z^5 + 5z^4\left(-\frac{1}{z}\right) + 10z^3\left(-\frac{1}{z}\right)^2$$
$$\quad + 10z^2\left(-\frac{1}{z}\right)^3 + 5z\left(-\frac{1}{z}\right)^4 + \left(-\frac{1}{z}\right)^5$$

$$= z^5 - 5z^3 + 10z - \frac{10}{z} + \frac{5}{z^3} - \frac{1}{z^5}$$

$$= \left(z^5 - \frac{1}{z^5}\right) - 5\left(z^3 - \frac{1}{z^3}\right) + 10\left(z - \frac{1}{z}\right)$$

$$= 2i\sin 5\theta - 5(2i\sin 3\theta) + 10(2i\sin\theta)$$

So $32i\sin^5\theta = 2i\sin 5\theta - 10i\sin 3\theta + 20i\sin\theta$

$$\Rightarrow \sin^5\theta = \frac{1}{16}(\sin 5\theta - 5\sin 3\theta + 10\sin\theta)$$

b $0, \dfrac{\pi}{6}, \dfrac{5\pi}{6}$

11 a $(\cos\theta + i\sin\theta)^5 = \cos 5\theta + i\sin 5\theta$

$$= \cos^5\theta + 5i\cos^4\theta\sin\theta + 10i^2\cos^3\theta\sin^2\theta$$
$$\quad + 10i^3\cos^2\theta\sin^3\theta + 5i^4\cos\theta\sin^4\theta + i^5\sin^5\theta$$

$$\Rightarrow \cos 5\theta + i\sin 5\theta = \cos^5\theta + 5i\cos^4\theta\sin\theta$$
$$\quad - 10\cos^3\theta\sin^2\theta - 10i\cos^2\theta\sin^3\theta$$
$$\quad + 5\cos\theta\sin^4\theta - i\sin^5\theta$$

Equating the real parts:

$$\cos 5\theta = \cos^5\theta - 10\cos^3\theta\sin^2\theta + 5\cos\theta\sin^4\theta$$
$$= \cos\theta(\cos^4\theta - 10\cos^2\theta(1 - \cos^2\theta) + 5(1 - \cos^2\theta)^2)$$
$$= \cos\theta(16\cos^4\theta - 20\cos^2\theta + 5)$$

b If $\cos 5\theta = 0$, then $\cos\theta(16\cos^4\theta - 20\cos^2\theta + 5) = 0$
If $x = \cos\theta$, then $x(16x^4 - 20x^2 + 5) = 0$ which has

solutions $x = 0$ and $x^2 = \dfrac{20 \pm \sqrt{80}}{32} = \dfrac{5 \pm \sqrt{5}}{8}$, by the

quadratic formula.

Since $\theta = \dfrac{\pi}{10}$ is a solution to $\cos 5\theta = 0$, $x = \cos\dfrac{\pi}{10}$

must be a solution to $x(16x^4 - 20x^2 + 5) = 0$.

Since $x \neq 0$, $\cos^2\left(\dfrac{\pi}{10}\right) = x^2 = \dfrac{5 \pm \sqrt{5}}{8}$, for some choice

of sign.

To find which, note that $\theta = \dfrac{3\pi}{10}$ gives another

solution and $\cos\dfrac{\pi}{10} > \cos\dfrac{3\pi}{10}$ by looking at the graph.

Hence $\theta = \dfrac{\pi}{10}$ corresponds to the larger of the two

solutions and $\cos^2\left(\dfrac{\pi}{10}\right) = \dfrac{5 + \sqrt{5}}{8}$

c $\cos^2\left(\dfrac{3\pi}{10}\right) = \dfrac{5 - \sqrt{5}}{8}$, $\cos^2\left(\dfrac{7\pi}{10}\right) = \dfrac{5 - \sqrt{5}}{8}$,

$\cos^2\left(\dfrac{9\pi}{10}\right) = \dfrac{5 + \sqrt{5}}{8}$

12 a $\tan 3\theta \equiv \dfrac{3\tan\theta - \tan^3\theta}{1 - 3\tan^2\theta}$

13 a $4\sqrt{2}\left(\cos\left(-\dfrac{\pi}{4}\right) + i\sin\left(-\dfrac{\pi}{4}\right)\right)$

b $z = \sqrt{2}e^{-\frac{\pi i}{20}}, \sqrt{2}e^{\frac{7\pi i}{20}}, \sqrt{2}e^{\frac{3\pi i}{4}}, \sqrt{2}e^{-\frac{9\pi i}{20}}, \sqrt{2}e^{-\frac{17\pi i}{20}}$

c

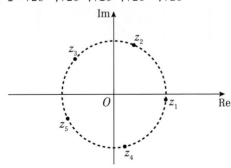

14 a $\sqrt{2}e^{-\frac{i\pi}{12}}, \sqrt{2}e^{\frac{7i\pi}{12}}, \sqrt{2}e^{-\frac{9i\pi}{12}}$

b

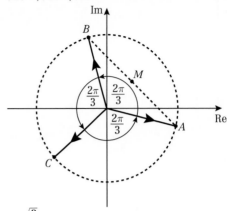

c $r = \dfrac{\sqrt{2}}{2}, \theta = \dfrac{\pi}{4}$

d $-\dfrac{i}{8}$

Challenge

Rewrite the equation as $\left(1 + \dfrac{1}{z}\right)^6 = 1$.

Then $1 + \dfrac{1}{z} = e^{\frac{k\pi i}{3}}$ for some $k \in \mathbb{Z}$, since it is a sixth root of

unity.

So $\dfrac{1}{z} = e^{\frac{k\pi i}{3}} - 1$

$$z = \frac{1}{e^{\frac{k\pi i}{3}} - 1} = \frac{1}{e^{\frac{k\pi i}{6}}\left(e^{\frac{k\pi i}{6}} - e^{-\frac{k\pi i}{6}}\right)} = \frac{1}{e^{\frac{k\pi i}{6}}\left(2i\sin\frac{k\pi}{6}\right)} = -\frac{ie^{-\frac{k\pi i}{6}}}{2\sin\frac{k\pi}{6}}$$

$$= -\frac{i(\cos\frac{k\pi}{6} - i\sin\frac{k\pi}{6})}{2\sin\frac{k\pi}{6}} = -\frac{\sin\frac{k\pi}{6} + i\cos\frac{k\pi}{6}}{2\sin\frac{k\pi}{6}} = -\frac{1}{2} - \frac{1}{2}i\cot\frac{k\pi}{6}$$

So the points lie on the straight line $z = -\dfrac{1}{2} + it$ for $t \in \mathbb{R}$.

CHAPTER 4
Prior knowledge check

1

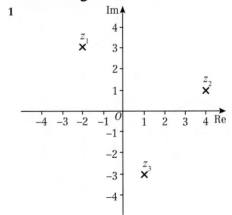

2

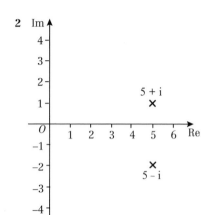

3

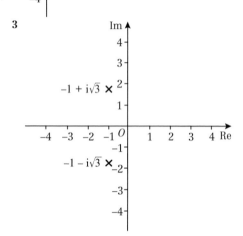

Exercise 4A

1 a

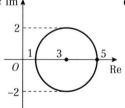

b

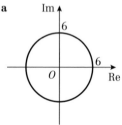

c

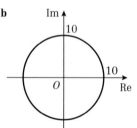

d

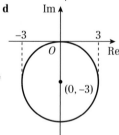

e

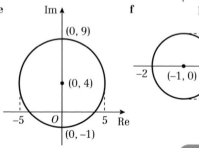

f

g

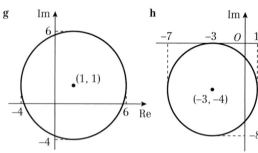

h

i

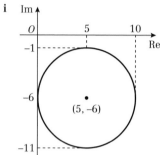

2 a

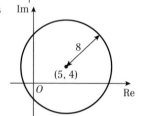

b i $(4 + \sqrt{39})$i and $(4 - \sqrt{39})$i

   ii $5 + 4\sqrt{3}$ and $5 - 4\sqrt{3}$

3 a

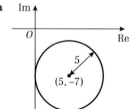

b $(x - 5)^2 + (y + 7)^2 = 25$

c $2\arctan\left(\frac{5}{7}\right) - \frac{\pi}{2} = -0.330$ rad (3 s.f.)

4 a $(x - 4)^2 + (y - 3)^2 = 8^2$

b

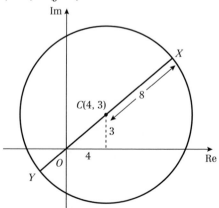

c $|z|_{\min} = 3$, $|z|_{\max} = 13$

Online Worked solutions are available in SolutionBank.

5 a

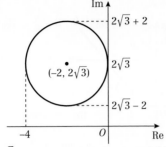

b $\frac{\pi}{2}$ **c** 2.51 rad

6 a 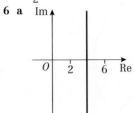   **b**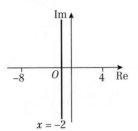

c 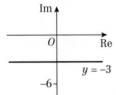   **d**

$y = 2.5$

-3

e 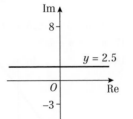   **f**

$y = \frac{-7}{2}$

g 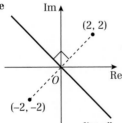   **h**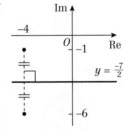

$y = 3x - 6$

i

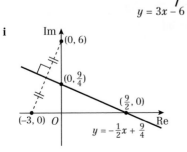

$y = -\frac{1}{2}x + \frac{9}{4}$

j

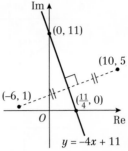

$y = -4x + 11$

7 a 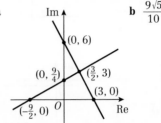   **b** $\frac{9\sqrt{5}}{10}$

8 a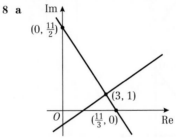

b $y = -\frac{3}{2}x + \frac{11}{2}$ **c** $\frac{11\sqrt{13}}{13}$

9 a 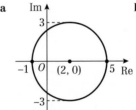   **b**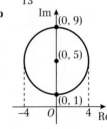

c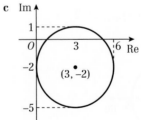

10 a 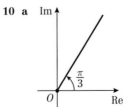   **b**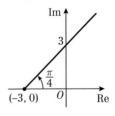

c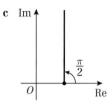

d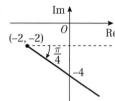

e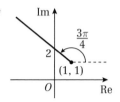

f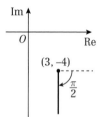

g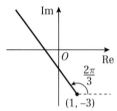

h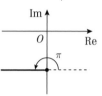

i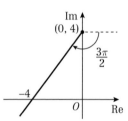

11 a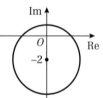

b Use the cosine rule to find $|z|^2 + 2|z| - 5 = 0$, solve to get $|z| = -1 + \sqrt{6}$

12 a $|z_{\text{max}}| = 6\sqrt{2} + 4$ and $|z_{\text{min}}| = 6\sqrt{2} - 4$

b $(-2.38, \pi)$

13 a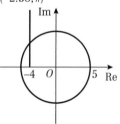

b $z = -4 + 3i$

14 a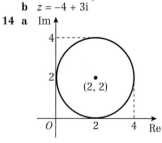

b $z = (2 + \sqrt{3}) + 3i$

15 a,b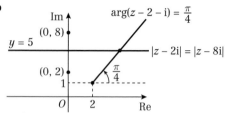

c $z = 6 + 5i$

16 a,b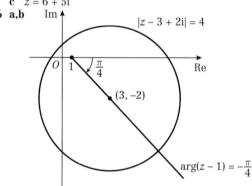

c $a = 3 + 2\sqrt{2}, b = -2 - 2\sqrt{2}$

17 a $z = 4 + 4i\sqrt{3}$ **b** $\arg(z - 8) = \frac{2\pi}{3}$

18 a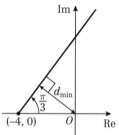

b Hence the minimum value of $|z|$ is $|z|_{\text{min}} = 2\sqrt{3}$

19 a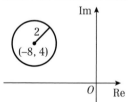

b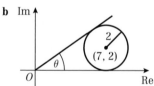

Maximum value of $\arg(z + 15 - 2i) = \theta$

$\sin\left(\frac{\theta}{2}\right) = \frac{2}{\sqrt{2^2 + 7^2}} = \frac{2}{\sqrt{53}}$

$\Rightarrow \theta = 2\arcsin\left(\frac{2}{\sqrt{53}}\right)$

c $\left(-8 + \sqrt{2}, 4 - \sqrt{2}\right)$ and $\left(-8 - \sqrt{2}, 4 + \sqrt{2}\right)$

Challenge

$0.37 < \theta < 2.77$

Exercise 4B

1 a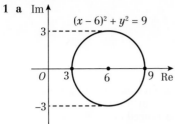
Im, $(x - 6)^2 + y^2 = 9$

b $\left(x + \frac{19}{15}\right)^2 + y^2 = \frac{256}{225}$
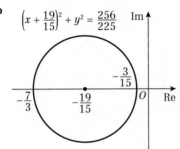

c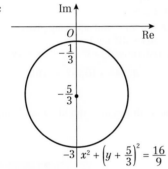
$x^2 + \left(y + \frac{5}{3}\right)^2 = \frac{16}{9}$

d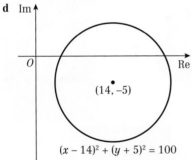
$(x - 14)^2 + (y + 5)^2 = 100$

e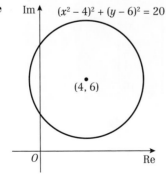
$(x^2 - 4)^2 + (y - 6)^2 = 20$

f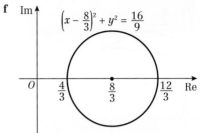
$\left(x - \frac{8}{3}\right)^2 + y^2 = \frac{16}{9}$

2 a $\arg\left(\frac{z}{z + 3}\right) = \frac{\pi}{4}$
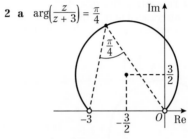

b $\arg\left(\frac{z - 3i}{z + 4}\right) = \frac{\pi}{6}$
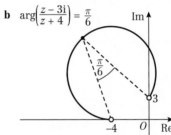

c $\arg\left(\frac{z}{z - 2}\right) = \frac{\pi}{3}$
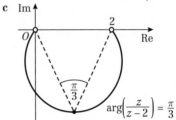

d $\arg\left(\frac{z - 3i}{z - 5}\right) = \frac{\pi}{4}$
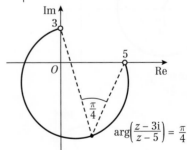

e $\arg z - \arg(z - 2 + 3i) = \frac{\pi}{3}$
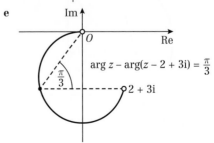

f $\arg\left(\dfrac{z-4i}{z+4}\right) = \dfrac{\pi}{2}$

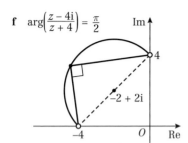

3 a Substituting $x + iy$ for z and squaring gives
$(x + 1)^2 + (y + 1)^2 = 4((x + 4)^2 + (y - 2)^2)$
which can be rearranged to $(x + 5)^2 + (y - 3)^2 = 8$,
which is the equation of a circle with centre $(-5, 3)$.

b $2\sqrt{2}$

4 a $\arg z - \arg(z + 4) = \dfrac{\pi}{4}$

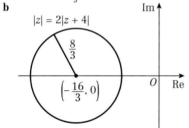

b $(-2, 2)$
c $2\sqrt{2}$
d $(x + 2)^2 + (y - 2)^2 = 8$
e $6\pi + 4$

5 a Substituting $x + iy$ for z and squaring gives
$x^2 + y^2 = 4((x + 4)^2 + y^2)$
which can be rearranged to $(x + \frac{16}{3})^2 + y^2 = \frac{64}{9}$,
which is the equation of a circle with centre $\left(-\frac{16}{3}, 0\right)$
and radius $\frac{8}{3}$

b

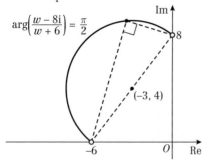

$|z| = 2|z + 4|$

c $-\dfrac{8}{3} \leqslant \text{Im}(z) \leqslant \dfrac{8}{3}$

6 $\dfrac{\pi}{4} \leqslant \arg z \leqslant \dfrac{3\pi}{4}$

7 a

$\arg\left(\dfrac{w - 8i}{w + 6}\right) = \dfrac{\pi}{2}$

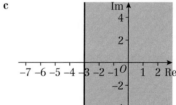

b $(x + 3)^2 + (y - 4)^2 = 25, x < 0, y > 0$
c $a = \dfrac{\pi}{2}, b = \pi$
d $-8 < \text{Re}(z) < 0$

8 $(x + 1)^2 + (y + 2)^2 = 8, y > 0$

9 a $\arg\left(\dfrac{z + 2}{z + 5}\right) = \dfrac{\pi}{4}$

b $\arg\left(\dfrac{z - i}{z - 4i}\right) = \dfrac{\pi}{6}$

c $\arg\left(\dfrac{z - 6 - i}{z - 1 - 2i}\right) = \dfrac{2\pi}{3}$

10 a Substituting $x + iy$ for z and squaring gives
$(x + 3)^2 + y^2 = 9((x - 5)^2 + y^2)$
which can be rearranged to
$x^2 + y^2 - 12x + 27 = 0$.

b

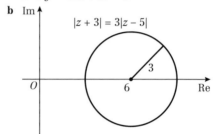

$|z + 3| = 3|z - 5|$

c $3\sqrt{3}\left(\cos\dfrac{\pi}{6} + i \sin\dfrac{\pi}{6}\right)$

11 a $z_1 = 6i, z_2 = 3, k = 2$

b Substituting $x + iy$ for z and squaring gives
$x^2 + (y - 6)^2 = 4((x - 3)^2 + y^2)$
which can be rearranged to $x^2 + y^2 - 8x + 4y = 0$.

c $\alpha = -\dfrac{3\pi}{4}$ **d** $\left(4 - \sqrt{10}, -2 - \sqrt{10}\right)$

Challenge
The locus is an ellipse with foci at a and at $-a$, and major axis of length b.

Exercise 4C

1 a

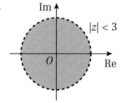

$|z| < 3$

b

c

d

$-2 - 8i$

e

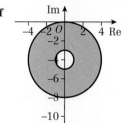

f

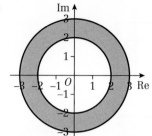

g

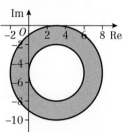

2

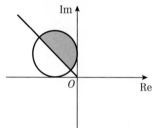

3

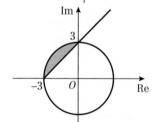

4

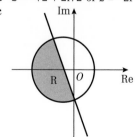

$|z - 2| = |z - 6 - 8i|$ $\arg(z - 4 - 2i) = \frac{\pi}{2}$

$\arg(z - 4 - 2i) = 0$

5 a i $y = -2\sqrt{2}x - 2\sqrt{2}$ **ii** $(x + 1)^2 + y^2 = 9$

b $z = -\sqrt{2} + 2i\sqrt{2}$ or $z = -2i$

c

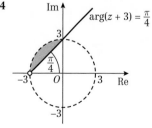

Challenge

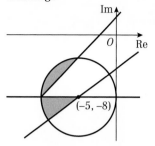

$(-5, -8)$

Exercise 4D

1 a

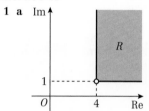

b

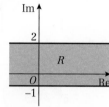

c

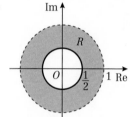

d

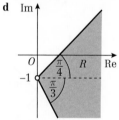

2

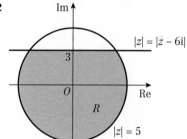

$|z| = |z - 6i|$

$|z| = 5$

3

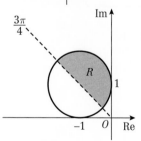

$\frac{3\pi}{4}$

4

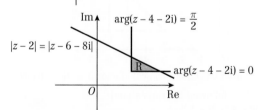

$\arg(z + 3) = \frac{\pi}{4}$

5 a

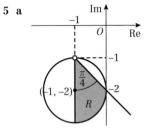

b

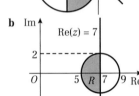

6 a

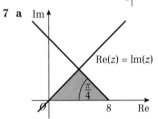

b $\dfrac{5\pi}{6} < \arg z < \dfrac{7\pi}{6}$

7 a

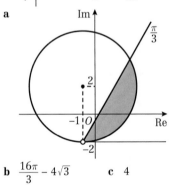

b 16

8 a

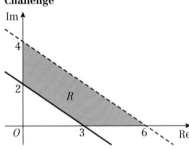

b $\dfrac{16\pi}{3} - 4\sqrt{3}$ **c** 4

Challenge

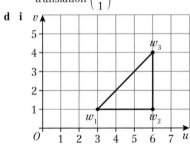

Exercise 4E

1 a i

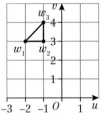

ii Translation $\begin{pmatrix} -3 \\ 2 \end{pmatrix}$

b i

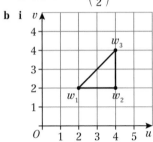

ii Enlargement by scale factor 2 with centre O

c i

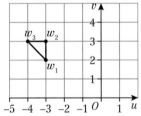

ii Rotation $\dfrac{\pi}{2}$ anticlockwise about O followed by
translation $\begin{pmatrix} -2 \\ 1 \end{pmatrix}$

d i

ii Enlargement by scale factor 3 with centre O
followed by translation $\begin{pmatrix} 0 \\ -2 \end{pmatrix}$

2 $w = 4z - 8 + 12i$

3 $w = 4\mathrm{i}z$

4 $(u + 1)^2 + (v - 3)^2 = 64$

5 a

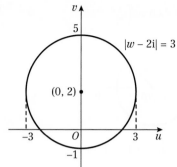

b

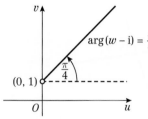

c

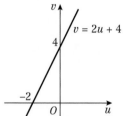

6 a Circle with centre $(0, 0)$ and radius $\frac{1}{2}$

  b Half-line from $(0, 0)$ at an angle of $-\frac{\pi}{4}$

  c Circle with centre $(-1, -\frac{1}{2})$ and radius $\frac{\sqrt{5}}{2}$

7 a The circle in the z-plane is $|z| = 3$, so the corresponding locus in the w-plane will be such that $|w| = |z|^2 = 9$, i.e. a circle with centre $(0, 0)$ and radius 9.
  $\arg w = \arg(z^2) = 2\arg z$
  Thus, if z moves around the circle $|z| = 3$ once, w will move around the circle $|w| = 9$ twice.

  b The non-negative real axis: $v = 0$, $u \geqslant 0$

  c The non-positive real axis: $v = 0$, $u \leqslant 0$

8 a i Substituting $u + \mathrm{i}v$ for w and squaring gives
  $u^2 + (v - 2)^2 = 4(u^2 + v^2)$ which can be rearranged to
  $u^2 + (v - \frac{2}{3})^2 = \frac{16}{9}$, which is the equation of a circle.

  ii Centre $(0, \frac{2}{3})$, radius $\frac{4}{3}$

  b

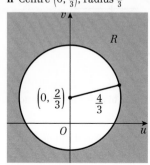

9 Rearrange to $z = \frac{2w - 1}{w}$, then $\left|\frac{2w - 1}{w}\right| = 2$
  $\Rightarrow |2w - 1| = 2|w| \Rightarrow |w - \frac{1}{2}| = |w|$
  This is the perpendicular bisector of $(0, 0)$ and $(\frac{1}{2}, 0)$, so is a line in the w-plane.

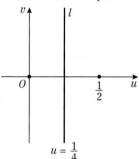

$u = \frac{1}{4}$

10 a Rearrange to get $z = -\frac{\mathrm{i}w - \mathrm{i}}{w - 1} \Rightarrow z - \mathrm{i} = -\frac{2\mathrm{i}w}{w - 1}$

  So $|z - \mathrm{i}| = \left|\frac{2w}{w - 1}\right| = 1 \Rightarrow 2|w| = |w - 1|$

  Substituting $u + \mathrm{i}v$ for w and squaring gives
  $4(u^2 + v^2) = (u - 1)^2 + v^2$, which can be rearranged
  to give $(u + \frac{1}{3})^2 + v^2 = \frac{4}{9}$, which is the equation of a
  circle with centre $(-\frac{1}{3}, 0)$ and radius $\frac{2}{3}$

  b

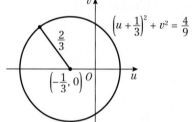

11 Rearrange to get $z = \frac{2w - 3}{w}$. Substitute $x + \mathrm{i}y$ for z and
  $u + \mathrm{i}v$ for w and rearrange to get $x = \frac{2u^2 - 3v + 2v^2}{u^2 + v^2}$
  and $y = \frac{3v}{u^2 + v^2}$
  Then the equation of line $2y = x$ gives
  $6v = 2u^2 - 3v + 2v^2$, which can be rearranged to
  $(u - \frac{3}{4})^2 + (v - \frac{3}{2})^2 = \frac{45}{16}$, which is the equation of a circle
  with centre $(\frac{3}{4}, \frac{3}{2})$ and radius $\frac{3\sqrt{5}}{4}$

12 a $v = 0$

  b

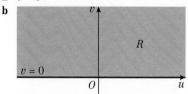

  c $|z| = 2 \Rightarrow 2|w + \mathrm{i}| = |w - \mathrm{i}|$, then substituting $u + \mathrm{i}v$ for
  w and squaring gives $4(u^2 + (v + 1)^2) = u^2 + (v - 1)^2$,
  which can be rearranged to give $u^2 + (v + \frac{5}{3})^2 = \frac{16}{9}$,
  which is the equation of a circle with centre $(0, -\frac{5}{3})$
  and radius $\frac{4}{3}$

13 Rearrange to get $z = \frac{w - 3\mathrm{i}}{w - 4}$. $|z| = 3 \Rightarrow 3|w - 4| = |w - 3\mathrm{i}|$,
  then substituting $u + \mathrm{i}v$ for w and squaring gives
  $9((u - 4)^2 + v^2) = u^2 + (v - 3)^2$, which can be rearranged
  to give $(u - \frac{9}{2})^2 + (v + \frac{3}{8})^2 = \frac{225}{64}$, which is the equation of
  a circle with centre $(\frac{9}{2}, -\frac{3}{8})$ and radius $\frac{15}{8}$

14 a Rearrange to get $z = \dfrac{1 - iw}{w}$ then substituting

$u + iv$ for w and rearranging gives

$z = \dfrac{u}{u^2 + v^2} - i\left(\dfrac{u^2 + v^2 + v}{u^2 + v^2}\right)$, so the real axis, $y = 0$,

becomes $\dfrac{u^2 + v^2 + v}{u^2 + v^2} = 0 \Rightarrow u^2 + v^2 + v = 0$, which

can be rearranged to $u^2 + (v + \frac{1}{2})^2 = \frac{1}{4}$, which is a

circle with centre $(0, \frac{1}{2})$ and radius $\frac{1}{2}$

b The line $x = 4$ becomes $\dfrac{u}{u^2 + v^2} = 4 \Rightarrow u = 4u^2 + 4v^2$

which can be rearranged to $(u - \frac{1}{8})^2 + v^2 = \frac{1}{64}$, which

is a circle with centre $\left(\frac{1}{8}, 0\right)$ and radius $\frac{1}{8}$

15 $w = z + \dfrac{4}{z} = z + \dfrac{4z^*}{|z|^2} = z + z^* = 2\text{Re}(z)$

Since $|z| = 2$, $-2 \leqslant 2\text{Re}(z) \leqslant 2$, so $w \in [-4, 4]$. $k = 4$.

16 Rearrange to get $z = \dfrac{1 - 3w}{w}$, then substituting $u + iv$

for w gives $z = \dfrac{u - 3u^2 - 3v^2}{u^2 + v^2} - i\left(\dfrac{v}{u^2 + v^2}\right)$, so the line

$2x - 2y + 7 = 0$ becomes $2(u - 3u^2 - 3v^2)$
$+ 2v + 7(u^2 + v^2) = 0$. This can be rearranged to
$(u + 1)^2 + (v + 1)^2 = 2$, which is the equation of a circle
with centre $(-1, -1)$ and radius $\sqrt{2}$.

Challenge
$w = iz + 2i$

Chapter review 4

1 a $(x + 1)^2 + (y - 1)^2 = 1$

b
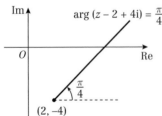

c $|z|_{min} = \sqrt{2} - 1$ **d** $|z - 1|_{min} = \sqrt{5} - 1$
$|z|_{max} = \sqrt{2} + 1$ $|z - 1|_{max} = \sqrt{5} + 1$

2 a
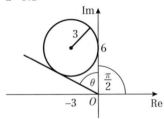

b $3\sqrt{2}$

3

Max value $= \dfrac{\pi}{2} + \theta$

$\sin\left(\dfrac{\theta}{2}\right) = \dfrac{3}{\sqrt{3^2 + 6^2}} = \dfrac{3}{\sqrt{45}} = \dfrac{1}{\sqrt{5}}$

$\Rightarrow \dfrac{\pi}{2} + \theta = \dfrac{\pi}{2} + 2\arcsin\left(\dfrac{1}{\sqrt{5}}\right)$

4 a Im

b $(3.96, 3.86)$ and $(1.14, -1.03)$

c $-\pi < \theta < -0.41, 0.41 < \theta < \pi$

5 a Im

b $y = \dfrac{11}{2}x + \dfrac{5}{4}$ **c** $\dfrac{\sqrt{5}}{10}$

6 a $y = \frac{1}{2}x + 3$

b $6 + 6i$

c Im

7 a i $y = x - 2$

    ii $(x - 2)^2 + y^2 = 8$

b $-2i, 4 + 2i$

c Im

8 a i $x = 2$

    ii line; perpendicular bisector of $(0, 0)$ and $(4, 0)$

b i $\left(x - \dfrac{16}{3}\right)^2 + y^2 = \dfrac{64}{9}$

    ii Circle with centre $(\frac{16}{3}, 0)$ and radius $\frac{8}{3}$

9 a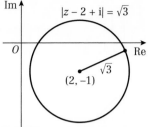
$|z - 2 + i| = \sqrt{3}$

centre $(2, -1)$, radius $\sqrt{3}$

b $m = \sqrt{3}$

c $\arg(z + i) = \dfrac{\pi}{3}$

d $a = \dfrac{1}{2} + i\left(\dfrac{\sqrt{3}}{2} - 1\right)$

10 a $\left(x - \dfrac{4}{3}\right)^2 + y^2 = \dfrac{25}{9}$

b $\dfrac{4 + \sqrt{34}}{6} + i\left(\dfrac{4 + \sqrt{34}}{6}\right)$

c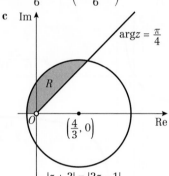
$\arg z = \dfrac{\pi}{4}$

$\left(\dfrac{4}{3}, 0\right)$

$|z + 2| = |2z - 1|$

11 a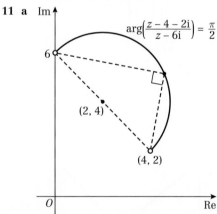
$\arg\left(\dfrac{z - 4 - 2i}{z - 6i}\right) = \dfrac{\pi}{2}$

$(2, 4)$, $(4, 2)$

b $2\sqrt{2}$

12 a Substituting $x + iy$ for z and squaring gives
$4((x + 3)^2 + y^2) = (x - 3)^2 + y^2$
which can be rearranged to $x^2 + y^2 + 10x + 9 = 0$.

b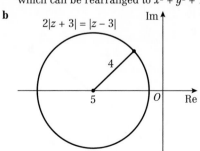
$2|z + 3| = |z - 3|$

c $\tan\theta = \pm\dfrac{3}{4}$

13 a A circular arc anticlockwise from $5 + 2i$ to $1 + 6i$. Since $\theta = \dfrac{\pi}{2}$, it is a semicircle. Centre is $(3, 4)$ and radius is $2\sqrt{2}$.

b $5 + 2\sqrt{2}$

14 a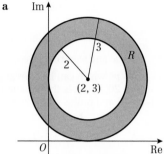

b 5π **c** yes

15 a $z = \dfrac{1}{w} = \dfrac{u}{u^2 + v^2} - i\left(\dfrac{v}{u^2 + v^2}\right)$, so the image of $x = \dfrac{1}{2}$ is $\dfrac{u}{u^2 + v^2} = \dfrac{1}{2}$, which can be rearranged to $(u - 1)^2 + v^2 = 1$, which is the equation of a circle with centre $(1, 0)$ and radius 1.

b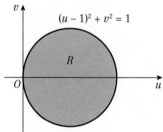
$(u - 1)^2 + v^2 = 1$

16 a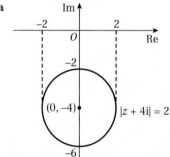
$(0, -4)$ $|z + 4i| = 2$

b 6

c i Circle with centre $(0, -8)$ and radius 4
  ii Circle with centre $(4, 0)$ and radius 2
 iii Circle with centre $(-4, 0)$ and radius 2
 iv Circle with centre $(0, 4)$ and radius 2

17 a $z = \dfrac{2 - iw}{w - 1}$
$= \dfrac{(2 + v)(u - 1) - uv}{(u - 1)^2 + v^2} + i\left(\dfrac{-u(u - 1) - v(2 + v)}{(u - 1)^2 + v^2}\right)$
So the line $x = 0$ has image $\dfrac{(2 + v)(u - 1) - uv}{(u - 1)^2 + v^2} = 0$, and this can be rearranged to $v = 2u - 2$, which is a line in the w-plane.

b $y = x$ has image with equation
$(2 + v)(u - 1) - uv = -u^2 + u - 2v - v^2$
which can be rearranged to $\left(u + \dfrac{1}{2}\right)^2 + \left(v + \dfrac{1}{2}\right)^2 = \dfrac{5}{2}$,
which is the equation of a circle with centre $\left(\dfrac{1}{2}, \dfrac{1}{2}\right)$ and radius $\sqrt{\dfrac{5}{2}} = \sqrt{\dfrac{10}{4}} = \dfrac{\sqrt{10}}{2}$

18 $z = \dfrac{4 - iw}{w + 1}$, so the image of the circle $|z| = 1$ is such that

$\left|\dfrac{4 - iw}{w + 1}\right| = 1 \Rightarrow |w + 4i| = |w + 1|$, and then substituting

$u + iv$ for w gives $u^2 + (v + 4)^2 = (u + 1)^2 + v^2$, which can be rearranged to $2u - 8v - 15 = 0$, which is the equation of line l.

19 Rearrange to get $z = \dfrac{w - 6}{w + 3i}$. $|z| = 2 \Rightarrow 2|w + 3i| = |w - 6|$,

then substituting $u + iv$ for w and squaring gives

$4(u^2 + (v + 3)^2) = (u - 6)^2 + v^2$, which can be rearranged to give $(u + 2)^2 + (v + 4)^2 = 20$, which is the equation of a circle with centre $(-2, -4)$ and radius $\sqrt{20} = 2\sqrt{5}$.

20 a $a = \frac{5}{2}, b = 0, c = -\frac{5}{2}$ **b** $\omega = 5$

21 a $a = \frac{17}{5}, b = -\frac{13}{5}, c = -\frac{13}{5}$ **b** $3 \pm \frac{4}{5}\sqrt{10}$

22 a $v = u - 1$

    b $x + y + 1 = 0$ has image $v + (u - 1) + ((u - 1)^2 + v^2) = 0$
       $\Rightarrow u^2 + v^2 - u + v = 0$
       This can be written as $(u - \frac{1}{2})^2 + (v + \frac{1}{2})^2 = \frac{1}{2}$, which
       is the equation of a circle with centre $(\frac{1}{2}, -\frac{1}{2})$ and

       radius $\dfrac{\sqrt{2}}{2}$

    c

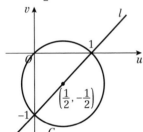

Challenge

1 a

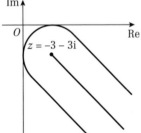

    b $3\sqrt{2} - 3$

2 $f(z) = -iz* + 1 + i$

Review exercise 1

1 $x < -4, -1 < x < 2$

2 $\{x : x < 0\} \cup \{x : 2 < x < 4\}$

3 $\{x : -3 < x < 0\} \cup \{x : x > 4\}$

4 $\{x : -\frac{1}{2} < x < 0\} \cup \{x : x > 3\}$

5 $\{x : x < -4k\} \cup \{x : -2k < x < 0\} \cup \{x : x > 2k\}$

6 a

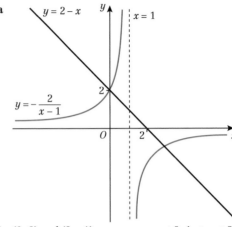

    b $(0, 2)$ and $(3, -1)$ **c** $x < 0, 1 < x < 3$

7 a

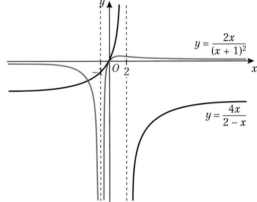

    b $(0, 0)$ and $\left(-\frac{5}{2}, -\frac{20}{9}\right)$

    c $\left\{x : x \leqslant -\frac{5}{2}\right\} \cup \{x : x > 2\} \cup \{x : x = 0\}$

8 a

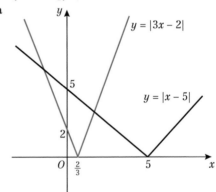

    b $\left(-\frac{3}{2}, \frac{13}{2}\right), \left(\frac{7}{4}, \frac{13}{4}\right)$

    c $x < -\frac{3}{2}, x > \frac{7}{4}$

9 a

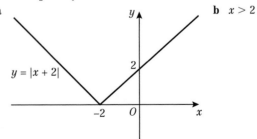

    b $x > 2$

10 a

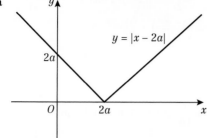

$y = |x - 2a|$

b $x < \frac{1}{3}a$

11 $\{x : x < 6 - 2\sqrt{3}\} \cup \{x : 4 < x < 6\}$

12 a

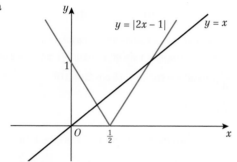

$y = |2x - 1|$ $y = x$

b $\left(\frac{1}{3}, \frac{1}{3}\right)$ and $(1, 1)$ **c** $\{x : x > \frac{1}{3}\} \cup \{x : x > 1\}$

13 $\{x : -5 < x < \frac{1}{3}\}$

14 $-\frac{1}{3}a \leqslant x \leqslant -\frac{1}{7}a$

15 a

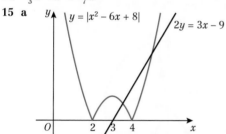

$y = |x^2 - 6x + 8|$ $2y = 3x - 9$

The curve meets the x-axis at $(2, 0)$ and $(4, 0)$.
The line meets the x-axis at $(3, 0)$.

b $\left(\frac{7}{2}, \frac{3}{4}\right)$, $(5, 3)$
$x < \frac{7}{2}, x > 5$

16 a

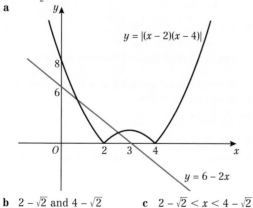

$y = |(x - 2)(x - 4)|$

$y = 6 - 2x$

b $2 - \sqrt{2}$ and $4 - \sqrt{2}$ **c** $2 - \sqrt{2} < x < 4 - \sqrt{2}$

17 a $x = -\frac{5}{2}, x = -\frac{7}{4}$ or $x = 1$

b $\{x : x < -\frac{5}{2}\} \cup \{x : -\frac{7}{4} < x < 1\}$

18 Using partial fractions,
$$\frac{2}{(r + 1)(r + 2)} = \frac{2}{r + 1} - \frac{2}{r + 2}$$
Using the method of differences,
$$\sum_{r=1}^{n} \frac{2}{(r + 1)(r + 2)} = \sum_{r=1}^{n}\left(\frac{2}{r + 1} - \frac{2}{r + 2}\right) = \frac{2}{2} - \frac{2}{n + 2}$$
$$= 1 - \frac{2}{n + 2} = \frac{n + 2 - 2}{n + 2} = \frac{n}{n + 2}$$

19 Using partial fractions,
$$\frac{4}{(r + 1)(r + 3)} = \frac{2}{r + 1} - \frac{2}{r + 3}$$
Using the method of differences,
$$\sum_{r=1}^{n} \frac{4}{(r + 1)(r + 3)} = \sum_{r=1}^{n}\left(\frac{2}{r + 1} - \frac{2}{r + 3}\right)$$
$$= \frac{2}{2} + \frac{2}{3} - \frac{2}{n + 2} - \frac{2}{n + 3} = \frac{5}{3} - \frac{2}{n + 2} - \frac{2}{n + 3}$$
$$= \frac{5(n + 2)(n + 3) - 3(n + 3) - 6(n + 2)}{3(n + 2)(n + 3)}$$
$$= \frac{5n^2 + 25n + 30 - 6n - 18 - 6n - 12}{3(n + 2)(n + 3)}$$
$$= \frac{5n^2 + 13n}{3(n + 2)(n + 3)} = \frac{n(5n + 13)}{3(n + 2)(n + 3)}$$
Hence, $a = 5, b = 13, c = 3$

20 a $\dfrac{r + 1}{r + 2} - \dfrac{r}{r + 1} = \dfrac{(r + 1)(r + 1) - r(r + 2)}{(r + 1)(r + 2)}$
$$= \frac{r^2 + 2r + 1 - r^2 - 2r}{(r + 1)(r + 2)} = \frac{1}{(r + 1)(r + 2)}$$

b $\dfrac{n}{2(n + 2)}$

21 a $f(x) = \dfrac{1}{x + 1} - \dfrac{2}{x + 2} + \dfrac{1}{x + 3}$

b $\dfrac{1}{6} - \dfrac{1}{n + 2} + \dfrac{1}{n + 3}$

22 a $\dfrac{2r - 1}{r^2(r - 1)^2}$

b Using the method of differences,
$$\sum_{r=2}^{n} \frac{2r - 1}{r^2(r - 1)^2} = \sum_{r=2}^{n}\left(\frac{1}{(r - 1)^2} - \frac{1}{r^2}\right) = \frac{1}{1^2} - \frac{1}{n^2} = 1 - \frac{1}{n^2}$$

23 a Using partial fractions,
$$\frac{4}{r(r + 2)} = \frac{2}{r} - \frac{2}{r + 2}$$
Using the method of differences,
$$\sum_{r=1}^{n} \frac{4}{r(r + 2)} = \sum_{r=1}^{n}\left(\frac{2}{r} - \frac{2}{r + 2}\right) = \frac{2}{1} + \frac{2}{2} - \frac{2}{n + 1} - \frac{2}{n + 2}$$
$$= 3 - \frac{2}{n + 1} - \frac{2}{n + 2}$$
$$= \frac{3(n + 1)(n + 2) - 2(n + 2) - 2(n + 1)}{(n + 1)(n + 2)}$$
$$= \frac{3n^2 + 9n + 6 - 2n - 4 - 2n - 2}{(n + 1)(n + 2)}$$
$$= \frac{3n^2 + 5n}{(n + 1)(n + 2)} = \frac{n(3n + 5)}{(n + 1)(n + 2)}$$
Hence $a = 3, b = 5$

b 0.0398

24 a Using partial fractions,
$$\frac{2}{4r^2 - 1} = \frac{1}{2r - 1} - \frac{1}{2r + 1}$$
Using the method of differences,
$$\sum_{r=1}^{n} \frac{2}{4r^2 - 1} = \sum_{r=1}^{n}\left(\frac{1}{2r - 1} - \frac{1}{2r + 1}\right) = 1 - \frac{1}{2n + 1}$$

b $\dfrac{20}{861}$

25 a $A = 24, B = 2$

b Using the identity from part **a**,

$$\sum_{r=1}^{n}(24r^2 + 2) = \sum_{r=1}^{n}((2r + 1)^3 - (2r - 1)^3)$$

$$24\sum_{r=1}^{n}r^2 + \sum_{r=1}^{n}2 = \sum_{r=1}^{n}((2r + 1)^3 - (2r - 1)^3)$$

Using the method of differences,

$$24\sum_{r=1}^{n}r^2 = 8n^3 + 12n^2 + 6n + 1 - 1 - 2n$$

$$= 8n^3 + 12n^2 + 4n = 4n(n + 1)(2n - 1)$$

$$\sum_{r=1}^{n}r^2 = \frac{4n(n + 1)(2n - 1)}{24} = \frac{1}{6}n(n + 1)(2n + 1)$$

c 194 380

26 Using partial fractions,

$$\frac{1}{r(r + 1)(r + 2)} = \frac{1}{2r} - \frac{1}{r + 1} + \frac{1}{2(r + 2)}$$

Using the method of differences,

$$\sum_{r=1}^{2n}\frac{1}{r(r + 1)(r + 2)} = \sum_{r=1}^{2n}\left(\frac{1}{2r} - \frac{1}{r + 1} + \frac{1}{2(r + 2)}\right)$$

$$= \frac{1}{4} - \frac{1}{2(2n + 1)} + \frac{1}{4(n + 1)}$$

$$= \frac{(n + 1)(2n + 1) - 2(n + 1) + (2n + 1)}{4(n + 1)(2n + 1)}$$

$$= \frac{2n^2 + 3n + 1 - 2n - 2 + 2n + 1}{4(n + 1)(2n + 1)}$$

$$= \frac{2n^2 + 3n}{4(n + 1)(2n + 1)} = \frac{n(2n + 3)}{4(n + 1)(2n + 1)}$$

Hence $a = 2, b = 3, c = 4$

27 a $\text{RHS} = r - 1 + \frac{1}{r} - \frac{1}{r + 1} = \frac{(r - 1)r(r + 1) + (r + 1) - r}{r(r + 1)}$

$$= \frac{r(r^2 - 1) + 1}{r(r + 1)} = \frac{r^3 - r + 1}{r(r + 1)} = \text{LHS}$$

b $\frac{n(n^2 + 1)}{2(n + 1)}$

28 $1 - \frac{1}{3^n(n + 1)}$

29 $\frac{\cos 2x + i \sin 2x}{\cos 9x - i \sin 9x} = \frac{\cos 2x + i \sin 2x}{\cos(-9x) + i \sin(-9x)}$

$$= \frac{e^{2xi}}{e^{-9xi}} = e^{11xi} = \cos 11x + i \sin 11x$$

Hence $n = 11$

30 a $\cos 5\theta + i \sin 5\theta = (\cos\theta + i \sin\theta)^5$

$= \cos^5\theta + 5i \cos^4\theta \sin\theta - 10 \cos^3\theta \sin^2\theta$
$\quad - 10i \cos^2\theta \sin^3\theta + 5 \cos\theta \sin^4\theta + i \sin^5\theta$

Equating real parts:

$\cos 5\theta = \cos^5\theta - 10 \cos^3\theta \sin^2\theta + 5 \cos\theta \sin^4\theta$
$= \cos^5\theta - 10 \cos^3\theta(1 - \cos^2\theta) + 5 \cos\theta(1 - \cos^2\theta)^2$
$= 16 \cos^5\theta - 20 \cos^3\theta + 5 \cos\theta$

b $x = 0.809, -0.309, -1$

31 a $\cos 5\theta + i \sin 5\theta = (\cos\theta + i \sin\theta)^5$

$= \cos^5\theta + 5i \cos^4\theta \sin\theta - 10 \cos^3\theta \sin^2\theta$
$\quad - 10i \cos^2\theta \sin^3\theta + 5 \cos\theta \sin^4\theta + i \sin^5\theta$

Equating imaginary parts:

$\sin 5\theta = 5 \cos^4\theta \sin\theta - 10 \cos^2\theta \sin^3\theta + \sin^5\theta$
$= \sin\theta(5 \cos^4\theta - 10 \cos^2\theta \sin^2\theta + \sin^4\theta)$
$= \sin\theta(5 \cos^4\theta - 10 \cos^2\theta(1 - \cos^2\theta) + (1 - \cos^2\theta)^2)$
$= \sin\theta(16 \cos^4\theta - 12 \cos^2\theta + 1)$

b $0, \frac{\pi}{4}, \frac{3\pi}{4}$, 1.209 (3 d.p.) and 1.932 (3 d.p)

32 a $\sin\theta = \frac{e^{i\theta} - e^{-i\theta}}{2i}$, if $z = e^{i\theta}$, then $\sin\theta = \frac{z - z^{-1}}{2i}$

$$\sin^5\theta = \left(\frac{z - z^{-1}}{2i}\right)^5$$

$$= \frac{1}{32i}(z^5 - 5z^3 + 10z - 10z^{-1} + 5z^{-3} - z^{-5})$$

$$= \frac{1}{16}\left(\frac{z^5 - z^{-5}}{2i} - \frac{5(z^3 - z^{-3})}{2i} + \frac{10(z - z^{-1})}{2i}\right)$$

$$= \frac{1}{16}(\sin 5\theta - 5 \sin 3\theta + 10 \sin\theta)$$

b $\int_0^{\frac{\pi}{2}} \sin^5\theta \, d\theta = \frac{1}{16}\int_0^{\frac{\pi}{2}}(\sin 5\theta - 5 \sin 3\theta + 10 \sin\theta)d\theta$

$$= \frac{1}{16}\left[-\frac{1}{5}\cos 5\theta + \frac{5}{3}\cos 3\theta - 10 \cos\theta\right]_0^{\frac{\pi}{2}}$$

$$= \frac{1}{16}\left(0 - \left(-\frac{1}{5} + \frac{5}{3} - 10\right)\right) = \frac{8}{15}$$

33 a $z^{-n} = \cos(-n\theta) + i \sin(-n\theta) = \cos n\theta - i \sin n\theta$

$z^n + z^{-n} = \cos n\theta + i \sin n\theta + \cos n\theta - i \sin n\theta = 2 \cos n\theta$

b $\frac{1}{32}(\cos 6\theta + 6 \cos 4\theta + 15 \cos 2\theta + 10)$

c $\int_0^{\frac{\pi}{2}} \cos^6\theta \, d\theta$

$$= \frac{1}{32}\int_0^{\frac{\pi}{2}}(\cos 6\theta + 6 \cos 4\theta + 15 \cos 2\theta + 10)d\theta$$

$$= \frac{1}{32}\left[\frac{1}{6}\sin 6\theta + \frac{6}{4}\sin 4\theta + \frac{15}{2}\sin 2\theta + 10\theta\right]_0^{\frac{\pi}{2}}$$

$$= \frac{1}{32}(5\pi - 0) = \frac{5\pi}{32}$$

34 a $z = \sqrt{2}e^{\frac{\pi i}{20}}, \sqrt{2}e^{\frac{9\pi i}{20}}, \sqrt{2}e^{\frac{17\pi i}{20}}, \sqrt{2}e^{-\frac{7\pi i}{20}}, \sqrt{2}e^{-\frac{3\pi i}{4}}$

b

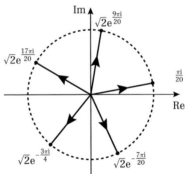

35 a $z = 4e^{\frac{\pi i}{9}}, 4e^{\frac{7\pi i}{9}}, 4e^{-\frac{5\pi}{9}}$

b $z^9 = \left(4e^{\frac{\pi i}{9}}\right)^9, \left(4e^{\frac{7\pi i}{9}}\right)^9, \left(4e^{-\frac{5\pi}{9}}\right)^9$

$$= 4^9 e^{i\pi}, 4^9 e^{7i\pi}, 4^9 e^{-5i\pi}$$

The value of all three of these expressions is $-4^9 = -2^{18}$

Hence the solutions satisfy $z^9 + 2^k = 0$, where $k = 18$.

36 $z = \cos\theta + i \sin\theta$, where

$\theta = \frac{\pi}{10}, \frac{5\pi}{10}\left(= \frac{\pi}{2}\right), \frac{9\pi}{10}, -\frac{3\pi}{10}, -\frac{7\pi}{10}$

37 a $2e^{\frac{\pi i}{15}}, 2e^{\frac{7\pi i}{15}}, 2e^{\frac{13\pi i}{15}}, 2e^{-\frac{\pi i}{15}}, 2e^{-\frac{11\pi i}{15}}$

b Vertices of a regular pentagon, inscribed in a circle radius 2, centred on the origin.

38 a

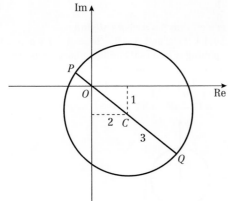

b Maximum value of $|z|$ is $3 + \sqrt{5}$
minimum value of $|z|$ is $3 - \sqrt{5}$

39 a

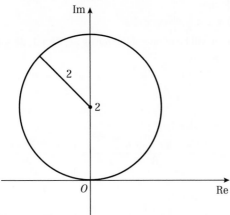

b 4

40 a

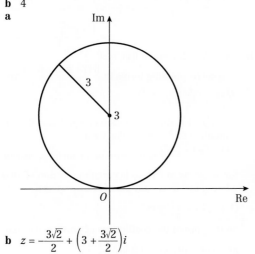

b $z = -\dfrac{3\sqrt{2}}{2} + \left(3 + \dfrac{3\sqrt{2}}{2}\right)i$

41

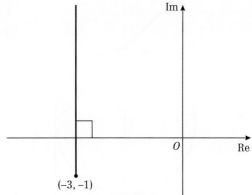

42 a

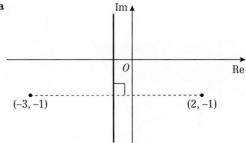

b $\frac{1}{2}$ **c** $-\frac{1}{2} - \frac{1}{2}i$

43 a Because $\dfrac{\pi}{4} < \dfrac{\pi}{2}$ **b** Centre $(1, 0)$

44 a $-1 + 3i$

b $\theta = \dfrac{11\pi}{12}$, $b = -\dfrac{7}{2} + \dfrac{5\sqrt{3} - 4}{2}i$

45 Radius 2, centre $(-1, 2)$

46 a 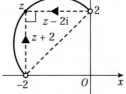 **b** $\sqrt{2}$

47 a L and M are both circles, so are similar.

b $\dfrac{2\sqrt{14}}{5}$

48 $\dfrac{3\pi}{2\sqrt{2}}$

49 $p = \frac{4}{3}$

50

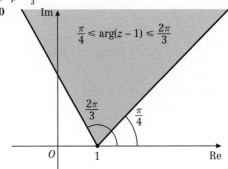

51

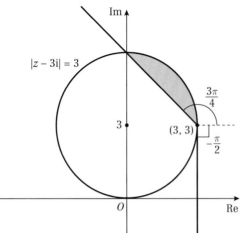

$|z - 3\mathrm{i}| = 3$

$\frac{3\pi}{4}$

(3, 3)

$-\frac{\pi}{2}$

52

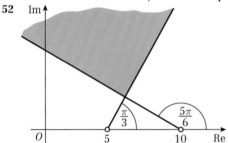

$\frac{\pi}{3}$ $\frac{5\pi}{6}$

53 a $k = 4$ **b** 10π

54 By sketching region, deduce that $\left(\dfrac{q - p}{2}\right)^2 = 2x$.

So $(q - p)^2 = 8x \Rightarrow q - p = \sqrt{8x}$

(For non-zero area, $q > p \Rightarrow q - p > 0$)

55 a 72   **b** $\mathrm{Im}(z) = 10$

56 Rearrange to get $z = \dfrac{2w - 1}{w - 2}$. $|z| = 1 \Rightarrow |w - 2| = |2w - 1|$

Substituting $u + iv$ for w and squaring gives
$(u - 2)^2 + v^2 = (2u - 1)^2 + v^2$, which can be rearranged
to give $u^2 + v^2 = 1$, which is the circle $|w| = 1$.

57 a Rearrange to get $z = \dfrac{-\mathrm{i}}{w - 1}$, and then substitute $u + \mathrm{i}v$

for w to get $z = \dfrac{-v}{(u - 1)^2 + v^2} + \mathrm{i}\dfrac{1 - u}{(u - 1)^2 + v^2}$

So $\mathrm{Im}(z) = \frac{1}{2} \Rightarrow \dfrac{1 - u}{(u - 1)^2 + v^2} = \frac{1}{2}$, and rearranging

gives $u^2 + v^2 = 1$, or $|w| = 1$.

b $w = \dfrac{(5 - \mathrm{i})z - 2\mathrm{i}}{z}$

58 a Rearrange to get $z = \dfrac{1 - \mathrm{i}w}{w - 1}$, and then subtitute

$u + \mathrm{i}v$ for w to get

$z = \dfrac{(v + 1)(u - 1) - uv}{(u - 1)^2 + v^2} + \mathrm{i}\dfrac{u(1 - u) - v(v + 1)}{(u - 1)^2 + v^2}$

When $\arg z = \dfrac{\pi}{4}$, $x = y$, so

$(v + 1)(u - 1) - uv = u(1 - u) - v(v + 1)$
and rearranging this gives $u^2 + v^2 = 1$, or $|w| = 1$.

b $v = -u$

c

$P(0, 1)$

O 1 x

d

O $Q\left(\dfrac{1}{2}, -\dfrac{1}{2}\right)$ x

59 a $\dfrac{1}{a}\mathrm{e}^{\mathrm{i}\theta}$

b $w = \mathrm{e}^{\mathrm{i}\theta} + a\mathrm{e}^{-\mathrm{i}\theta} = A\cos\theta + \mathrm{i}B\sin\theta$

So $A + B = 2$ and $A - B = 2a \Rightarrow A = 1 + a, B = 1 - a$

Splitting w into real and imaginary parts gives
$u = (1 + a)\cos\theta$ and $v = (1 - a)\sin\theta$

$\Rightarrow \left(\dfrac{u}{1 + a}\right)^2 + \left(\dfrac{v}{1 - a}\right)^2 = 1$

$\Rightarrow u^2(1 - a)^2 + v^2(1 + a)^2 = (1 - a^2)^2$

c

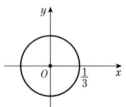

$\dfrac{1}{3}$

Challenge

1 $0 < x < \dfrac{\pi}{6}, \dfrac{5\pi}{6} < x < \pi$

2 a n will be of one of the forms $3k$, $3k + 1$, $3k - 1$:

$n = 3k$:

$\dfrac{1^{3k} + \left(\mathrm{e}^{\frac{2\pi\mathrm{i}}{3}}\right)^{3k} + \left(\mathrm{e}^{\frac{2\pi\mathrm{i}}{3}}\right)^{6k}}{3} = \dfrac{1 + \mathrm{e}^{2\pi k\mathrm{i}} + \mathrm{e}^{4\pi k\mathrm{i}}}{3} =$

$\dfrac{1 + 1 + 1}{3} = 1$

$n = 3k + 1$:

$\dfrac{1^{3k+1} + \left(\mathrm{e}^{\frac{2\pi\mathrm{i}}{3}}\right)^{3k+1} + \left(\mathrm{e}^{\frac{2\pi\mathrm{i}}{3}}\right)^{6k+2}}{3} = \dfrac{1 + \mathrm{e}^{2\pi k\mathrm{i}+\frac{2\pi\mathrm{i}}{3}} + \mathrm{e}^{4\pi k\mathrm{i}+\frac{4\pi\mathrm{i}}{3}}}{3}$

$= \dfrac{1 + \mathrm{e}^{\frac{2\pi\mathrm{i}}{3}} + \mathrm{e}^{\frac{4\pi\mathrm{i}}{3}}}{3} = 0$

$n = 3k - 1$:

$\dfrac{1^{3k-1} + \left(\mathrm{e}^{\frac{2\pi\mathrm{i}}{3}}\right)^{3k-1} + \left(\mathrm{e}^{\frac{2\pi\mathrm{i}}{3}}\right)^{6k-2}}{3} = \dfrac{1 + \mathrm{e}^{2\pi k\mathrm{i}-\frac{2\pi\mathrm{i}}{3}} + \mathrm{e}^{4\pi k\mathrm{i}-\frac{4\pi\mathrm{i}}{3}}}{3}$

$= \dfrac{1 + \mathrm{e}^{-\frac{2\pi\mathrm{i}}{3}} + \mathrm{e}^{-\frac{4\pi\mathrm{i}}{3}}}{3} = 0$

b Consider jth term of f(x), $a_j x^j$.

The corresponding terms in $\dfrac{\mathrm{f}(1) + \mathrm{f}(\omega) + \mathrm{f}(\omega^2)}{3}$ are:

$\dfrac{a_j(1)^j}{3} + \dfrac{a_j(\omega)^j}{3} + \dfrac{a_j(\omega^2)^j}{3}$

From part **a**, this expression is equal to a_j if j is 0 or
a multiple of 3, and 0 otherwise.

$\dfrac{\mathrm{f}(1) + \mathrm{f}(\omega) + \mathrm{f}(\omega^2)}{3}$ is the sum of all such expressions

for all terms in f(x), so is equal to the sum of all a_j
where j is 0 or a multiple of 3, as required.

c $(1 + x)45 = \sum\limits_{r=0}^{45}\binom{45}{r}x^r$.

So the sum of the coefficients of powers of x that

are 0 or multiples of 3 is $\sum\limits_{r=0}^{15}\binom{45}{3r}$.

From part **b**, this is equal to

$\dfrac{(1 + 1)^{45} + (1 + \omega)^{45} + (1 + \omega^2)^{45}}{3}$

$= \dfrac{2^{45} + (-\omega^2)^{45} + (-\omega)^{45}}{3} = \dfrac{2^{45} - 2}{3}$

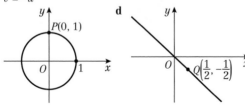

CHAPTER 5

Prior knowledge check

1 $y = (x - 1)e^x + c$

2 $y^2 = 4 - x^2$

3 **a** $-\frac{3}{2}\ln|50 - 2t| + c$ **b** $-\frac{1}{4}\ln|\cos(4x)| + c$

Exercise 5A

1 $y = x^2 + c$ where c is constant

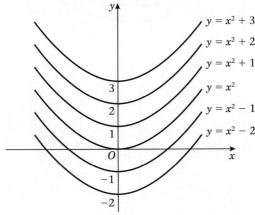

2 $y = Ae^x$ where A is constant

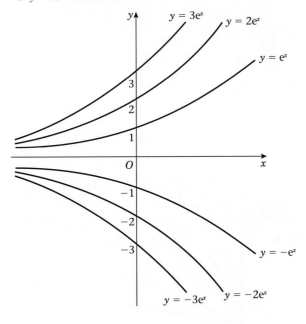

3 $y = \dfrac{x^3}{3} + c$ where c is constant

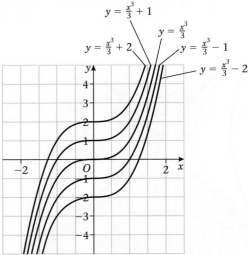

4 $y = \ln Ax$, where A is constant

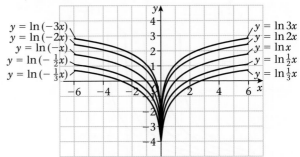

5 $y = Ax^2$, where A is constant

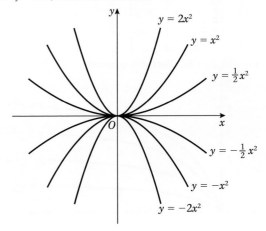

6 $y^2 - x^2 = 2c$, where c is constant

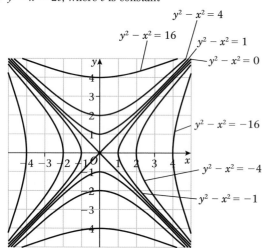

7 $y = \ln\dfrac{1}{(-x - c)}$, where c is constant

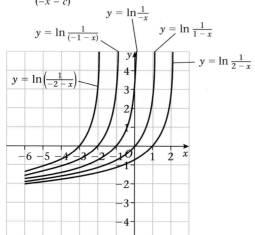

8 $y = \dfrac{Ax}{x + 1}$, $x > 0$, where A is constant

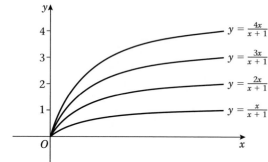

9 $y = \sin x + c$, where c is constant

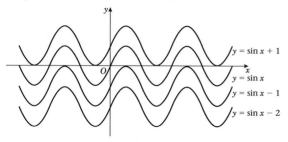

10 $y = A \sin x$, where A is constant

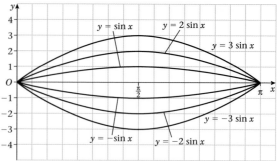

11 $x = \tan t + c$ for $-\dfrac{\pi}{2} < t < \dfrac{\pi}{2}$, where c is constant

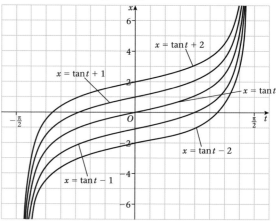

12 $x = \dfrac{Ae^t}{1 + Ae^t}$, where A is constant

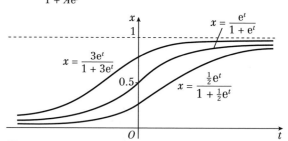

13 a

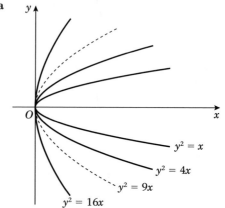

b $y^2 = 9x$

Online Worked solutions are available in SolutionBank.

14 a $y^2 + 5x^2 = 45$

b

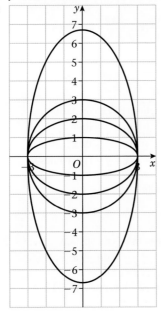

Exercise 5B

1 a $y = \frac{1}{x}\sin x + \frac{c}{x}$ **b** $y = xe^{2x} - e^{2x} + ce^x$

c $y = 3x\operatorname{cosec}x + c\operatorname{cosec}x$ **d** $y = xe^x + cx$

e $y = \ln\left(\frac{1}{2} + \frac{c}{x^2}\right)$ **f** $y = \pm\sqrt{\frac{1}{6}x^2 + \frac{c}{2x}}$

2 a $y = \frac{x + c}{e^{x^2}}$ **b** $y \to 0$

3 a $y = 1 + \frac{1}{x} + \frac{c}{x^2}$

b $1 + \frac{1}{x} + \frac{1}{4x^2}$

$1 + \frac{1}{x} + \frac{1}{x^2}$

$y = 1 + \frac{1}{x} + \frac{5}{x^2}$

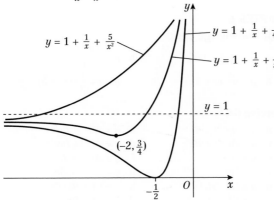

4 a $y = \dfrac{\ln\frac{A(x+1)}{(x+2)}}{\ln x}$ **b** $y = \dfrac{\ln\frac{16}{3}\frac{(x+1)}{(x+2)}}{\ln x}$

5 a $y = \frac{1}{3}e^x + ce^{-2x}$ **b** $y = -\cot x + c\operatorname{cosec}x$

c $y = xe^{\cos x} + ce^{\cos x}$ **d** $y = e^{2x} + ce^x$

e $y = \left(\frac{x^2}{2} + c\right)\cos x$ **f** $y = \frac{1}{x}\ln x + \frac{c}{x}$

g $y = x\ln(x+2) + cx$ **h** $y = \frac{1}{4}x + cx^{-\frac{1}{3}}$

i $y = (x+2)\ln(x+2) + c(x+2)$

j $y = \frac{1}{x^3}e^x - \frac{1}{x^4}e^x + \frac{c}{x^4}$

6 $y = \frac{1}{x}e^x - \frac{1}{x^2}e^x + \frac{1}{x^2}$

7 $y = -\frac{1}{3x^2} + \frac{4x}{3}$

8 a $y = \frac{1}{3}(x^2 + 1)^2 + \frac{c}{(x^2 + 1)}$

b $y = \frac{1}{3}(x^2 + 1)^2 - \frac{2}{3(x^2 + 1)}$

9 a $y = 1 + \frac{c}{\sec x + \tan x}$

b $y = 1 + \frac{1}{\sec x + \tan x}$ or $y = 1 + \frac{\cos x}{1 + \sin x}$

10 a $y = A\cos x + \sin x$ **b** $y = -3\cos x + \sin x$

c $x = \frac{\pi}{2} \Rightarrow y = A \times 0 + 1 = 1$

$x = \frac{3\pi}{2} \Rightarrow y = A \times 0 - 1 = -1$

so $\left(\frac{\pi}{2}, 1\right)$ and $\left(\frac{3\pi}{2}, 1\right)$ lie on all possible solution curves.

11 $y = e^{\frac{bx}{a}} + c$

Exercise 5C

1 a $y^2 = 2x^2(\ln x + c)$ **b** $y^3 = 3x^3(\ln x + c)$

c $y = \frac{-x}{\ln x + c}$ **d** $y^3 = x^3(Ax - 1)$

2 a Given $z = y^{-2}$, $y = z^{-\frac{1}{2}}$ and $\frac{dy}{dx} = x^3(Ax - 1)$

So $\frac{dy}{dx} + \left(\frac{1}{2}\tan x\right)y = -(2\sec x)y^3$

$\Rightarrow -\frac{1}{2}z^{-\frac{3}{2}}\frac{dz}{dx} + \left(\frac{1}{2}\tan x\right)z^{-\frac{1}{2}} = -2\sec x z^{-\frac{3}{2}}$

$\therefore \frac{dz}{dx} - z\tan x = 4\sec x$

b $y = \sqrt{\frac{\cos x}{4x + c}}$

3 a Given that $z = x^{\frac{1}{2}}$, $x = z^2$ and $\frac{dx}{dt} = 2z\frac{dz}{dt}$

So the equation $\frac{dx}{dt} + t^2 x = t^2 x^{\frac{1}{2}}$ becomes

$2z\frac{dz}{dt} + t^2 z^2 = t^2 z$

Divide through by $2z$: $\frac{dz}{dt} + \frac{1}{2}t^2 z = \frac{1}{2}t^2$

b $x = \left(1 + ce^{-\frac{1}{4}t^2}\right)^2$

4 a Let $z = y^{-1}$, then $y = z^{-1}$ and $\frac{dy}{dx} = -z^{-2}\frac{dz}{dx}$

So $\frac{dy}{dx} - \frac{1}{x}y = \frac{(x+1)^3}{x}y^2$ becomes

$-z^{-2}\frac{dz}{dx} - \frac{1}{x}z^{-1} = \frac{(x+1)^3}{x}z^{-2}$

Multiply through by $-z^2$: $\frac{dz}{dx} + \frac{1}{x}z = -\frac{(x+1)^3}{x}$

b $y = \frac{4x}{4c - (x+1)^4}$

5 a $(1 + x^2)\frac{dz}{dx} + 2xz = 1$ **b** $y = \sqrt{\frac{x + c}{1 + x^2}}$

c $y = \sqrt{\frac{x + 4}{1 + x^2}}$

6 $\frac{dy}{dx} = \frac{dy}{dz} \times \frac{dz}{dx} = \frac{1}{-(n-1)y^{-n}} \times \frac{dz}{dx}$

So differential equation becomes

$-\frac{y^n}{n-1} \times \frac{dz}{dx} + Py = Qy^n$

$\Rightarrow \frac{dz}{dx} - (n - y)Py^{-(n-1)} = -Q(n-1)$

and then $\frac{dz}{dx} - (n-1)Pz = -Q(n-1)$

7 a Differential equation becomes $\frac{du}{dx} = \frac{1}{1} + u$

b This solves to give $u + \frac{1}{2}u^2 = x + c$.

$2(y + 2x) + (y + 2x)^2 - 2x = k$ $(k = 2c)$

$\Rightarrow 4x^2 + 4xy + y^2 + 2y + 2x = k$

Challenge

Substitute $y = \frac{1}{v}$, $\frac{dy}{dx} = -\frac{1}{v^2}\frac{dv}{dx}$

Differential equation becomes

$x^2\left(-\frac{1}{v^2}\frac{dv}{dx}\right) - \frac{x}{v} = \frac{1}{v^2}$

$\Rightarrow x\frac{dv}{dx} + v = -\frac{1}{x}$

Integrate both sides to get $xv = -\ln x + C$

Substitute $v = \frac{1}{y}$ to get $y = \frac{-x}{\ln x + C}$

Chapter review 5

1 $y = 2\sin x + c\cos x$

2 $y = 5 + c(1-x^2)^{\frac{1}{2}}$

3 $y = -\frac{x}{2} + \frac{c}{x}$

4 $y = \frac{2}{5}x^{\frac{3}{2}} + \frac{c}{x}$

5 $y = \frac{1}{2} + ce^{-x^2}$

6 $y = 2x + cx\sqrt{1-x^2}$

7 a $y = \frac{ke^{\lambda x}}{\lambda - a} + ce^{ax}$ b $y = \frac{kx^{n+1}}{n+1}e^{ax} + ce^{ax}$

8 $y = \sin x + A\cosec x$

9 a Given that $z = y^{-1}$, then $y = z^{-1}$ so $\frac{dy}{dx} = -z^{-2}\frac{dz}{dx}$

The equation $x\frac{dy}{dx} + y = y^2\ln x$ becomes

$-xz^{-2}\frac{dz}{dx} + z^{-1} = z^{-2}\ln x$

Dividing through by $-xz^{-2}$ gives $\frac{dz}{dx} - \frac{z}{x} = -\frac{\ln x}{x}$

  b $y = \frac{1}{1 + cx + \ln x}$, where c is a constant.

10 a Given that $z = y^2$, $y = z^{\frac{1}{2}}$ and $\frac{dy}{dx} = \frac{1}{2}z^{-\frac{1}{2}}\frac{dz}{dx}$

the differential equation becomes

$\cos x\, z^{-\frac{1}{2}}\frac{dz}{dx} - z^{\frac{1}{2}}\sin x + z^{-\frac{1}{2}} = 0$

Divide through by $z^{-\frac{1}{2}}$: $\cos x\frac{dz}{dx} - z\sin x = -1$

  b $z = c\sec x - x\sec x$

  c $y^2 = c\sec x - x\sec x$, where c is a constant

11 a Given that $z = \frac{y}{x}$, $y = zx$ so $\frac{dy}{dx} = z + x\frac{dz}{dx}$

The equation $(x^2 - y^2)\frac{dy}{dx} - xy = 0$ becomes

$(x^2 - z^2x^2)\left(z + x\frac{dz}{dx}\right) - xzx = 0$

$\Rightarrow (1-z^2)z + (1-z^2)x\frac{dz}{dx} - z = 0$

$\Rightarrow x\frac{dz}{dx} = \frac{z}{1-z^2} - z$

$\Rightarrow x\frac{dz}{dx} = \frac{z^3}{1-z^2}$

  b $2y^2(\ln y + c) + x^2 = 0$, where c is a constant

12 a $z = \frac{y}{x} \Rightarrow y = xz$ and $\frac{dy}{dx} = z + x\frac{dz}{dx}$

So $\frac{dy}{dx} = \frac{y(x+y)}{x(y-x)}$ becomes $z + x\frac{dz}{dx} = \frac{xz(x+xz)}{x(xz-x)}$

$\Rightarrow z + x\frac{dz}{dx} = \frac{z(1+z)}{(z-1)}$

So $x\frac{dz}{dx} = \frac{z(1+z)}{z-1} - z = \frac{2z}{z-1}$

  b $\frac{y}{2x} - \frac{1}{2}\ln y = \frac{1}{2}\ln x + c$, where c is a constant.

13 a Given that $z = \frac{y}{x}$, $y = zx$ and $\frac{dy}{dx} = z + x\frac{dz}{dx}$

The equation $\frac{dy}{dx} = \frac{-3xy}{y^2 - 3x^2}$ becomes

$z + x\frac{dz}{dx} = \frac{-3x^2z}{z^2x^2 - 3x^2}$

So $x\frac{dz}{dx} = \frac{-3z}{z^2 - 3} - z = \frac{-z^3}{z^2 - 3}$

  b $\ln y + \frac{3x^2}{2y^2} = c$, where c is a constant.

14 a Let $u = x + y$, then $\frac{du}{dx} = 1 + \frac{dy}{dx}$ and so

$\frac{dy}{dx} = (x+y+1)(x+y-1)$ becomes

$\frac{du}{dx} - 1 = (u+1)(u-1) = u^2 - 1$

$\Rightarrow \frac{du}{dx} = u^2$

  b $y = \frac{-1}{x+c} - x$, where c is a constant

15 a Given that $u = y - x - 2$, $\frac{du}{dx} = \frac{dy}{dx} - 1$

So $\frac{dy}{dx} = (y - x - 2)^2$ becomes $\frac{du}{dx} + 1 = u^2$

$\Rightarrow \frac{du}{dx} = u^2 - 1$

  b $y = x + 2 + \frac{1 + Ae^{2x}}{1 - Ae^{2x}}$, where A is a positive constant.

16 a $v = u^{-\frac{1}{2}}$, $\frac{dv}{dt} = -\frac{1}{2}u^{-\frac{3}{2}}\frac{du}{dt}$

Equation becomes $-\frac{1}{2}u^{-\frac{3}{2}}\frac{du}{dt} \times t + u^{-\frac{1}{2}} = 2t^3u^{-\frac{3}{2}}$ which

rearranges to $\frac{du}{dt} - \frac{2u}{t} = -4t^2$.

  b Using integrating factor $e^{-2\int\frac{1}{t}dt} = e^{-2\ln t} = t^{-2}$, get

$\frac{d}{dt}(ut^{-2}) = -4 \Rightarrow ut^{-2} = -4t + c$, and $u = -4t^3 + ct^2$.

Then the general solution for the original equation

is $v = \frac{1}{\sqrt{t^2(c - 4t)}}$

CHAPTER 6
Prior knowledge check

1 a $y = Ax^2 + 1$ b $y = \frac{\frac{2}{3}x^3 + c}{x}$

2 a $y = e^{\frac{x}{2}}\left(e^{\frac{x}{2}} + 1\right)$ b $y = \frac{1}{2}x(x^2 + 5)$

Exercise 6A

1 a $y = Ae^{-3x} + Be^{-2x}$ b $y = Ae^{2x} + Be^{6x}$

  c $y = Ae^{-5x} + Be^{3x}$ d $y = Ae^{7x} + Be^{-4x}$

  e $y = A + Be^{-5x}$ f $y = Ae^{-\frac{1}{3}x} + Be^{-2x}$

  g $y = Ae^{-\frac{1}{4}x} + Be^{2x}$ h $y = Ae^{-\frac{1}{5}x} + Be^{\frac{2x}{3}}$

2 a $y = (A + Bx)e^{-5x}$ b $y = (A + Bx)e^{9x}$

  c $y = (A + Bx)e^{-x}$ d $y = (A + Bx)e^{4x}$

  e $y = (A + Bx)e^{-\frac{x}{4}}$ f $y = (A + Bx)e^{\frac{x}{2}}$

  g $y = (A + Bx)e^{-\frac{5x}{2}}$ h $y = (A + Bx)e^{-\sqrt{3}x}$

3 a $y = A\cos 5x + B\sin 5x$ b $y = A\cos 9x + B\sin 9x$

  c $y = A\cos x + B\sin x$ d $y = A\cos\frac{4}{3}x + B\sin\frac{4}{3}x$

  e $y = e^{-4x}(A\cos x + B\sin x)$ f $y = e^{2x}(A\cos x + B\sin x)$

  g $y = e^{-10x}(A\cos 3x + B\sin 3x)$

  h $y = e^{-\frac{\sqrt{3}}{2}x}(A\cos\frac{3}{2}x + B\sin\frac{3}{2}x)$

4 a $y = (A + Bx)e^{-7x}$

b $y = Ae^{-4x} + Be^{3x}$

c $y = e^{-2x}(A\cos 3x + B\sin 3x)$

d $y = (A + Bx)e^{\frac{3x}{4}}$

e $y = e^{\frac{1}{3}x}(A\cos\frac{2}{3}x + B\sin\frac{2}{3}x)$

f $y = Ae^{\frac{2}{3}x} + Be^{-\frac{x}{2}}$

5 a i $x = Ae^{(-k+\sqrt{k^2-9})t} + Be^{(-k-\sqrt{k^2-9})t}$

   ii $x = e^{-t}(A\sin((\sqrt{9-k^2})t) + B\cos((\sqrt{9-k^2})t))$

   iii $x = (A + Bt)e^{-kt}$

b i $x = e^{-2t}(A\cos(\sqrt{5}t) + B\sin(\sqrt{5}t))$

   ii $x \to 0$

6 From auxiliary equation:

$\alpha = -\dfrac{b}{2a}$ (using quadratic formula)

$b^2 = 4ac$ (setting discriminant $= 0$)

$y = (A + Bx)e^{\alpha x}$

$\dfrac{dy}{dx} = \alpha e^{\alpha x}(A + Bx) + Be^{\alpha x}$

$\dfrac{d^2y}{dx^2} = B\alpha e^{\alpha x} + \alpha^2 e^{\alpha x}(A + Bx) + \alpha Be^{\alpha x}$

Substituting these 5 relationships into

$a\dfrac{d^2y}{dx^2} + b\dfrac{dy}{dx} + cy$

yields a result of 0, so $(A + Bx)e^{\alpha x}$ is a solution

7 Substitute $y = Af(x) + Bg(x)$ into differential equation:

$a(Af''(x) + Bg''(x)) + b(Af'(x) + Bg'(x)) + c(Af(x) + Bg(x))$

$= A(af''(x) + bf'(x) + cf(x)) + B(ag''(x) + bg'(x) + cg(x))$

$= A(0) + B(0)$

$= 0$

Challenge

$Ae^{\alpha x} + Be^{\beta x} = Ae^{px}e^{qix} + Be^{px}e^{-qix}$

$\qquad\qquad = e^{px}((A + B)\cos qx + i(A - B)\sin qx)$

Set $B = A^*$, so that $A = \lambda + \mu i$ and $B = \lambda - \mu i$, $\lambda, \mu \in \mathbb{R}$.

Then $A + B = 2\lambda$ and $i(A - B) = -2\mu$

Hence setting $\lambda = \frac{1}{2}C$ and $\mu = -\frac{1}{2}D$ gives the required result.

Exercise 6B

1 a $y = Ae^{-x} + Be^{-5x} + 2$

b $y = Ae^{6x} + Be^{2x} + 2 + 3x$

c $y = Ae^{-4x} + Be^{3x} - 2e^{2x}$

d $y = Ae^{-5x} + Be^{3x} - \frac{1}{3}$

e $y = (A + Bx)e^{4x} + 1 + \frac{1}{2}x$

f $y = (A + Bx)e^{-x} + 4\sin 2x - 3\cos 2x$

g $y = A\cos 9x + B\sin 9x + \frac{1}{6}e^{3x}$

h $y = A\cos 2x + B\sin 2x + \frac{1}{3}\sin x$

i $y = e^{2x}(A\cos x + B\sin x) + 3 + 8x + 5x^2$

j $y = e^x(A\cos 5x + B\sin 5x) + \frac{1}{25}e^x$

2 a $\frac{1}{4}x^2 - \frac{1}{8}x + \frac{7}{32}$

b $y = Ae^{4x} + Be^x + \frac{1}{4}x^2 - \frac{1}{8}x + \frac{7}{32}$

3 a $Ae^{6x} + B$

b $y = Ae^{6x} + B - \frac{1}{9}x^3 + \frac{1}{36}x^2 - \frac{17}{108}x$

4 $y = A + Be^{-4x} + 2x^3 - \frac{3}{2}x^2 - \frac{3}{4}x$

5 a C.F. contains a term in xe^x. Results in setting up equation in the form of $e^x = 0$. Not possible.

b $\lambda = \frac{1}{2}$

c $y = (A + Bx + \frac{1}{2}x^2)e^x$

6 a $y = Ae^{-t} + Be^{-3t} + \frac{5}{3} - \frac{4k}{9} + \frac{kt}{3}$

b $y = 2t - 1$

Challenge

$y = A\cos x + B\sin x + \left(x - \frac{4}{5}\right)e^{2x}$

Exercise 6C

1 a $y = Ae^{-3x} + Be^{-3x} + e^x$ **b** $y = e^{-3x} - e^{-2x} + e^x$

2 a $y = A + Be^{-2x} + \frac{3}{2}e^{2x}$ **b** $y = 2 - \frac{3}{2}e^{-2x} + \frac{3}{2}e^{2x}$

3 $y = \frac{1}{6}e^{-6x} + \frac{1}{6}e^{7x} - \frac{1}{3}$

4 a $y = A\cos 3x + B\sin 3x + 2\sin x$

b $y = \cos 3x + 2\sin 3x + 2\sin x$

5 a $y = e^{-\frac{1}{2}x}(A\cos x + B\sin x) + \sin x$

b $y = \sin x\left(1 - e^{-\frac{1}{2}x}\right)$

6 a $x = Ae^{2t} + Be^{2t} + t$ **b** $x = e^t + e^{2t} + t$

7 a $x = e^{3t} + e^{-3t} - \sin t$

8 a $x = Ae^{2t} + Bte^{2t} + \frac{1}{2}t^3e^{2t}$ **b** $x = (t + \frac{1}{2}t^3)e^{2t}$

9 a $x = \frac{1}{2}\left(\cos\frac{6}{5}t + \sin\frac{6}{5}t + 1\right)$

10 a $x = e^t(A\cos t + B\sin t) + t^2 + 2t + 1$

b $x = e^t\sin t + 1 + 2t + t^2$ or $x = e^t\sin t + (1 + t)^2$

11 a $y = Ae^x + Be^{2x} + 3xe^{2x}$ **b** $y = 3e^x - 3e^{2x} + 3xe^{2x}$

12 a $y = \frac{1}{18}\sin 3x - \frac{x}{6}\cos 3x$

13 a $x = e^{-t} - e^{-3t}$

b Setting $\frac{dx}{dy} = 0$ gives $t = \frac{1}{2}\ln 3$, then substituting

this into $x = e^{-t} - e^{-3t}$ gives $x = \frac{2\sqrt{3}}{9}$

Since $\frac{d^2x}{dt^2} < 0$, this is the maximum.

Exercise 6D

1 a $y = \dfrac{A}{x^4} + \dfrac{B}{x}$ **b** $y = (A + B\ln x) \times \dfrac{1}{x^2}$

c $y = \dfrac{A}{x^2} + \dfrac{B}{x^3}$ **d** $y = \dfrac{A}{x^7} + Bx^4$

e $y = Ax^7 + \dfrac{B}{x^2}$ **f** $y = \dfrac{1}{x}(A\cos\ln x + B\sin\ln x)$

2 a $y = \dfrac{z}{x} \Rightarrow xy = z$ and $x\dfrac{dy}{dx} + y = \dfrac{dz}{dx}$

Also $x\dfrac{d^2y}{dx^2} + \dfrac{dy}{dx} + \dfrac{dy}{dx} = \dfrac{d^2z}{dx^2}$

So the equation $x\dfrac{d^2y}{dx^2} + (2 - 4x)\dfrac{dy}{dx} - 4y = 0$

becomes $\dfrac{d^2z}{dx^2} - 4\left(\dfrac{dz}{dx} - y\right) - 4y = 0$

which rearranges to give $\dfrac{d^2z}{dx^2} - 4\dfrac{dz}{dx} = 0$

b $z = A + Be^{4x}$ **c** $y = \dfrac{A}{x} + \dfrac{B}{x}e^{4x}$

3 a $y = \dfrac{z}{x^2} \Rightarrow x^2y = z$

So $x^2\dfrac{dy}{dx} + 2xy = \dfrac{dz}{dx}$ **(1)**

and $x^2\dfrac{d^2y}{dx^2} + 2x\dfrac{dy}{dx} + 2x\dfrac{dy}{dx} + 2y = \dfrac{d^2z}{dx^2}$ **(2)**

The differential equation becomes

$\left(x^2\dfrac{d^2y}{dx^2} + 4x\dfrac{dy}{dx} + 2y\right) + \left(2x^2\dfrac{dy}{dx} + 4xy\right) + 2x^2y = e^{-x}$

Using results **(1)** and **(2)**,

$\dfrac{d^2z}{dx^2} + 2\dfrac{dz}{dx} + 2z = e^{-x}$

b $z = e^{-x}(A\cos x + B\sin x + 1)$

c $y = \dfrac{e^{-x}}{x^2}(A\cos x + B\sin x + 1)$

4 a $z = \sin x \Rightarrow \dfrac{dz}{dx} = \cos x$

So $\dfrac{dy}{dx} = \dfrac{dy}{dz} \times \cos x$

and $\dfrac{d^2y}{dx^2} = \dfrac{d^2y}{dz^2}\cos^2 x - \dfrac{dy}{dz}\sin x$

The equation becomes

$\cos^3 x \dfrac{d^2y}{dz^2} - \cos x \sin x \dfrac{dy}{dz} + \cos x \sin x \dfrac{dy}{dz} -$

$2y\cos^3 x = 2\cos^5 x$

Dividing by $\cos^3 x$ gives

$\dfrac{d^2y}{dz^2} - 2y = 2\cos^2 x = 2(1 - z^2)$

b $y = Ae^{\sqrt{2}\sin x} + Be^{-\sqrt{2}\sin x} + \sin^2 x$

5 a $x = ut, \dfrac{dx}{dt} = u + t\dfrac{du}{dt}, \dfrac{d^2x}{dt^2} = 2\dfrac{du}{dt} + t\dfrac{d^2u}{dt^2}$

So differential equation becomes

$t^2\left(2\dfrac{du}{dt} + t\dfrac{d^2u}{dt^2}\right) - 2t\left(u + t\dfrac{du}{dt}\right) = -2(1 - 2t^2)ut$

which rearranges to give $t^3\left(\dfrac{d^2u}{dt^2} - 4u\right) = 0$

$\Rightarrow \dfrac{d^2u}{dt^2} - 4u = 0$

b $x = t(Ae^{2t} + Be^{-2t})$

c $x = t\left(\dfrac{3}{4e^2}e^{2t} + \dfrac{5}{4e^{-2}}e^{-2t}\right)$

Challenge

$y = A\ln x + B + 3x^2$

Chapter review 6

1 a $y = e^x\cos x + A\cos x$

   b $y = e^x\cos x - (1 + e^\pi)\cos x$

2 $y = -\frac{1}{10}(3\sin x + \cos x) + \frac{1}{10}e^{3x}$

3 $y = \dfrac{2(3e^{2x^2} - 1)}{3e^{2x^2} + 1}$

4 $y = e^{-\frac{1}{2}x}\left(A\cos\dfrac{\sqrt{3}}{2}x + B\sin\dfrac{\sqrt{3}}{2}x\right)$

5 $y = (A + Bx)e^{6x}$

6 $y = A + Be^{4x}$

7 $y = \cos kx + \dfrac{1}{k}\sin kx$

8 $y = e^x\sin 3x$

9 a $k = \frac{1}{9}$

   b $y = e^{2x}(A\cos 3x + B\sin 3x) + \frac{1}{9}e^{2x}$

10 $y = Ae^x + Be^{-x} + 2xe^x$

11 a $y = (A + Bx)e^{2x}$

   b They are part of the complementary function.

   c $k = 2$ and $y = (A + Bx + 2x^2)e^{2x}$

12 $y = \sin 2t + 2\cos 2t - \cos 3t$

13 a $k = 1, \mu = 2, \lambda = 3$

   b $y = Ae^x + Be^{2x} + xe^{2x} + 2x + 3$

14 a $y = 4e^{-\frac{x}{4}}\sin\frac{1}{2}x + x + 3$

   b As $x \to \infty$, $e^{-\frac{x}{4}} \to 0$, so $4e^{-\frac{x}{4}}\sin\frac{1}{2}x \to 0$ and $y \approx x + 3$.

15 $y = \frac{5}{6}e^{-2x} + \frac{1}{6}(\cos 3x - \sin 3x)$

16 a $x = Ae^{-4t} + Bte^{-4t} + \frac{1}{32}\sin 4t$

   b $x = \frac{1}{2}e^{-4t} + \frac{15}{8}te^{-4t} + \frac{1}{32}\sin 4t$

   c Will oscillate as a sine wave with amplitude $\frac{1}{32}$ and period $\dfrac{\pi}{2}$

17 $y = \frac{1}{2}\cos(\sin x) + \frac{5}{2}\sin(\sin x) + \frac{1}{2}e^{\sin x}$

Challenge

1 a $y = \pm\sqrt{\dfrac{x + c}{1 + x^2}}$ **b** $y = \sqrt{\dfrac{x + 4}{1 + x^2}}$

2 a $y = \dfrac{A}{x} + \dfrac{B}{x^2} + \frac{1}{2}\ln x - \frac{3}{4}$ **b** $y = \dfrac{4}{x} - \dfrac{9}{4x^2} + \frac{1}{2}\ln x - \frac{3}{4}$

3 a Let $u = \dfrac{dy}{dx}$, so equation becomes $\dfrac{du}{dx} = u^2$

$\Rightarrow \displaystyle\int \dfrac{1}{u^2}\,du = \int dx \Rightarrow -\dfrac{1}{u} = x + B$

$\Rightarrow \dfrac{dy}{dx} = -\dfrac{1}{x + B} \Rightarrow y = A - \ln(x + b)$

CHAPTER 7

Prior knowledge check

1 a $-3x^2\sin(1 + x^3)$ **b** $\dfrac{-(\sin x + \cos x)}{e^x\sin^2 x}$

2 Auxilliary equation $\lambda^2 + 2\lambda + 2 = 0$ has solution $\lambda = -1 \pm i$, so general solution is
$y(x) = Ae^{-x}\sin x + Be^{-x}\cos x$

Exercise 7A

1 a $f'(x) = 2e^{2x}, f''(x) = 4e^{2x}, f'''(x) = 2^3e^{2x} = 8e^{2x},$
   $f^{(n)}(x) = 2^n e^{2x}$

   b $f'(x) = n(1 + x)^{n-1}, f''(x) = n(n - 1)(1 + x)^{n-2},$
   $f'''(x) = n(n - 1)(n - 2)(1 + x)^{n-3}, f^{(n)}(x) = n!$

   c $f'(x) = e^x + xe^x, f''(x) = 2e^x + xe^x, f'''(x) = 3e^x + xe^x,$
   $f^{(n)}(x) = ne^x + xe^x$

   d $f'(x) = (1 + x)^{-1}, f''(x) = -(1 + x)^{-2}, f'''(x) = 2(1 + x)^{-3},$
   $f^{(n)}(x) = (-1)^{n-1}(n - 1)!(1 + x)^{-n}$

2 a $\dfrac{d^n y}{dx^n} = 3^n e^{2+3x} = 3^n y$ **b** e^2

3 a $\dfrac{dy}{dx} = 3 \times \cos 3x \times 2\sin 3x$
   $= 6\sin x\cos x = 3\sin 6x$

   b $\dfrac{d^2y}{dx^2} = 18\cos 6x, \dfrac{d^3y}{dx^3} = -108\sin 6x, \dfrac{d^4y}{dx^4} = -648\cos 6x$

   c 648

4 a $f'(x) = 2xe^{-x} - x^2e^{-x}$
   $f''(x) = (2e^{-x} - 2xe^{-x}) - (2xe^{-x} - x^2e^{-x})$
   $= e^{-x}(2 - 4x + x^2)$
   $f'''(x) = e^{-x}(-4 + 2x) - e^{-x}(2 - 4x + x^2)$
   $= e^{-x}(-6 + 6x - x^2)$

   b $f''''(x) = e^{-x}(6 - 2x) - e^{-x}(-6 + 6x - x^2)$
   $= e^{-x}(12 - 8x + x^2)$
   so $f''''(2) = e^{-2}(12 - 16 + 4) = 0$

5 a Given that $y = \sec x, \dfrac{dy}{dx} = \sec x\tan x$
   $\dfrac{d^2y}{dx^2} = \sec x(\sec^2 x) + (\sec x\tan x)\tan x$
   $= \sec x(\sec^2 x + \tan^2 x) = 2\sec^3 x - \sec x$

   b $\dfrac{d^3y}{dx^3} = 6\sec^2 x(\sec x\tan x) - \sec x\tan x$
   $= \sec x\tan x(6\sec^2 x - 1)$
   When $x = \dfrac{\pi}{4}, \dfrac{d^3y}{dx^3} = (\sqrt{2})(1)(6(2) - 1) = 11\sqrt{2}$

6 a $\dfrac{d^2}{dx^2}(y^2) = \dfrac{d}{dx}\left(2y\dfrac{dy}{dx}\right) = 2y\dfrac{d^2y}{dx^2} + 2\left(\dfrac{dy}{dx}\right)^2$

   b $2\left(y\dfrac{d^3y}{dx^3} + 3\dfrac{dy}{dx} \times \dfrac{d^2y}{dx^2}\right)$

7 a $f'(x) = \dfrac{1}{x + \sqrt{1 + x^2}} \times \left(1 + \dfrac{x}{\sqrt{1 + x^2}}\right) = \dfrac{1}{\sqrt{1 + x^2}}$
   So $\sqrt{1 + x^2}\,f'(x) = 1$

b Differentiating this equation w.r.t. x,

$$\sqrt{1+x^2}\,f''(x) + \frac{x}{\sqrt{1+x^2}}f'(x) = 0$$

$$\Rightarrow (1+x^2)f''(x) + xf'(x) = 0$$

c Differentiating this equation w.r.t. x

$$((1+x^2)f'''(x) + 2xf''(x)) + (f'(x) + xf''(x)) = 0$$

$$\Rightarrow (1+x^2)f'''(x) + 3xf''(x) + f'(x) = 0$$

d $f'(0) = 1$, $f''(0) = 0$, $f'''(0) = -1$

Exercise 7B

1 a $f(x) = (1-x)^{-1}$ $\Rightarrow f(0) = 1$

$f'(x) = -1(1-x)^{-2}(-1) = (1-x)^{-2}$ $\Rightarrow f'(0) = 1$

$f''(x) = -2(1-x)^{-3}(-1) = 2(1-x)^{-3}$ $\Rightarrow f''(0) = 2$

$f'''(x) = -(3 \times 2)(1-x)^{-4}(-1) = (3 \times 2)(1-x)^{-4}$

$\Rightarrow f'''(0) = 3!$

General term:

$f^{(r)}(x) = r(r-1)\dots2(1-x)^{-(r+1)} = r!(1-x)^{-(r+1)}$

$\Rightarrow f^{(r)}(0) = r!$

Using $f(x) = f(0) + f'(0)x + \dfrac{f''(0)}{2!}x^2 + \dots + \dfrac{f^{(r)}(0)}{r!}x^r + \dots$

$(1-x)^{-1} = 1 + x + \dfrac{2}{2!}x^2 + \dots + \dfrac{r!}{r!}x^r + \dots$

$= 1 + x + x^2 + \dots + x^r + \dots$

b $f(x) = \sqrt{1+x} = (1+x)^{\frac{1}{2}}$ $\Rightarrow f(0) = 1$

$f'(x) = \frac{1}{2}(1+x)^{-\frac{1}{2}}$ $\Rightarrow f'(0) = \frac{1}{2}$

$f''(x) = \frac{1}{2}\left(-\frac{1}{2}\right)(1+x)^{-\frac{3}{2}}$ $\Rightarrow f''(0) = -\frac{1}{4}$

$f'''(x) = \frac{1}{2}\left(-\frac{1}{2}\right)\left(-\frac{3}{2}\right)(1+x)^{-\frac{5}{2}}$ $\Rightarrow f'''(0) = \frac{3}{8}$

Using Maclaurin's expansion,

$\sqrt{1+x} = 1 + \frac{1}{2}x + \dfrac{\left(-\frac{1}{4}\right)}{2!}x^2 + \dfrac{\left(\frac{3}{8}\right)}{3!}x^3 - \dots$

$= 1 + \dfrac{x}{2} - \dfrac{x^2}{8} + \dfrac{x^3}{16} - \dots$

2 $f(x) = e^{\sin x}$ $\Rightarrow f(0) = 1$

$f'(x) = \cos x\, e^{\sin x}$ $\Rightarrow f'(0) = 1$

$f''(x) = \cos^2 x\, e^{\sin x} - \sin x\, e^{\sin x}$ $\Rightarrow f''(0) = 1$

Using Maclaurin's expansion,

$e^{\sin x} = 1 + x + \frac{1}{2!}x^2 + \dots = 1 + x + \frac{1}{2}x^2 \dots$

3 a $f(x) = \cos x$ $\Rightarrow f(0) = 1$

$f'(x) = -\sin x$ $\Rightarrow f'(0) = 0$

$f''(x) = -\cos x$ $\Rightarrow f''(0) = -1$

$f'''(x) = \sin x$ $\Rightarrow f'''(0) = 0$

$f''''(x) = \cos x$ $\Rightarrow f''''(0) = 1$

The process repeats itself every 4th derivative.

Using Maclaurin's expansion,

$\cos x = 1 + \dfrac{-1}{2!}x^2 + \dfrac{1}{4!}x^4 + \dots + \dfrac{(-1)^r}{(2r)!}x^{2r} + \dots$

$= 1 - \dfrac{x^2}{2!} + \dfrac{x^4}{4!} + \dots + \dfrac{(-1)^r}{(2r)!}x^{2r} + \dots$

b Using $\cos x \approx 1 - \dfrac{x^2}{2!} + \dfrac{x^4}{4!}$ with $x = \dfrac{\pi}{6}$,

$\cos x \approx 1 - \dfrac{\pi^2}{72} + \dfrac{\pi^4}{31104} = 0.86605\dots$ which is

correct to 3 d.p.

4 a $e = 2.718$ (3 d.p.)

b $\ln\left(\frac{6}{5}\right) = 0.182$ (3 d.p.)

5 a $1 + 3x + \frac{9}{2}x^2 + \frac{9}{2}x^3 + \frac{27}{8}x^4 + \dots$

b $2x - 2x^2 + \frac{8}{3}x^3 - 4x^4 + \dots$

c $x^2 - \dfrac{x^4}{3} + \dots$

6 $\cos\left(x - \dfrac{\pi}{4}\right) = \cos x \cos\dfrac{\pi}{4} + \sin x \sin\dfrac{\pi}{4}$

$= \dfrac{1}{\sqrt{2}}(\cos x + \sin x)$

$= \dfrac{1}{\sqrt{2}}\left(\left(1 - \dfrac{x^2}{2!} + \dfrac{x^4}{4!} - \dots\right) + \left(x - \dfrac{x^3}{3!} + \dfrac{x^5}{5!} - \dots\right)\right)$

$= \dfrac{1}{\sqrt{2}}\left(1 + x - \dfrac{x^2}{2} - \dfrac{x^3}{6} + \dfrac{x^4}{24} - \dots\right)$

7 a $f(x) = (1-x)^2\ln(1-x)$

$f'(x) = (1-x)^2 \times \dfrac{-1}{1-x} + 2(1-x)(-1)\ln(1-x)$

$= x - 1 - 2(1-x)\ln(1-x)$

$f''(x) = 1 - 2\left((1-x) \times \dfrac{-1}{1-x} + (-1)\ln(1-x)\right)$

$= 3 + 2\ln(1-x)$

b $f(0) = 0$, $f'(0) = -1$, $f''(0) = 3$, $f'''(0) = -2$

c $-x + \frac{3}{2}x^2 - \frac{1}{3}x^3$

8 a $\sin x = x - \dfrac{x^3}{3!} + \dfrac{x^5}{5!} - \dots = x - \frac{1}{6}x^3 + \frac{1}{120}x^5 - \dots$

$\cos x = 1 - \dfrac{x^2}{2!} + \dfrac{x^4}{4!} - \dots = 1 - \frac{1}{2}x^2 + \frac{1}{24}x^4 - \dots$

$3\sin x - 4x\cos x + x$

$= 3\left(x - \frac{1}{6}x^3 + \frac{1}{120}x^5 - \dots\right) - 4x\left(x - \frac{1}{2}x^3 + \frac{1}{24}x^5 - \dots\right) + x$

$= \frac{3}{2}x^3 - \frac{17}{120}x^5 + \dots$

b $\frac{3}{2}$

9 a $f'(x) = \dfrac{1}{\cos x} \times (-\sin x) = -\tan x$

b $f'(0) = 0$, $f''(0) = -1$, $f'''(0) = 0$, $f''''(0) = -2$

c $\dfrac{-x^2}{2} - \dfrac{x^4}{12}$

d $\ln\left(\cos\dfrac{\pi}{4}\right) = \ln(2^{-\frac{1}{2}}) = -\frac{1}{2}\ln 2$

And by the Maclaurin series we have also

$\ln\left(\cos\dfrac{\pi}{4}\right) \approx -\dfrac{\left(\frac{\pi}{4}\right)^2}{2} - \dfrac{\left(\frac{\pi}{4}\right)^4}{12}$

$\ln 2 \approx \dfrac{\pi^2}{16}\left(1 + \dfrac{\pi^2}{96}\right)$

10 $f(x) = \tan x \Rightarrow f(0) = 0$

$f'(x) = \sec^2 x \Rightarrow f'(0) = 1$

$f''(x) = 2\sec^2 x \tan x \Rightarrow f''(0) = 0$

$f'''(x) = 4\sec^2 x \tan^2 x + 2\sec^4 x = 6\sec^4 x - 4\sec^2 x$

$= 2(\sec^4 x + 2\sec^2 x \tan^2 x) \Rightarrow f'''(0) = 2$

$f''''(x) = 24\sec^4 x \tan x - 8\sec^2 x \tan x \Rightarrow f''''(0) = 0$

$f'''''(x) = 24\sec^4 x \tan^2 x + 24\sec^6 x - 8\sec^2 x \tan^2 x$

$\quad - 8\sec^4 x \Rightarrow f'''''(0) = 16$

So the Maclaurin series is

$0 + 1x + \dfrac{0}{2!}x^2 + \dfrac{2}{3!}x^3 + \dfrac{0}{4!}x^4 + \dfrac{16}{5!}x^5 + \dots$

$= x + \dfrac{1}{3}x^3 + \dfrac{2}{15}x^5 + \dots$

Challenge

a $e^x = 1 + x + \dfrac{x^2}{2!} + \dfrac{x^3}{3!}\dots + \dfrac{x^r}{r!} + \dots$

$a_r = \dfrac{x^r}{r!}$; $a_{r+1} = \dfrac{x^{r+1}}{(r+1)!}$

$\lim_{r\to\infty}\left|\dfrac{a_{r+1}}{a_r}\right| = \lim_{r\to\infty}\left|\dfrac{x^{r+1}}{(r+1)!} \times \dfrac{r!}{x^r}\right| = \lim_{r\to\infty}\dfrac{|x|}{r+1} < 1$

b $\ln(1+x) = x - \frac{x^2}{2} + \frac{x^3}{3} - \ldots + (-1)^{r+1}\frac{x^r}{r} + \ldots$

$a_r = (-1)^{r+1}\frac{x^r}{r}; \; a_{r+1} = (-1)^{r+2}\frac{x^{r+1}}{r+1}$

$\lim_{r\to\infty}\left|\frac{a_{r+1}}{a_r}\right| = \lim_{r\to\infty}\left|\frac{(-1)^{r+2}x^{r+1}}{r+1} \times \frac{r}{(-1)^{r+1}x^r}\right| = \lim_{r\to\infty}\left|\frac{rx}{r+1}\right|$

$= \lim_{r\to\infty}\left|\frac{x}{1+\frac{1}{r}}\right| = |x|$

So $\ln(1+x)$ converges for $-1 < x < 1$ and diverges for $x > 1$.

Exercise 7C

1 a $1 - x + \frac{x^2}{2} - \frac{x^3}{6} + \ldots$ valid for all values of x

b $1 + 4x + 8x^2 + \frac{32x^3}{3} + \ldots$ valid for all values of x

c $e\left(1 + x + \frac{x^2}{2} + \frac{x^3}{6} + \ldots\right)$ valid for all values of x

d $-x - \frac{x^2}{2} - \frac{x^3}{3} - \frac{x^4}{4} - \ldots$ $-1 \leqslant x < 1$

e $\frac{x}{2} - \frac{x^3}{48} + \frac{x^5}{3840} - \frac{x^7}{645\,120} + \ldots$ valid for all values of x

f $\ln 2 + \frac{3x}{2} - \frac{9x^2}{8} + \frac{9x^3}{8} + \ldots$ $-\frac{2}{3} < x \leqslant \frac{2}{3}$

2 a $\ln(1+x) = x - \frac{x^2}{2} + \frac{x^3}{3} - \frac{x^4}{4} + \frac{x^5}{5} - \ldots, \; -1 < x \leqslant 1$

$\ln(1-x) = -x - \frac{x^2}{2} - \frac{x^3}{3} - \frac{x^4}{4} + \frac{x^5}{5} - \ldots, \; -1 \leqslant x < 1$

$\ln\left(\frac{1+x}{1-x}\right) = \ln(1+x) - \ln(1-x) = 2\left(x + \frac{x^3}{3} + \frac{x^5}{5} + \ldots\right)$

As x must be in both the intervals $-1 < x \leqslant 1$ and $-1 \leqslant x < 1$, x must be in the interval $-1 < x < 1$.

b $\left(x + \frac{x^3}{3} + \frac{x^5}{5} + \ldots\right), \; -1 < x < 1$

c $x = -\frac{1}{5}; \; -0.0027\%$ (4 d.p.)

d $\ln\left(\frac{1+\frac{3}{5}}{1-\frac{3}{5}}\right)^{\frac{1}{2}} = \frac{1}{2}\ln(4) = \ln(2)$

and the series from **b** gives

$\frac{3}{5} + \frac{\left(\frac{3}{5}\right)^3}{3} + \frac{\left(\frac{3}{5}\right)^5}{5} + 0.69\ldots$

Which is $\ln 2$ correct to 2 d.p.

3 $e^{2x} = 1 + 2x + \frac{(2x)^2}{2!} + \frac{(2x)^3}{3!} + \ldots = 1 + 2x + 2x^2 + \frac{4x^3}{3} + \ldots$

$e^{-x} = 1 - x + \frac{(-x)^2}{2!} + \frac{(-x)^3}{3!} + \ldots = 1 - x + \frac{x^2}{2} - \frac{x^3}{6} + \ldots$

So $e^{2x} - e^{-x} \approx 3x + \frac{3}{2}x^2$ if terms in x^3 and above may be neglected.

4 a $3x\sin 2x = 3x\left(2x - \frac{4x^3}{3} + \ldots\right)$

$\cos 3x = \left(1 - \frac{9x^2}{2} + \frac{27x^4}{8} - \ldots\right)$

So we get that

$3x\sin 2x - \cos 3x = 6x^2 - 4x^3 - \left(1 - \frac{9x^2}{2} + \frac{27x^4}{8}\right) + \ldots$

$= -1 + \frac{21}{2}x^2 - \frac{59}{8}x^4 + \ldots$

b $\frac{21}{2}$

5 a $x - \frac{5x^2}{2} + \frac{7x^3}{3} - \frac{17x^4}{4} + \ldots, \; \frac{1}{2} < x \leqslant \frac{1}{2}$

b $2\ln 3 + \frac{2x}{3} - \frac{x^2}{9} + \frac{2x^3}{81} - \frac{x^4}{162} + \ldots, \; -3 < x \leqslant 3$

6 a $1 - 2x^2 + \frac{2x^4}{3} - \frac{4x^6}{45} + \frac{2x^8}{315} - \ldots$

b $x^2 - \frac{x^4}{3} + \frac{2x^6}{45} - \frac{x^8}{315} + \ldots$

7 $p = \frac{2}{3}, \; q = -\frac{1}{8}$

8 a $x + 2x^2 + \frac{17x^3}{6} + \frac{11x^4}{3} + \ldots$

b 1

9 a $(1 - 3x)\ln(1 + 2x)$

$= (1 - 3x)\left(2x - 2x^2 + \frac{8x^3}{3} - 4x^4 + \ldots\right)$

$= 2x - 8x^2 + \frac{26}{3}x^3 - 12x^4 + \ldots$

b $e^{2x}\sin x$

$= \left(1 + 2x + \frac{(2x)^2}{2!} + \frac{(2x)^3}{3!} + \frac{(2x)^4}{4!} + \ldots\right)\left(x - \frac{x^3}{3!} + \ldots\right)$

$= \left(1 + 2x + 2x^2 + \frac{4x^3}{3} + \frac{2x^4}{3} + \ldots\right)\left(x - \frac{x^3}{6} + \ldots\right)$

$= x + 2x^2 + \frac{11}{6}x^3 + x^4 + \ldots$

c $\sqrt{1+x^2}\,e^{-x} = (1 + x^2)^{\frac{1}{2}}\,e^{-x}$

$= \left(1 + \frac{1}{2}x^2 + \left(\frac{1}{2}\right)\left(-\frac{1}{2}\right)\frac{(x^2)^2}{2!} + \ldots\right)\left(1 - x + \frac{x^2}{2!} - \frac{x^3}{3!} + \frac{x^4}{4!} + \ldots\right)$

$= \left(1 + \frac{x^2}{2} - \frac{x^4}{8} + \ldots\right)\left(1 - x + \frac{x^2}{2} - \frac{x^3}{6} + \frac{x^4}{24} + \ldots\right)$

$= 1 - x + x^2 - \frac{2}{3}x^3 + \frac{1}{6}x^4 + \ldots$

10 a $1 - \frac{x^2}{2} + \frac{x^4}{8} - \frac{x^6}{48} + \frac{x^8}{384} - \ldots$

b 1.711 (3 d.p.)

11 a $e^{px}\sin 3x$

$= \left(1 + px + \frac{(px)^2}{2!} + \frac{(px)^3}{3!} + \ldots\right)\left(3x - \frac{(3x)^3}{3!} + \ldots\right)$

$= \left(1 + px + \frac{p^2x^2}{2} + \frac{p^3x^3}{6} + \ldots\right)\left(3x - \frac{9x^3}{2} + \ldots\right)$

$= 3x + 3px^2 + \frac{3(p^2 - 3)x^3}{2} + \ldots$

b $q = -2 \quad p = \frac{2}{3} \quad k = -\frac{13}{2}$

12 a $e^{x-\ln x} = e^x \times e^{-\ln x} = e^x \times e^{\ln x^{-1}} = \frac{e^x}{x}$

$\Rightarrow e^{x-\ln x}\sin x = \frac{e^x\sin x}{x}$

$f(x) = \frac{\left(1 + x + \frac{x^2}{2} + \frac{x^3}{6} + \ldots\right)\left(x - \frac{x^3}{6} + \ldots\right)}{x}, \; x > 0$

$= \left(1 + x + \frac{x^2}{2} + \frac{x^3}{6} + \ldots\right)\left(1 - \frac{x^2}{6} + \ldots\right)$

$= 1 + x + \frac{x^2}{3}$ ignoring terms in x^4 and above

b $f(0.1) = \frac{e^{0.1}\sin 0.1}{0.1} = 1.103329\ldots$

Using the approximation in part **a**,

$f(0.1) = 1 + 0.1 + 0.00333333 = 1.103333\ldots$

This result is correct to 6 s.f.

13 a $\frac{d^4y}{dx^4} = 16(\sin 2x - \cos 2x) = 16y$

b $y = -1 + 2x + 2x^2 - \frac{4}{3}x^3 - \frac{2}{3}x^4 + \ldots$

Challenge

a $\gamma = 1 + \frac{1}{2}\beta^2 + \frac{3}{8}\beta^4$

b 19.6 years (3 s.f.)   **c** 0.0027%

d As β is larger, the error in γ is larger, so the approximation would be less accurate.

Exercise 7D

1 a $1 + \frac{1}{2}(x-1) - \frac{1}{8}(x-1)^2 + \frac{1}{16}(x-1)^3 - \frac{5}{128}(x-1)^4 + \dots$

b 1.095 (3 d.p.)

2 a $1 + \frac{x-e}{e} - \frac{(x-e)^2}{2e^2} + \dots$

b $\sqrt{3} + 4\left(x - \frac{\pi}{3}\right) + 4\sqrt{3}\left(x - \frac{\pi}{3}\right)^2 + \frac{40}{3}\left(x - \frac{\pi}{3}\right)^3 + \dots$

c $\cos 1 - \sin 1\,(x-1) - \frac{\cos 1}{2}(x-1)^2$
$+ \frac{\sin 1}{6}(x-1)^3 + \frac{\cos 1}{24}(x-1)^4 + \dots$

3 a i $\frac{\sqrt{2}}{2}\left(1 - x - \frac{1}{2}x^2 + \frac{1}{6}x^3 + \frac{1}{24}x^4 - \dots\right)$

ii $\ln 5 + \frac{1}{5}x - \frac{1}{50}x^2 + \frac{1}{375}x^3 - \frac{1}{2500}x^4 + \dots$

iii $\frac{1}{2}\left(-\sqrt{3} + x + \frac{\sqrt{3}}{2!}x^2 - \frac{1}{3!}x^3 - \frac{\sqrt{3}}{4!}x^4 + \dots\right)$

b 1.649 (4 s.f.)

4 b $e^{-1}\left(-1 + \frac{1}{2}(x+1)^2 + \frac{1}{3}(x+1)^3 + \frac{1}{8}(x+1)^4 + \dots\right)$

5 a $(x-1) + \frac{5}{2}(x-1)^2 + \frac{11}{6}(x-1)^3 + \frac{1}{4}(x-1)^4 + \dots$

b 0.4059 (4 d.p.)

6 $-\frac{3}{4} + \frac{25}{16}x - \frac{75}{64}x^2 + \dots$

7 $\frac{\sqrt{3}}{2} + 1\left(x - \frac{\pi}{6}\right) - \sqrt{3}\left(x - \frac{\pi}{6}\right)^2 - \frac{2}{3}\left(x - \frac{\pi}{6}\right)^3$
$+ \frac{\sqrt{3}}{3}\left(x - \frac{\pi}{6}\right)^4 + \dots$

8 a $\left.\frac{dy}{dx}\right|_3 = -\frac{1}{16}$

$\left.\frac{d^2y}{dx^2}\right|_3 = \frac{3}{128}$

b $y = \frac{1}{\sqrt{(1+x)}} = \frac{1}{2} - \frac{1}{16}(x-3) + \frac{3}{256}(x-3)^2 + \dots$

9 $f(x) = \ln x, f'(x) = \frac{1}{x}, f''(x) = -\frac{1}{x^2}, f'''(x) = \frac{2}{x^3}$

$f^k(x) = (-1)^{k-1}\frac{(k-1)!}{x^k} \Rightarrow f^k(2) = (-1)^{k-1}\frac{(k-1)!}{2^k}$

Substituting into the Taylor series expansion gives

$f(x) = \ln 2 + \sum_{n=1}^{\infty}\frac{1}{n!}(-1)^{n-1}\frac{(n-1)!}{2^n}(x-2)^n$

$= \ln 2 + \sum_{n=1}^{\infty}(-1)^{n-1}\frac{(x-2)^n}{n\,2^n}$

Challenge

a $\ln(\cos 2x) = -2(x-\pi)^2 - \frac{4}{3}(x-\pi)^4 - \dots$

b -0.1433 (4 d.p.)

Exercise 7E

1 $y = 1 + \frac{x}{2} + x^2 + \frac{x^3}{3} + \frac{x^4}{6} + \dots$

2 $y = x - \frac{x^3}{6} + \dots$

3 $y = 2 - x + x^2 - \frac{x^3}{6} \dots$

4 $y = 1 + 2x - \frac{1}{2}x^2 - \frac{2}{3}x^3 + \frac{1}{8}x^4 + \dots$

5 $y = 1 - (x-1) + \frac{5}{2}(x-1)^2 - \frac{5}{3}(x-1)^3 + \dots$

6 $y = 1 + x - x^2 + \frac{1}{2}x^4 + \dots$

7 a Differentiating $(1+2x)\frac{dy}{dx} = x + 2y^2$ with respect to x

$(1+2x)\frac{d^2y}{dx^2} + 2\frac{dy}{dx} = 1 + 4y\frac{dy}{dx}$ **(1)**

Differentiating **(1)** gives

$(1+2x)\frac{d^3y}{dx^3} + 2\frac{d^2y}{dx^2} + 2\frac{d^2y}{dx^2} = 4y\frac{d^2y}{dx^2} + 4\left(\frac{dy}{dx}\right)^2$

$\Rightarrow (1+2x)\frac{d^3y}{dx^3} + 4(1-y)\frac{d^2y}{dx^2} = 4\left(\frac{dy}{dx}\right)^2$ **(2)**

b $y = 1 + 2x + \frac{5}{2}x^2 + \frac{8}{3}x^3 \dots$

8 $y = \sqrt{2} + \sqrt{2}\left(x - \frac{\pi}{4}\right) + \frac{3\sqrt{2}}{2}\left(x - \frac{\pi}{4}\right)^2 + \dots$

9 a i Differentiating $\frac{dy}{dx} - x^2 - y^2 = 0$ with respect to x

gives $\frac{d^2y}{dx^2} - 2y\frac{dy}{dx} - 2x = 0$ **(1)**

ii Differentiating **(1)** gives

$\frac{d^3y}{dx^3} - 2y\frac{d^2y}{dx^2} - 2\left(\frac{dy}{dx}\right)^2 - 2 = 0$

So $\frac{d^3y}{dx^3} - 2y\frac{d^2y}{dx^2} - 2\left(\frac{dy}{dx}\right)^2 = 2$ **(2)**

b $\frac{d^4y}{dx^4} - 2y\frac{d^3y}{dx^3} - 6\left(\frac{dy}{dx}\right)\frac{d^2y}{dx^2} = 0$

c $y = 1 + x + x^2 + \frac{4}{3}x^3 + \frac{7}{6}x^4 + \dots$

10 Differentiating $\cos x\frac{dy}{dx} + y\sin x + 2y^3 = 0$ **(1)**

with respect to x gives

$\cos x\frac{d^2y}{dx^2} - \sin x\frac{dy}{dx} + y\cos x + \sin x\frac{dy}{dx} + 6y^2\frac{dy}{dx} = 0$ **(2)**

Differentiating again

$\cos x\frac{d^3y}{dx^3} - \sin x\frac{d^2y}{dx^2} - y\sin x + \cos x\frac{dy}{dx} + 6y^2\frac{d^2y}{dx^2} + 12y\left(\frac{dy}{dx}\right)^2 = 0$ **(3)**

Substituting $x_0 = 0, y_0 = 1$ into **(1)** gives $\left.\frac{dy}{dx}\right|_0 + 2(1) = 0$,
so $\left.\frac{dy}{dx}\right|_0 = -2$

Substituting $x_0 = 0, y_0 = 1, \left.\frac{dy}{dx}\right|_0 = -2$ into **(2)** gives

$\left.\frac{d^2y}{dx^2}\right|_0 + 1 + 6(1)(-2) = 0$, so $\left.\frac{d^2y}{dx^2}\right|_0 = 11$

Substituting $x_0 = 0, y_0 = 1, \left.\frac{dy}{dx}\right|_0 = -2, \left.\frac{d^2y}{dx^2}\right|_0 = 11$
into **(3)** gives

$\left.\frac{d^3y}{dx^3}\right|_0 + (1)(-2) + 6(1)(11) + 12(1)(-2)^2$,

so $\left.\frac{d^3y}{dx^2}\right|_0 = -112$

Substituting these values into the Taylor series, gives

$y = 1 + (-2)x + \frac{11}{2!}x^2 + \frac{(-112)}{3!}x^3 + \dots$

$y = 1 - 2x + \frac{11}{2}x^2 - \frac{56}{3}x^3 + \dots$

Ignoring terms in x^4 and higher powers,

$y \approx 1 - 2x + \frac{11}{2}x^2 - \frac{56}{3}x^3$

11 a Repeated differentiation gives:

$\frac{d^3y}{dx^3} = 4\frac{dy}{dx} + 4x\frac{d^2y}{dx^2} - 2\frac{dy}{dx} = 2\frac{dy}{dx} + 4x\frac{d^2y}{dx^2}$

$\frac{d^4y}{dx^4} = 2\frac{d^2y}{dx^2} + 4\frac{d^2y}{dx^2} + 4x\frac{d^3y}{dx^3} = 6\frac{d^2y}{dx^2} + 4x\frac{d^3y}{dx^3}$

$\frac{d^5y}{dx^5} = 6\frac{d^3y}{dx^3} + 4\frac{d^3y}{dx^3} + 4x\frac{d^4y}{dx^4} = 4x\frac{d^4y}{dx^4} + 10\frac{d^3y}{dx^3}$

$p = 4$ and $q = 10$

b $y = 2 + 2(x - 1) + 2(x - 1)^2 + \frac{10}{3}(x - 1)^3 + \frac{13}{3}(x - 1)^4$
$+ \frac{77}{15}(x - 1)^5 + \dots$

Chapter review 7

1 a $\dfrac{d^n y}{dx^n} = (-2)^n e^{1-2x}$

b $\dfrac{d^8 y}{dx^8} = (-2)^8 e^{1 - 2\ln 32} = 256 e^{1 + \ln 32^{-2}}$

$= 256(e^1)\left(e^{\ln\frac{1}{1024}}\right) = \dfrac{256}{1024}e^1 = \dfrac{e}{4}$

2 a $f'(0) = \frac{1}{2}$, $f''(0) = \frac{1}{4}$

b $f'''(x) = \dfrac{(1 + e^x)^2 e^x - e^x 2(1 + e^x)e^x}{(1 + e^x)^4} = \dfrac{e^x(1 - e^x)}{(1 + e^x)^3}$

$f'''(0) = 0$

c $\ln 2 + \dfrac{x}{2} + \dfrac{x^2}{8} + \dots$

3 a $1 - 8x^2 + \frac{32}{3}x^4 - \frac{256}{45}x^6 + \dots$

b $\cos 4x = 1 - 2\sin^2 2x$

so $2\sin^2 2x = 1 - \cos 4x = 8x^2 - \frac{32}{3}x^4 + \frac{256}{45}x^6 + \dots$

so $\sin^2 2x = 4x^2 - \frac{16}{3}x^4 + \frac{128}{45}x^6 + \dots$

4 Using $e^x = 1 + x + \dfrac{x^2}{2} + \dfrac{x^3}{6} + \dfrac{x^4}{24} + \dots$ and

$\cos x = 1 - \dfrac{x^2}{2} + \dfrac{x^4}{24} - \dots$

$e^{\cos x} = e^{\left(1 - \frac{x^2}{2} + \frac{x^4}{24}\right)} = e \times e^{-\frac{x^2}{2}} \times e^{\frac{x^4}{24}}$

$= e\left(1 + \left(-\dfrac{x^2}{2}\right) + \dfrac{1}{2}\left(-\dfrac{x^2}{2}\right)^2 + \dots\right)\left(1 + \dfrac{x^4}{24} + \dots\right)$

$= e\left(1 - \dfrac{x^2}{2} + \dfrac{x^4}{8} + \dfrac{x^4}{24} + \dots\right) = e\left(1 - \dfrac{x^2}{2} + \dfrac{x^4}{6} + \dots\right)$

5 $-3x^2 - 2x^3 - \dots$

6 $x + \dfrac{x^3}{6} + \dots$

7 a $\dfrac{d}{dx}(e^x)$

$= \dfrac{d}{dx}\left(1 + x + \dfrac{x^2}{2!} + \dfrac{x^3}{3!} + \dfrac{x^4}{4!} + \dots + \dfrac{x^r}{r!} + \dfrac{x^{r+1}}{(r+1)!} + \dots\right)$

$= 0 + 1 + \dfrac{2x}{2!} + \dfrac{3x^2}{3!} + \dfrac{4x^3}{4!} + \dots + \dfrac{(r+1)x^r}{(r+1)!} + \dots$

$= 1 + x + \dfrac{x^2}{2!} + \dfrac{x^3}{3!} + \dots + \dfrac{x^r}{r!} + \dots = e^x$

b $\dfrac{d}{dx}(\sin x) = \dfrac{d}{dx}\left(x - \dfrac{x^3}{3!} + \dfrac{x^5}{5!} - \dots + (-1)^r \dfrac{x^{2r+1}}{(2r+1)!} + \dots\right)$

$= 1 - \dfrac{3x^2}{3!} + \dfrac{5x^4}{5!} - \dots + (-1)^r \dfrac{(2r+1)x^{2r}}{(2r+1)!} + \dots$

$= 1 - \dfrac{x^2}{2!} + \dfrac{x^4}{4!} - \dots + (-1)^r \dfrac{x^{2r}}{(2r)!} \dots = \cos x$

c $\dfrac{d}{dx}(\cos x) = \dfrac{d}{dx}\left(1 - \dfrac{x^2}{2!} + \dfrac{x^4}{4!} - \dfrac{x^6}{6!} \dots + (-1)^r \dfrac{x^{2r}}{(2r)!}\right.$

$\left. + (-1)^{r+1} \dfrac{x^{2r+2}}{(2r+2)!} + \dots\right)$

$= -\dfrac{2x}{2!} + \dfrac{4x^3}{4!} - \dfrac{6x^5}{6!} \dots + (-1)^r \dfrac{2rx^{2r-1}}{(2r)!}$

$+ (-1)^{r+1} \dfrac{(2r+2)x^{2r+1}}{(2r+2)!} + .$

$= -\left(x - \dfrac{x^3}{3!} + \dfrac{x^5}{5!} - \dots + (-1)^r \dfrac{x^{2r+1}}{(2r+1)!}\right) = -\sin x$

8 a $\cos x = 1 - \left(\dfrac{x^2}{2} - \dfrac{x^4}{24} + \dots\right)$

$\Rightarrow \sec x = \dfrac{1}{\cos x} = \left(1 - \left(\dfrac{x^2}{2} - \dfrac{x^4}{24} + \dots\right)\right)^{-1}$

$\sec x = 1 + (-1)\left(-\left(\dfrac{x^2}{2} - \dfrac{x^4}{24}\right)\right)$

$+ \dfrac{(-1)(-2)}{2!}\left(-\left(\dfrac{x^2}{2} - \dfrac{x^4}{24}\right)\right)^2 + \dots$

$= 1 + \tfrac{1}{2}x^2 + \tfrac{5}{24}x^4 + \dots$

b $x + \dfrac{x^3}{3} + \dfrac{2}{15}x^5 + \dots$

9 $1 + x - 4x^2 - \dfrac{13}{3}x^3 + \dots$

10 $f'(x) = (1 + x)(1 + 2\ln(1 + x))$

$f''(x) = 3 + 2\ln(1 + x)$

$f'''(x) = \dfrac{2}{1 + x}$

$(1 + x)^2 \ln(1 + x) = x + \tfrac{3}{2}x^2 + \tfrac{1}{3}x^3 + \dots$

11 a $x - \dfrac{x^2}{2} + \dfrac{x^3}{6} - \dfrac{x^4}{12} + \dots$

b 0.116 (3 d.p.)

12 a $f(x) = e^{\tan x} = e^{x + \frac{x^3}{3} + \dots} = e^{x \dots} \times e^{\frac{x^3}{3}}$

$= \left(1 + x + \dfrac{x^2}{2!} + \dfrac{x^3}{3!} + \dots\right)\left(1 + \dfrac{x^3}{3} + \dots\right)$

$= 1 + x + \dfrac{x^2}{2} + \dfrac{x^3}{2} + \dots$

b $1 - x + \dfrac{x^2}{2} - \dfrac{x^3}{2} + \dots$

13 a $f(x) = \ln\cos x$ $f(0) = 0$

$f'(x) = \dfrac{-\sin x}{\cos x} = -\tan x$ $f'(0) = 0$

$f''(x) = -\sec^2 x$ $f''(0) = -1$

$f'''(x) = -2\sec^2 x \tan x$ $f'''(0) = 0$

$f''''(x) = -2\sec^4 x - 4\sec^2 x \tan^2 x$ $f''''(0) = -2$

Substituting into Maclaurin,

$\ln\cos x = (-1)\dfrac{x^2}{2!} + (-2)\dfrac{x^4}{4!} + \dots = -\dfrac{x^2}{2} - \dfrac{x^4}{12} + \dots$

b Using $1 + \cos x = 2\cos^2\dfrac{x}{2}$,

$\ln(1 + \cos x) = \ln 2\cos^2\dfrac{x}{2} = \ln 2 + 2\ln\cos\dfrac{x}{2}$

so $\ln(1 + \cos x) = \ln 2 + 2\left(-\dfrac{1}{2}\left(\dfrac{x}{2}\right)^2 - \dfrac{1}{12}\left(\dfrac{x}{2}\right)^4 - \dots\right)$

$= \ln 2 - \dfrac{x^2}{4} - \dfrac{x^4}{96} - \dots$

14 a $\dfrac{dy}{dx} = 3(e^{3x} + e^{-3x})$, $\dfrac{d^2 y}{dx^2} = 9(e^{3x} + e^{-3x})$,

$\dfrac{d^3 y}{dx^3} = 27(e^{3x} + e^{-3x})$, $\dfrac{d^4 y}{dx^4} = 81(e^{3x} - e^{-3x}) = 81y$

b $y = 6x + 9x^3 + \dfrac{81}{20}x^5 + \dots$

c $\dfrac{2(3)^{2n-1}x^{2n-1}}{(2n - 1)!}$

15 Let $f(x) = \left(x - \dfrac{\pi}{4}\right)\cot x$ and $a = \dfrac{\pi}{4} \Rightarrow f(a) = 0$

$f'(x) = \left(x - \dfrac{\pi}{4}\right)(-\csc^2 x) + \cot x \Rightarrow f'(a) = 1$

$f''(x) = \left(x - \dfrac{\pi}{4}\right)2\cot x\csc^2 x + (-2\csc^2 x) \Rightarrow f''(a) = -4$

$f'''(x) = \left(x - \dfrac{\pi}{4}\right)(-2\csc^4 x - 4\cot^2 x\csc^2 x)$

$+ 6\cot x\csc^2 x \Rightarrow f'''(a) = 12$

Substituting into the Taylor series expansion gives

$f(x) = 0 + 1\left(x - \dfrac{\pi}{4}\right) + \dfrac{-4}{2!}\left(x - \dfrac{\pi}{4}\right)^2 + \dfrac{12}{3!}\left(x - \dfrac{\pi}{4}\right)^3 + \dots$

$= \left(x - \dfrac{\pi}{4}\right) - 2\left(x - \dfrac{\pi}{4}\right)^2 + 2\left(x - \dfrac{\pi}{4}\right)^3 + \dots$ as required

16 a $f'(0) = \frac{1}{2}$, $f''(0) = \frac{1}{4}$

b $f'''(x) = \dfrac{e^x(e^x - 1)}{(e^x + 1)^3} \Rightarrow f'''(0) = \dfrac{1(1 - 1)}{(1 + 1)^3} = 0$

c $\ln 2 + \dfrac{x}{2} + \dfrac{x^2}{8} + \dots$

$x < 0$

17 a $1 - 8x^2 + \dfrac{32}{3}x^4 - \dfrac{256}{45}x^6 + \dots$

18 $e^{\cos x} = e(e^{\cos x - 1})$

$$= e\left(1 + \left(-\frac{x^2}{2} + \frac{x^4}{24} + \dots\right) + \frac{\left(-\frac{x^2}{2} + \dots\right)^2}{2} + \dots\right)$$

$$= e\left(1 - \frac{x^2}{2} + \frac{x^4}{24} + \frac{x^4}{8} + \dots\right) \approx e\left(1 - \frac{x^2}{2} + \frac{x^4}{6}\right)$$

19 a $y = 2x + \frac{3}{2}x^2 + \frac{1}{2}x^3 + \dots$ **b** 0.2155

20 $-3x^2 - 2x^3 - \dots$

21 $y = 2 + 4x + x^2 - \frac{2}{3}x^3 + \dots$

22 a $y = x + \frac{x^3}{6} + \dots$ **b** $\frac{2}{3}$

23 a $\frac{d}{dx}(e^x) = \frac{d}{dx}\left(1 + x + \frac{x^2}{2!} + \frac{x^3}{3!} + \frac{x^4}{4!} + \dots + \frac{x^r}{r!} + \frac{x^{r+1}}{(r+1)!} + \dots\right)$

$$= 1 + \frac{2x}{2!} + \frac{3x^2}{3!} + \frac{4x^3}{4!} + \dots + \frac{(r+1)x^r}{(r+1)!} + \dots$$

$$= 1 + x + \frac{x^2}{2!} + \frac{x^3}{3!} + \dots + \frac{x^r}{r!} + \dots$$

$$= e^x$$

b $\frac{d}{dx}(\sin x) = \frac{d}{dx}\left(x - \frac{x^3}{3!} + \frac{x^5}{5!} - \dots + (-1)^r \frac{x^{2r+1}}{(2r+1)!} + \dots\right)$

$$= 1 - \frac{3x^2}{3!} + \frac{5x^4}{5!} - \dots + (-1)^r \frac{(2r+1)x^{2r}}{(2r+1)!} + \dots$$

$$= 1 - \frac{x^2}{2!} + \frac{x^4}{4!} - \frac{x^6}{6!} + \dots + (-1)^r \frac{x^{2r}}{(2r)!} + \dots = \cos x$$

c $\frac{d}{dx}(\cos x) = \frac{d}{dx}\left(1 - \frac{x^2}{2!} + \frac{x^4}{4!} - \frac{x^6}{6!} + \dots + (-1)^r \frac{x^{2r}}{(2r)!} + \right.$

$$\left. (-1)^{r+1} \frac{x^{2r+2}}{(2r+2)!} + \dots\right)$$

$$= -\frac{2x}{2!} + \frac{4x^3}{4!} - \frac{6x^5}{6!} + \dots + (-1)^r \frac{2rx^{2r-1}}{(2r)!} + $$

$$(-1)^{r+1} \frac{(2r+2)x^{2r+1}}{(2r+2)!} + \dots$$

$$= -x + \frac{x^3}{3!} - \frac{x^5}{5!} + \dots + (-1)^{r+1} \frac{x^{2r+1}}{(2r+1)!} + \dots$$

$$= -\left(x - \frac{x^3}{3!} + \frac{x^5}{5!} - \dots + (-1)^r \frac{x^{2r+1}}{(2r+1)!} + \dots\right)$$

$$= -\sin x$$

24 $y = 2(x-1) + \frac{1}{2}(x-1)^2 - \frac{1}{2}(x-1)^3 + \dots$

25 a You can write $\cos x = 1 - \left(\frac{x^2}{2} - \frac{x^4}{24} + \dots\right)$; it is not necessary to have higher powers

$$\sec x = \frac{1}{\cos x} = \frac{1}{1 - \left(\frac{x^2}{2} - \frac{x^4}{24} + \dots\right)}$$

$$= \left(1 - \left(\frac{x^2}{2} - \frac{x^4}{24} + \dots\right)\right)^{-1}$$

Using the binomial expansion but only requring powers up to x^4

$$\sec x = 1 + (-1)\left(-\left(\frac{x^2}{2} - \frac{x^4}{24}\right)\right)$$

$$+ \frac{(-1)(-2)}{2!}\left(-\left(\frac{x^2}{2} - \frac{x^4}{24}\right)\right)^2 + \dots$$

$$= 1 + \left(\frac{x^2}{2} - \frac{x^4}{24}\right) + \frac{x^4}{4} + \text{higher powers of } x$$

$$= 1 + \frac{x^2}{2} + \frac{5}{24}x^4 + \dots$$

b $x + \frac{x^3}{3} + \frac{2}{15}x^5 + \dots$

26 $1 + x - 4x^2 - \frac{13}{3}x^3 + \dots$

27 a $y = 2 + x - x^2 - \frac{x^3}{6} + \dots$

b Differentiating with respect to x gives

$$\frac{d^4y}{dx^4} + 2x\frac{d^2y}{dx^2} + 2\frac{dy}{dx} + x^2\frac{d^3y}{dx^3} + 2x\frac{d^2y}{dx^2} + \frac{d^2y}{dx^2} = 0 \quad \textbf{(1)}$$

Substituting $x = 0$, $\left.\frac{dy}{dx}\right|_0 = 1$, $\left.\frac{d^2y}{dx^2}\right|_0 = -2$

and $\left.\frac{d^3y}{dx^3}\right|_0 = -1$ into **(1)** gives,

at $x = 0$, $\frac{d^4y}{dx^4} + 2(1) + (-2) = 0$, so $\frac{d^4y}{dx^4} = 0$

28 a $f'(x) = (1+x)^2 \frac{1}{1+x} + 2(1+x)\ln(1+x)$

$$= (1+x)(1 + 2\ln(1+x))$$

$$f''(x) = (1+x)\left(\frac{2}{1+x}\right) + (1 + 2\ln(1+x))$$

$$= 3 + 2\ln(1+x)$$

$$f'''(x) = \frac{2}{1+x}$$

b $x + \frac{3}{2}x^2 + \frac{1}{3}x^3 + \dots$

29 a $x - \frac{x^2}{2} + \frac{x^3}{6} - \frac{x^4}{12} + \dots$ **b** 0.116 (3 d.p.)

30 a $f(x) = e^{\tan x} = e^{x + \frac{x^3}{3} + \dots} = e^x \times e^{\frac{x^3}{3}}$

(As only terms up to x^3 are required, only first two terms of $\tan x$ are needed.)

$$= \left(1 + x + \frac{x^2}{2!} + \frac{x^3}{3!} + \dots\right)\left(1 + \frac{x^3}{3} + \dots\right)$$

no other terms required.

$$= \left(1 + \frac{x^3}{3} + x + \frac{x^2}{2!} + \frac{x^3}{3!} + \dots\right)$$

$$= 1 + x + \frac{x^2}{2} + \frac{x^3}{2} + \dots$$

b $1 - x + \frac{x^2}{2} - \frac{x^3}{2} + \dots$

31 a $\frac{d^3y}{dx^3} = -\frac{1}{y}\left(\frac{dy}{dx}\left(3\frac{d^2y}{dx^2} + 1\right)\right)$

b $y = 1 + x - x^2 + \frac{5x^3}{6} + \dots$

c The approximation is best for small values of x (close to 0). $x = 0.2$, therefore, would be acceptable, but not $x = 50$.

32 a
$f(x) = \ln\cos x$	$f(0) = 0$
$f'(x) = \frac{-\sin x}{\cos x} = -\tan x$	$f'(0) = 0$
$f''(x) = -\sec^2 x$	$f''(0) = -1$
$f'''(x) = -2\sec^2 x\tan x$	$f'''(0) = 0$
$f''''(x) = -2\sec^4 x - 4\sec^2 x\tan^2 x$	$f''''(0) = -2$

Substituting into Maclaurin:

$$\ln\cos x = (-1)\frac{x^2}{2!} + (-2)\frac{x^4}{4!} + \dots = -\frac{x^2}{2} - \frac{x^4}{12} - \dots$$

b Using $1 + \cos x \equiv 2\cos^2\left(\frac{x}{2}\right)$,

$$\ln(1 + \cos x) = \ln\left(2\cos^2\left(\frac{x}{2}\right)\right) = \ln 2 + 2\ln\cos\left(\frac{x}{2}\right)$$

so $\ln(1 + \cos x) = \ln 2 + 2\left(-\frac{1}{2}\left(\frac{x}{2}\right)^2 - \frac{1}{12}\left(\frac{x}{2}\right)^4 - \dots\right)$

$$= \ln 2 - \frac{x^2}{4} - \frac{x^4}{96} - \dots$$

33 a Let $y = 3^x$, then $\ln y = \ln 3^x = x\ln 3 \Rightarrow y = e^{x\ln 3}$

so $3^x = e^{x\ln 3}$

$$1 + x\ln 3 + \frac{x^2(\ln 3)^2}{2} + \frac{x^3(\ln 3)^3}{6} + \dots$$

b 1.73 (3 s.f.)

34 a $f(x) = \text{cosec}\, x$

$f'(x) = -\text{cosec}\, x\cot x$

i $f''(x) = -\text{cosec}\, x(-\text{cosec}^2 x) + \cot x(\text{cosec}\, x\cot x)$

$$= \text{cosec}\, x(\text{cosec}^2 x + \cot^2 x)$$

$$= \text{cosec}\, x(\text{cosec}^2 x + (\text{cosec}^2 x - 1))$$

$$= \text{cosec}\, x(2\,\text{cosec}^2 x - 1)$$

ii $f'''(x) = \operatorname{cosec} x(-4\operatorname{cosec}^2 x \cot x) -$
$\operatorname{cosec} x \cot x(2\operatorname{cosec}^2 x - 1)$
$= -\operatorname{cosec} x \cot x(6\operatorname{cosec}^2 x - 1)$

b $\sqrt{2} - \sqrt{2}\left(x - \frac{\pi}{4}\right) + \frac{3\sqrt{2}}{2}\left(x - \frac{\pi}{4}\right)^2 - \frac{11\sqrt{2}}{6}\left(x - \frac{\pi}{4}\right)^3 + \dots$

35 a $f'(x) = \dfrac{-\pi \sin\left(\frac{\pi x}{2}\right)}{1 + 2\cos\left(\frac{\pi x}{2}\right)}$

$f''(x) = -\dfrac{\pi^2 \cos\left(\frac{\pi x}{2}\right)}{2\left(1 + 2\cos\left(\frac{\pi x}{2}\right)\right)} - \dfrac{\pi^2 \sin^2\left(\frac{\pi x}{2}\right)}{\left(1 + 2\cos\left(\frac{\pi x}{2}\right)\right)^2}$

b $f(1) = 0$, $f'(1) = -\pi$ and $f''(1) = -\pi^2$, so
$f(x) = -\pi(x - 1) - \frac{\pi^2}{2}(x - 1)^2 + \dots$

Challenge

a Base case: $n = 1$ we have $\dfrac{d}{dx}\ln x = \dfrac{1}{x}$

Suppose that $\dfrac{d^n}{dx^n}\ln x = (-1)^{n+1}\dfrac{(n-1)!}{x^n}$, then
$\dfrac{d^{n+1}}{dx^{n+1}}\ln x = \dfrac{d}{dx}(-1)^{n+1}\dfrac{(n-1)!}{x^n} = (-1)^{n+2}\dfrac{n!}{x^{n+1}}$

b $\ln x = \ln a + \displaystyle\sum_{n=1}^{\infty}(-1)^{n+1}\dfrac{(x-a)^n}{na^n}$

CHAPTER 8
Prior knowledge check

1 0.5π

2 $\dfrac{\pi}{6}, \dfrac{5\pi}{6}$

3 a Circle centre $(0,3)$, radius 3

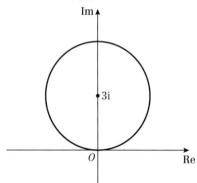

b $\dfrac{9\pi}{2}$

Exercise 8A

1 a $(13, 1.176)$ **b** $(13, 1.966)$
c $(13, -1.966)$ **d** $(\sqrt{13}, -0.983)$
e $\left(2, -\dfrac{\pi}{6}\right)$

2 a $(3\sqrt{3}, 3)$ **b** $(3\sqrt{3}, -3)$
c $(-3\sqrt{2}, 3\sqrt{2})$ **d** $(-5\sqrt{2}, -5\sqrt{2})$
e $(-2, 0)$

3 a $x^2 + y^2 = 4$ **b** $x = 3$
c $y = 5$ **d** $x^2 = 4ay$ or $y = \dfrac{x^2}{4a}$
e $x^2 + y^2 = 2ax$ or $(x - a)^2 + y^2 = a^2$
f $x^2 + y^2 = 3ay$ or $x^2 + \left(y - \dfrac{3a}{2}\right)^2 = \dfrac{9a^2}{4}$
g $(x^2 + y^2)^{\frac{3}{2}} = 8y^2$ **h** $(x^2 + y^2)^{\frac{3}{2}} = 2x^2$
i $x^2 = 1$

4 a $r = 4$ **b** $r^2 = 8\operatorname{cosec} 2\theta$
c $r^2 = \sin 2\theta$ **d** $r = 2\cos\theta$
e $r^2 = \dfrac{4}{1 + \sin 2\theta}$ **f** $r = \dfrac{3}{\sqrt{2}}\sec\left(\theta + \dfrac{\pi}{4}\right)$
g $\theta = \arctan 2$ **h** $r = \dfrac{a}{2}\operatorname{cosec}\left(\theta + \dfrac{\pi}{3}\right)$
i $r = \tan\theta \sec\theta + a\sec\theta$

Challenge
Consider the triangle formed by the two points and the origin and use the cosine rule to find d.

Exercise 8B

1 a
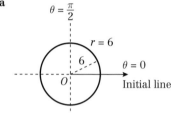

b
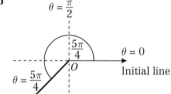

c
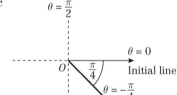

d
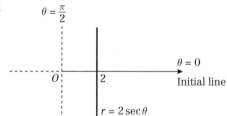

e
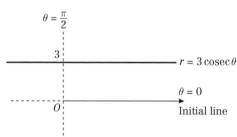

f

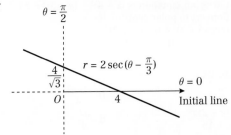

$\theta = \dfrac{\pi}{2}$

$r = 2\sec\left(\theta - \dfrac{\pi}{3}\right)$

$\dfrac{4}{\sqrt{3}}$

O 4 $\theta = 0$ Initial line

g

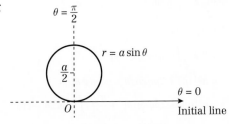

$\theta = \dfrac{\pi}{2}$

$r = a\sin\theta$

$\dfrac{a}{2}$

O $\theta = 0$ Initial line

h

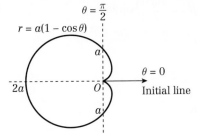

$r = a(1 - \cos\theta)$

$\theta = \dfrac{\pi}{2}$

a

$2a$ O $\theta = 0$ Initial line

a

i

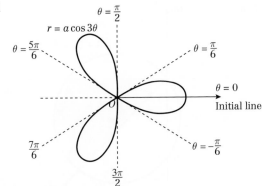

$r = a\cos 3\theta$

$\theta = \dfrac{\pi}{2}$

$\theta = \dfrac{5\pi}{6}$ $\theta = \dfrac{\pi}{6}$

O $\theta = 0$ Initial line

$\dfrac{7\pi}{6}$ $\theta = -\dfrac{\pi}{6}$

$\dfrac{3\pi}{2}$

j

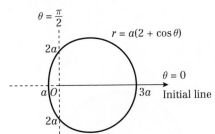

$\theta = \dfrac{\pi}{2}$

$r = a(2 + \cos\theta)$

$2a$

a O $3a$ $\theta = 0$ Initial line

$2a$

k

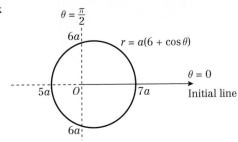

$\theta = \dfrac{\pi}{2}$

$6a$ $r = a(6 + \cos\theta)$

$5a$ O $7a$ $\theta = 0$ Initial line

$6a$

l

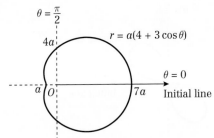

$\theta = \dfrac{\pi}{2}$

$r = a(4 + 3\cos\theta)$

$4a$

a O $7a$ $\theta = 0$ Initial line

m

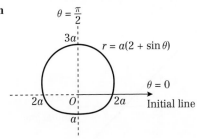

$\theta = \dfrac{\pi}{2}$

$3a$ $r = a(2 + \sin\theta)$

$2a$ O $2a$ $\theta = 0$ Initial line

a

n

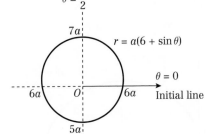

$\theta = \dfrac{\pi}{2}$

$7a$ $r = a(6 + \sin\theta)$

$6a$ O $6a$ $\theta = 0$ Initial line

$5a$

o

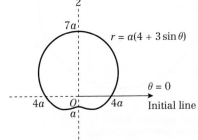

$\theta = \dfrac{\pi}{2}$

$7a$ $r = a(4 + 3\sin\theta)$

$4a$ O $4a$ $\theta = 0$ Initial line

a

p

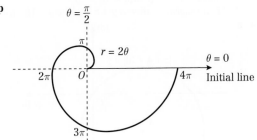

$\theta = \dfrac{\pi}{2}$

π $r = 2\theta$

2π O 4π $\theta = 0$ Initial line

3π

q

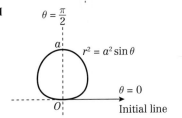

$\theta = \dfrac{\pi}{2}$

a $r^2 = a^2\sin\theta$

O $\theta = 0$ Initial line

r

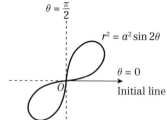

$\theta = \frac{\pi}{2}$

$r^2 = a^2 \sin 2\theta$

$\theta = 0$

Initial line

2

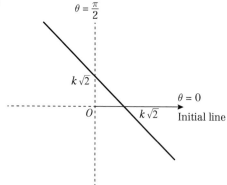

$\theta = \frac{\pi}{2}$

$k\sqrt{2}$

$\theta = 0$

O $k\sqrt{2}$ Initial line

3 a

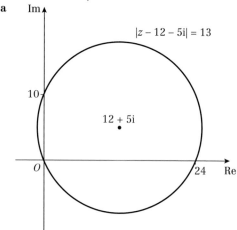

Im

$|z - 12 - 5i| = 13$

10

$12 + 5i$

O 24   Re

b Cartesian equation is $(x - 12)^2 + (y - 5)^2 = 169$
Convert to polar coordinates:
$(r\cos\theta - 12)^2 + (r\sin\theta - 5)^2 = 169$
Then rearrange this to get $r = 24\cos\theta + 10\sin\theta$

4 a

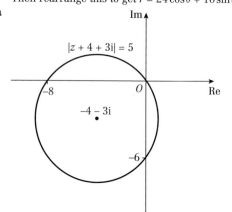

Im

$|z + 4 + 3i| = 5$

-8 O Re

$-4 - 3i$

-6

b Cartesian equation is $(x + 4)^2 + (y + 3)^2 = 25$
Convert to polar coordinates:
$(r\cos\theta + 4)^2 + (r\sin\theta + 3)^2 = 25$
Then rearrange to get $r = -8\cos\theta - 6\sin\theta$

Exercise 8C

1 a $\dfrac{\pi a^2}{8}$ b $\dfrac{3\pi a^2}{4}$

c $\dfrac{(\pi + 2)a^2}{48}$ d $\dfrac{a^2}{4}$

e $\dfrac{a^2 \ln\sqrt{2}}{2}$ or $\dfrac{a^2 \ln 2}{4}$ f $\dfrac{2a^2\pi^3}{3}$

g $\dfrac{a^2}{4}(11\pi + 24)$

2 Area $= 2 \times \dfrac{1}{2}\displaystyle\int_0^\pi a^2(p + q\cos\theta)^2\,d\theta$

$\qquad = a^2\displaystyle\int_0^\pi (p^2 + 2pq\cos\theta + q^2\cos^2\theta)\,d\theta$

$\qquad = a^2[p^2\theta + 2pq\sin\theta]_0^\pi + \dfrac{a^2 q^2}{2}\displaystyle\int_0^\pi (\cos 2\theta + 1)\,d\theta$

$\qquad = a^2 p^2 \pi + \dfrac{a^2 q^2}{2}\left[\dfrac{1}{2}\sin 2\theta + \theta\right]_0^\pi$

$\qquad = a^2 p^2 \pi + \dfrac{a^2 q^2 \pi}{2} = \dfrac{2p^2 + q^2}{2}\pi a^2$

3 $\dfrac{\pi a^2}{12}$

4 $a = 9$

5 $\dfrac{a^2}{4}\left(\dfrac{\pi}{4} - \dfrac{3\sqrt{3}}{16}\right)$

6 $\dfrac{5\pi}{4}$

7 a

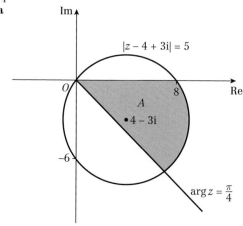

Im

$|z - 4 + 3i| = 5$

O 8   Re

A

$\bullet 4 - 3i$

-6

$\arg z = \dfrac{\pi}{4}$

b 35.1

8 a

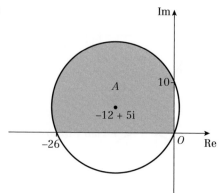

Im

A

10

$\bullet$
$-12 + 5i$

-26 O Re

b 385

9   0.0966
10 0.79

Challenge

a $k = \dfrac{3}{7\pi}$ b $\dfrac{12\pi}{7}$

Exercise 8D

1   $(2a, 0), \left(\dfrac{a}{2}, \dfrac{2\pi}{3}\right)$ and $\left(\dfrac{a}{2}, \dfrac{-2\pi}{3}\right)$

2   a $(9.15, 1.11)$ b $(212, 2.68)$

3   a $\left(\dfrac{2a}{3}, \pm 0.421\right)$ b $r = \pm \dfrac{a\sqrt{6}}{9} \operatorname{cosec}\theta$

4   $\left(\dfrac{15}{2}a, \pm 1.32\right)$

5   $r\cos\theta = 3$ $r\cos\theta = -1$ $r = 3\sec\theta$ $r = -\sec\theta$

6   $\left(2a, \dfrac{\pi}{4}\right)$

7   $\dfrac{3 + \sqrt{73}}{4}$

8   0.212

Chapter review 8

1   $\dfrac{9\pi a^2}{8}$

2   a, b
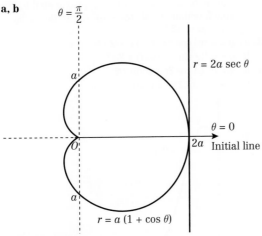
$r = 2a\sec\theta$
$r = a(1 + \cos\theta)$

c $\cos\alpha = \dfrac{\sqrt{5} - 1}{2}$

3
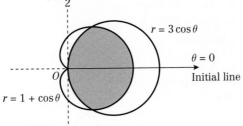
$r = 3\cos\theta$
$r = 1 + \cos\theta$
Area $= \dfrac{5\pi}{4}$

4   $\left(a\sqrt{\dfrac{\sqrt{3}}{2}}, \dfrac{\pi}{6}\right), \left(a\sqrt{\dfrac{\sqrt{3}}{2}}, \dfrac{7\pi}{6}\right)$ and $\left(0, \dfrac{\pi}{2}\right)$

5   a
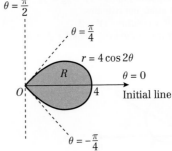
$r = 4\cos 2\theta$

b 2π

6
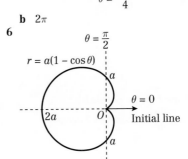
$r = a(1 - \cos\theta)$
Maximum value at $(2a, \pi)$

7   a
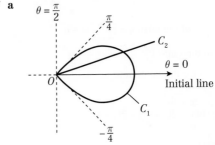
C_2
C_1

b $\dfrac{\pi}{6} - \dfrac{\sqrt{3}}{8}$

8   a
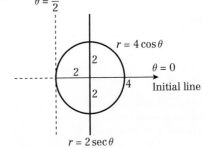
$r = 4\cos\theta$
$r = 2\sec\theta$

b $\left(2\sqrt{2}, \dfrac{\pi}{4}\right), \quad \left(2\sqrt{2}, -\dfrac{\pi}{4}\right)$

9   a $\left(\dfrac{3}{2}a, \dfrac{\pi}{3}\right)$ b $\dfrac{5\pi}{8}a^2$

10 a $y^2 = x^2 - 1$ b $y = \dfrac{1}{2x}$

11 a
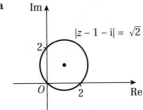
$|z - 1 - i| = \sqrt{2}$

b Cartesian equation is $(x - 1)^2 - (y + 1)^2 = 2$
Convert to polar coordinates:
$(r\cos\theta - 1)^2 + (r\sin\theta - 1)^2 = 2$
Then rearrange to get $r = 2\cos\theta + 2\sin\theta$

c
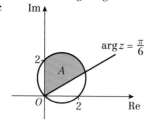

d 3.59
12 2.09
13 1.52

Challenge
$x = r\cos\theta = \sqrt{2}\,\theta\cos\theta$, $y = r\sin\theta = \sqrt{2}\,\theta\sin\theta$
$\dfrac{dx}{d\theta} = \sqrt{2}\cos\theta - \sqrt{2}\,\theta\sin\theta$, $\dfrac{dy}{d\theta} = \sqrt{2}\sin\theta + \sqrt{2}\,\theta\cos\theta$
So $\dfrac{dy}{dx} = \dfrac{\sin\theta + \theta\cos\theta}{\cos\theta - \theta\sin\theta}$
At $\theta = \dfrac{\pi}{4}$ the gradient of the tangent is $\dfrac{1 + \dfrac{\pi}{4}}{1 - \dfrac{\pi}{4}} = \dfrac{4 + \pi}{4 - \pi}$
So the tangent is of the form $y = \left(\dfrac{4 + \pi}{4 - \pi}\right)x + c$
Substituting in the point $\left(\dfrac{\pi}{4}, \dfrac{\pi}{4}\right)$, $c = \dfrac{\pi^2}{2(\pi - 4)}$
So the equation for the tangent is
$y = \left(\dfrac{4 + \pi}{4 - \pi x}\right) + \dfrac{\pi^2}{(2\pi - 4)}$
Rearranging, this is $2(\pi - 4)y + 2(\pi + 4)x = \pi^2$

Review exercise 2
1 $y = x^2 - x + \dfrac{c}{x^4}$
2 $y = \dfrac{x^3}{2} + cx$
3 $y = \dfrac{x + \ln x + c}{(x + 1)^2}$
4 $y = \dfrac{1}{2}(e^{2x} + 3)\cos x$
5 $y = \dfrac{2\sin^3 x}{3\sin 2x} + \dfrac{c}{\sin 2x}$
6 $y = \dfrac{5e^x}{4(1 + x)} - \dfrac{xe^{-x}}{2(1 + x)} - \dfrac{e^{-x}}{4(1 + x)}$
7 a $y = \sin x \cos x + c\cos x$
   b $\cos x = 0$, $0 \leqslant x \leqslant 2\pi \Rightarrow x = \dfrac{\pi}{2}, \dfrac{3\pi}{2}$
   The points $\left(\dfrac{\pi}{2}, 0\right)$ and $\left(\dfrac{3\pi}{2}, 0\right)$ lie on all of the
   solution curves for the differential equation.
   c
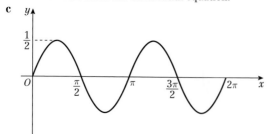

8 a $y = \dfrac{x}{2} - \dfrac{1}{4} + ce^{-2x}$ **b** $\left(\dfrac{1}{2}\ln 5, \dfrac{1}{4}\ln 5\right)$

c
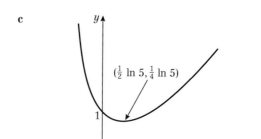

9 $\theta = 3e^{-2t}\cos t$
10 a $k = 12$
   b $y = 2\cos 2x - \dfrac{\pi}{4}\sin 2x + 3x\sin 2x$
11 a $a = 5$, $b = 1$
   b $y = e^{2x}(3 + 2x) + 5 + x$
12 a $y = e^{-2x}(A\cos x + B\sin x) + \sin 2x - 8\cos 2x$
   b As $x \to \infty$, $e^{-kx} \to 0 \Rightarrow y \to \sin 2x - 8\cos 2x$
   Let $\sin 2x - 8\cos 2x = R\sin(2x - \alpha)$
   $\qquad\qquad\qquad = R\sin 2x \cos\alpha - R\cos 2x \sin\alpha$
   Equating the coefficients of $\cos 2x$ and $\sin 2x$
   $\Rightarrow R = \sqrt{65}$, $\tan\alpha = 8$
   Hence, for large x, y can be approximated by the
   sine function $\sqrt{65}\sin(2x - \alpha)$, where $\tan$
   $\alpha = 8$ ($\alpha \approx 82.9°$)
13 a $y = e^{-t}(A\cos t + B\sin t) + 2e^{-t}$
   b $y = e^{-t}(2\sin t - \cos t) + 2e^{-t}$
14 a $x = e^{-t}(A\cos 2t + B\sin 2t)$
   b $x = e^{-t}(\cos 2t + \sin 2t)$
   c
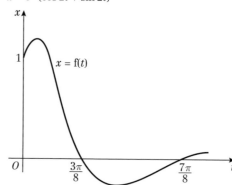

15 a $y = Ae^{-\frac{1}{2}t} + Be^{-3t} + t^2 - t + 1$
   b $y = \dfrac{4}{5}\left(e^{-\frac{1}{2}t} - e^{-3t}\right) + t^2 - t + 1$
   c 1.45 (3 s.f.)
16 a $\lambda = 2$
   b $y = A\cos 3x + B\sin 3x + 2x\cos 3x$
   c $y = (1 + 2x)\cos 3x$
   d
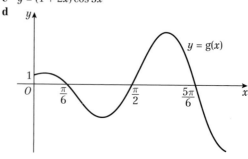

17 a $y = Kt^2 e^{3t}, \dfrac{dy}{dt} = 2Kt e^{3t} + 3Kt^2 e^{3t}, \dfrac{d^2y}{dt^2} = 2K e^{3t}$
$+ 12Kt e^{3t} + 9Kt^2 e^{3t}$
Substituting into the differential equation
$2K e^{3t} + 12Kt e^{3t} + 9Kt^2 e^{3t} - 12Kt e^{3t} - 18Kt^2 e^{3t}$
$+ 9Kt^2 e^{3t} = 4 e^{3t}$
$\Rightarrow 2K = 4 \Rightarrow K = 2$
$2t^2 e^{3t}$ is a particular integral of the differential equation

b $y = (A + Bt + 2t^2)e^{3t}$

c $y = (3 - 8t + 2t^2)e^{3t}$

d

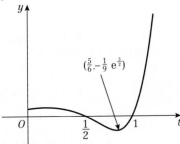

$\left(\frac{5}{6}, -\frac{1}{9} e^{\frac{5}{2}}\right)$

18 a $x = A e^{-\frac{1}{2}t} + B e^{-2t} + t + 2$

b $x = e^{-2t} + t + 2$

19 a $A = \frac{1}{2}$

b $x = \left(1 + t + \frac{1}{2}t^2\right)e^{-t}$

c $\dfrac{dx}{dt} = (1 + t)e^{-t} - \left(1 + t + \frac{1}{2}t^2\right)e^{-t} = -\frac{1}{2}t^2 e^{-t} \leq 0$,
for all real t
When $t = 0$, $x = 1$ and x has a negative gradient for all positive t, x is a decreasing function of t. Hence, for $t \geq 0$, $x \leq 1$.

20 a $k = 3$

b $y = A \sin x + 3x$

c At $x = \pi$, $y = A \sin \pi + 3\pi = 3\pi$
This is independent of the value of A. Hence, all curves given by the solution in part **a** pass through $(\pi, 3\pi)$.
$\dfrac{dy}{dx} = A \cos x + 3$
At $x = \dfrac{\pi}{2}$, $\dfrac{dy}{dx} = A \cos \dfrac{\pi}{2} + 3 = 3$
This is independent of the value of A. Hence, all curves given by the solution in part **a** have an equal gradient of 3 at $x = \dfrac{\pi}{2}$

d $y = 3x - \dfrac{3\pi}{2} \sin x$

e For a minimum $\dfrac{dy}{dx} = 3 - \dfrac{3\pi}{2} \cos x = 0$
$\cos x = \dfrac{2}{\pi} \Rightarrow x = \arccos \dfrac{2}{\pi}$
$\dfrac{d^2y}{dx^2} = \dfrac{3\pi}{2} \sin x$
In the interval $0 \leq x \leq \dfrac{\pi}{2}$, $\dfrac{d^2y}{dx^2} > 0 \Rightarrow$ minimum
$\sin^2 x = 1 - \cos^2 x = 1 - \dfrac{4}{\pi^2} = \dfrac{\pi^2 - 4}{\pi^2}$
In the interval $0 \leq x \leq \dfrac{\pi}{2}$, $\sin x = \dfrac{\sqrt{\pi^2 - 4}}{\pi^2}$
$y = 3 \arccos \dfrac{2}{\pi} - \dfrac{3}{2}\sqrt{\pi^2 - 4}$

21 a $y = \dfrac{C e^{2x} - 2x - 1}{4}$ **b** $y = \dfrac{9 e^{2x} - 2x - 1}{4}$

22 a $y = vx, \dfrac{dy}{dx} = x\dfrac{dv}{dx} + v$
$x\dfrac{dv}{dx} + v = \dfrac{(4x + vx)(x + vx)}{x^2} = 4 + 5v + v^2$
$\Rightarrow x\dfrac{dv}{dx} = 4 + 4v + v^2 = (2 + v)^2$

b $v = -2 - \dfrac{1}{\ln x + c}$

23 a $y = vx, \dfrac{dy}{dx} = x\dfrac{dv}{dx} + v$
$x\dfrac{dv}{dx} + v = \dfrac{3x - 4vx}{4x + 3vx} = \dfrac{3 - 4v}{4 + 3v}$
$x\dfrac{dv}{dx} = \dfrac{3 - 4v}{4 + 3v} - v = -\dfrac{3v^2 + 8v - 3}{3v + 4}$

b $3v^2 + 8v - 3 = \dfrac{C}{x^2}$

c $y = xv \Rightarrow v = \dfrac{y}{x} \Rightarrow \dfrac{3y^2}{x^2} + \dfrac{8y}{x} - 3 = \dfrac{C}{x^2}$
$\Rightarrow 3y^2 + 8yx - 3x^2 = C$
$y = 7$ at $x = 1 \Rightarrow C = 200$
Factorising the LHS, $(3y - x)(y + 3x) = 200$

24 a $\dfrac{d\mu}{dx} = -2y^{-3}\dfrac{dy}{dx} \Rightarrow \dfrac{dy}{dx} = -\dfrac{y^3}{2}\dfrac{d\mu}{dx}$
So $-\dfrac{1}{2}\dfrac{d\mu}{dx} + 2x\mu = x e^{-x^2}$
$\Rightarrow \dfrac{d\mu}{dx} - 4x\mu = -2x e^{-x^2}$

b $\mu = \dfrac{1}{3} e^{-x^2} + C e^{2x^2}$ **c** $\dfrac{1}{y^2} = \dfrac{1}{3} e^{-x^2} + \dfrac{2}{3} e^{2x^2}$

25 a $\dfrac{dy}{dx} = v + x\dfrac{dv}{dx}, \dfrac{d^2y}{dx^2} = 2\dfrac{dv}{dx} + x\dfrac{d^2v}{dx^2}$
So $x^2\left(x\dfrac{d^2v}{dx^2} + 2\dfrac{dv}{dx}\right) - 2x\left(v + x\dfrac{dv}{dx}\right) + (2 + 9x^2)vx = x^5$
$\Rightarrow x^3\dfrac{d^2v}{dx^2} + 9x^3v = x^5 \Rightarrow \dfrac{d^2v}{dx^2} + 9v = x^2$

b $v = A\cos 3x + B\sin 3x + \dfrac{1}{9}x^2 - \dfrac{2}{81}$

c $y = Ax\cos 3x + Bx\sin 3x + \dfrac{1}{9}x^3 - \dfrac{2}{81}x$

26 a $2t^{\frac{1}{2}}\dfrac{dy}{dt}$

b $4t\dfrac{d^2y}{dt^2} + 2\dfrac{dy}{dt} + \left(6t^{\frac{1}{2}} - \dfrac{1}{t^{\frac{1}{2}}}\right)2t^{\frac{1}{2}}\dfrac{dy}{dt} - 16ty = 4t e^{2t}$
$\Rightarrow 4t\dfrac{d^2y}{dt^2} + 12t\dfrac{dy}{dt} - 16ty = 4t e^{2t}$

c $y = A e^{t^2} + B e^{-4t^2} + \dfrac{1}{6}e^{2x^2} \Rightarrow \dfrac{d^2y}{dt^2} + 3\dfrac{dy}{dt} - 4y = e^{2t}$

27 a $t\dfrac{dy}{dt}$

b $\dfrac{d^2y}{dx^2} = \dfrac{dt}{dx} \times \dfrac{d}{dt}\left(\dfrac{dy}{dx}\right) = t\dfrac{d}{dt}\left(t\dfrac{dy}{dt}\right)$
$= t\left(\dfrac{dy}{dt} + t\dfrac{d^2y}{dt^2}\right) = t^2\dfrac{d^2y}{dt^2} + t\dfrac{dy}{dt}$

c $\left(t^2\dfrac{d^2y}{dt^2} + t\dfrac{dy}{dt}\right) - (1 - 6t)t\dfrac{dy}{dt} + 10yt^2 = 5t^2 \sin 2t$
$\Rightarrow \dfrac{d^2y}{dt^2} + 6\dfrac{dy}{dt} + 10y = 5\sin 2t$

d $y = e^{-3e^x}(A\cos(e^x) + B\sin(e^x)) + \dfrac{1}{6}\sin(2 e^x) - \dfrac{1}{3}\cos(2 e^x)$

28 $\cos x = 1 - \dfrac{x^2}{2!} + \dfrac{x^4}{4!} - \ldots = 1 - \dfrac{x^2}{2!}$, neglecting terms in x^3 and higher powers

$\sin x = x - \dfrac{x^3}{3!} + \dfrac{x^5}{5!} - \ldots = x$, neglecting terms in x^3 and higher powers

$11 \sin x - 6 \cos x + 5 = 11x - 6\left(1 - \dfrac{x^2}{2}\right) + 5$

$\qquad\qquad = -1 + 11x + 3x^2$

$A = -1, B = 11, C = 3$

29 LHS $= \ln(x^2 - x + 1) + \ln(x + 1) - 3\ln x$

$= \ln((x^2 - x + 1)(x + 1)) - \ln x^3$

$= \ln\left(\dfrac{x^3 + 1}{x^3}\right) = \ln\left(1 + \dfrac{1}{x^3}\right)$

Substituting $\dfrac{1}{x^3}$ for x and n for r in the series

$\ln(1 + x) = x - \dfrac{x^2}{2} + \dfrac{x^3}{3} + \ldots + \dfrac{(-1)^{r+1}x^r}{r} + \ldots$

LHS $= \dfrac{1}{x^3} - \dfrac{1}{2x^6} + \ldots + \dfrac{(-1)^{n-1}}{nx^{3n}} + \ldots$

30 $A = 1, B = -2, C = -\dfrac{21}{2}, D = \dfrac{71}{3}$

31 a $\dfrac{1}{3} - \dfrac{2}{9}x + \dfrac{4}{27}x^2 - \dfrac{8}{81}x^3 + \ldots$

b $\dfrac{2}{3}x - \dfrac{4}{9}x^2 - \dfrac{4}{27}x^3 + \dfrac{8}{81}x^4 + \ldots$

32 a $-\dfrac{x^2}{2} - \dfrac{x^4}{12} - \ldots$ **b** $\dfrac{x^2}{2} + \dfrac{x^4}{12} + \ldots$

33 a Let $u = 1 + \cos 2x$, then $f(x) = \ln u$

$\dfrac{du}{dx} = -2\sin 2x$

$f'(x) = f'(u)\dfrac{du}{dx} = \dfrac{1}{u}\dfrac{du}{dx} = \dfrac{1}{1 + \cos 2x} \times (-2\sin 2x)$

$= \dfrac{-4\sin x \cos x}{2\cos^2 x} = \dfrac{-2\sin x}{\cos x} = -2\tan x$

b $f''(x) = -2\sec^2 x$

$f'''(x) = -4\sec^2 x \tan x$

$f''''(x) = -8\sec x \sec x \tan x \tan x - 4\sec^2 x \sec^2 x$

$= -8\sec^2 x \tan^2 x - 4\sec^4 x$

c $\ln 2 - x^2 - \dfrac{1}{6}x^4 + \ldots$

34 a $-2\left(x - \dfrac{\pi}{4}\right) + \dfrac{4}{3}\left(x - \dfrac{\pi}{4}\right)^3 - \dfrac{4}{15}\left(x - \dfrac{\pi}{4}\right)^5 + \ldots$

b $-0.416\,147$ (6 d.p.)

35 a $-\ln 2 + \sqrt{3}\left(x - \dfrac{\pi}{6}\right) - 2\left(x - \dfrac{\pi}{6}\right)^2 + \dfrac{4\sqrt{3}}{3}\left(x - \dfrac{\pi}{6}\right)^3 + \ldots$

b $-0.735\,166$ (6 d.p.)

36 a $\dfrac{dy}{dx} = \sec^2 x$

$\dfrac{d^2y}{dx^2} = 2\sec^2 x \tan x$

$\dfrac{d^3y}{dx^3} = 4\sec^2 x \tan^2 x + 2\sec^4 x$

b $1 + 2\left(x - \dfrac{\pi}{4}\right) + 2\left(x - \dfrac{\pi}{4}\right)^2 + \dfrac{8}{3}\left(x - \dfrac{\pi}{4}\right)^3 + \ldots$

c Let $x = \dfrac{3\pi}{10} \Rightarrow x - \dfrac{\pi}{4} = \dfrac{\pi}{20}$

$\tan \dfrac{3\pi}{10} = 1 + 2\left(\dfrac{\pi}{20}\right) + 2\left(\dfrac{\pi}{20}\right)^2 + \dfrac{8}{3}\left(\dfrac{\pi}{20}\right)^3$

$= 1 + \dfrac{\pi}{10} + \dfrac{\pi^2}{200} + \dfrac{\pi^3}{3000}$

37 $(x - 1) - \dfrac{1}{2}(x - 1)^2 + \dfrac{1}{3}(x - 1)^3 + \ldots$

38 a $\dfrac{d^3y}{dx^3} = 1$ **b** $2 - x - 2x^2 + \dfrac{1}{6}x^3 + \ldots$

39 a Differentiate the equation with respect to x:

$2\dfrac{dy}{dx} + (1 + 2x)\dfrac{d^2y}{dx^2} = 1 + 8y\dfrac{dy}{dx}$

$(1 + 2x)\dfrac{d^2y}{dx^2} = 1 + 8y\dfrac{dy}{dx} - 2\dfrac{dy}{dx} = 1 + 2(4y - 1)\dfrac{dy}{dx}$

b $2\dfrac{d^2y}{dx^2} + (1 + 2x)\dfrac{d^3y}{dx^3} = 8\left(\dfrac{dy}{dx}\right)^2 + 2(4y - 1)\dfrac{d^2y}{dx^2} \ldots$

c $\dfrac{1}{2} + x + \dfrac{3}{2}x^2 + \dfrac{4}{3}x^3 + \ldots$

40 a $1 + x + 2x^2 + 2x^3 + \ldots$ **b** 1.12 (2 d.p.)

41 a $1.5 + 0.8x - 0.208x^2 + 0.131\,982x^3 + \ldots$

b 1.578 (3 d.p.)

42 a $-\dfrac{1}{y}\dfrac{dy}{dx}\left(3\dfrac{d^2y}{dx^2} + 1\right)$ **b** $1 + x - x^2 + \dfrac{5}{6}x^3 + \ldots$

c The series expansion up to and including the term in x^3 can be used to estimate y if x is small. So it would be sensible to use it at $x = 0.2$ but not at $x = 50$.

43 a $1 + \dfrac{3}{2}x^2 + 2x^3 + \dfrac{5}{4}x^4 + \ldots$ **b** 1.08 (2 d.p.)

44 a $r = 2$ **b** $r = 3\sec\theta$

c $r = 2\sqrt{3}\sec\left(\theta - \dfrac{\pi}{6}\right)$

45 a

$r = a\cos 3\theta$

$\theta = \dfrac{\pi}{6}$

$\theta = -\dfrac{\pi}{6}$

O a Initial line

b $\dfrac{\pi}{12}a^2$

46 a

$\theta = \dfrac{\pi}{4}$ $\theta = \dfrac{\pi}{6}$

$r = 3\cos 2\theta$

O 3 Initial line

$\theta = -\dfrac{\pi}{4}$

b $\dfrac{3}{32}(2\pi - 3\sqrt{3})$ **c** $\dfrac{2\sqrt{6}}{3}$

47 a

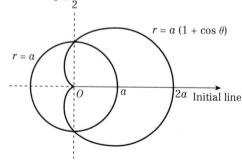

$\theta = \dfrac{\pi}{2}$

$r = a(1 + \cos\theta)$

$r = a$

O a $2a$ Initial line

b $r = \dfrac{3\sqrt{3}a}{4}\operatorname{cosec}\theta$

$r = -\dfrac{3\sqrt{3}a}{4}\operatorname{cosec}\theta$

$\theta = \pi$

c The circle and the cardioid meet when
$a = a(1 + \cos\theta) \Rightarrow \cos\theta = 0 \Rightarrow \theta = \pm\dfrac{\pi}{2}$

$A = 2 \times \dfrac{1}{2}\displaystyle\int_{0}^{\frac{\pi}{2}} r^2\,d\theta$

$\displaystyle\int_{0}^{\frac{\pi}{2}} r^2\,d\theta = \int_{0}^{\frac{\pi}{2}} a^2(1 + \cos\theta)^2\,d\theta$

$\qquad = \displaystyle\int_{0}^{\frac{\pi}{2}} a^2(1 + 2\cos\theta + \cos^2\theta)\,d\theta$

$\qquad = \displaystyle\int_{0}^{\frac{\pi}{2}} a^2\left(1 + 2\cos\theta + \dfrac{1}{2}\cos 2\theta + \dfrac{1}{2}\right)d\theta$

$\qquad = a^2 \displaystyle\int_{0}^{\frac{\pi}{2}} \left(2\cos\theta + \dfrac{1}{2}\cos 2\theta + \dfrac{3}{2}\right)d\theta$

$\qquad = a^2\left[2\sin\theta + \dfrac{1}{4}\sin 2\theta + \dfrac{3\theta}{2}\right]_{0}^{\frac{\pi}{2}} = a^2\left(\dfrac{3\pi}{4} + 2\right)$

The required area is A less half the circle

$a^2\left(\dfrac{3\pi}{4} + 2\right) - \dfrac{1}{2}\pi a^2 = \left(\dfrac{\pi + 8}{4}\right)a^2$

48 a $\theta = \dfrac{\pi}{2}$

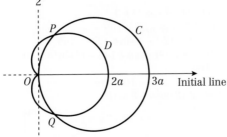

b $P\left(\dfrac{3}{2}a, \dfrac{\pi}{3}\right), Q\left(\dfrac{3}{2}a, -\dfrac{\pi}{3}\right)$

c $\dfrac{a^2}{16}(4\pi + 9\sqrt{3})$

d Let the smaller area enclosed by C and the half-line $\theta = \dfrac{\pi}{3}$ be A_2:

$R = \pi\left(\dfrac{3a}{2}\right)^2 - 2A_1 - 2A_2$

$\quad = \dfrac{9a^2\pi}{4} - \dfrac{2a^2}{16}(4\pi + 9\sqrt{3}) - \dfrac{6a^2}{16}(2\pi - 3\sqrt{3})$

$\quad = \dfrac{9a^2\pi}{4} - \dfrac{a^2\pi}{2} - \dfrac{9\sqrt{3}a^2}{8} - \dfrac{3a^2\pi}{4} + \dfrac{9\sqrt{3}a^2}{8} = \pi a^2$

49 a

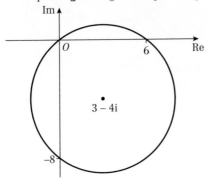

b In Cartesian form: $(x - 3)^2 + (y + 4)^2 = 25$

$\Rightarrow (r\cos\theta - 3)^2 + (r\sin\theta + 4)^2 = 25$

$\Rightarrow r^2\cos^2\theta - 6r\cos\theta + 9 + r^2\sin^2\theta + 8r\sin\theta$
$\qquad + 16 = 25$

$\Rightarrow r^2(\cos^2\theta + \sin^2\theta) - 6r\cos\theta + 8r\sin\theta = 0$

$\Rightarrow r^2(\cos^2\theta + \sin^2\theta) = r(6\cos\theta - 8\sin\theta)$

$\Rightarrow r = (6\cos\theta - 8\sin\theta)$

c 63.3

50 a

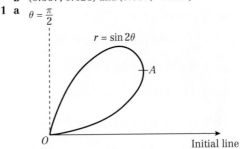

b (0.667, 0.421) and (0.667, −0.421)

51 a

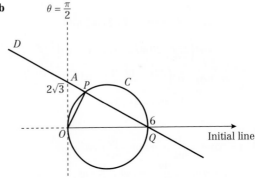

b (0.943, 0.615)

52 a $(x - 3)^2 + y^2 = 9$

$x + \sqrt{3}y = 6$

b

$\theta = \dfrac{\pi}{2}$

c $P\left(3, \dfrac{\pi}{3}\right), Q(6, 0)$

53 $\dfrac{1}{2}a^2$

54 $A = \dfrac{1}{2}\displaystyle\int_{\frac{\pi}{8}}^{\frac{\pi}{4}} r^2\,d\theta = \dfrac{1}{2}\int_{\frac{\pi}{8}}^{\frac{\pi}{4}} 16a^2\cos^2 2\theta\,d\theta$

$\qquad = 4a^2 \displaystyle\int_{\frac{\pi}{8}}^{\frac{\pi}{4}} (1 + \cos 4\theta)\,d\theta = 4a^2\left[\theta + \dfrac{1}{4}\sin 4\theta\right]_{\frac{\pi}{8}}^{\frac{\pi}{4}}$

$\qquad = 4a^2\left(\dfrac{\pi}{8} - \dfrac{1}{4}\right) = \dfrac{1}{2}a^2(\pi - 2)$

55 $\dfrac{9}{8}\pi a^2$

56 a $\theta = \dfrac{\pi}{12}, \dfrac{5\pi}{12}$ **b** $\dfrac{\pi}{12} - \dfrac{\sqrt{3}}{16}$

57 a $P(4a, 1.107), Q(4a, -1.107)$

b $\dfrac{5\sqrt{5}}{4}$ m

c $\dfrac{2875\pi}{32}$ m²

58 a $\frac{3}{2}\pi a^2$

  b $A:\left(\frac{1}{2}a, \frac{2\pi}{3}\right), B:\left(\frac{1}{2}a, -\frac{2\pi}{3}\right)$

  c $\frac{9}{4}a$

  d $\frac{27\sqrt{3}}{8}a^2$

  e 113 cm^2 (3 s.f.)

59 a $A:\left(\frac{3}{2}a, -\frac{\pi}{3}\right), B:\left(\frac{3}{2}a, \frac{\pi}{3}\right)$

  b $AB = 2 \times \frac{3}{2}a \sin\frac{\pi}{3} = \frac{3\sqrt{3}}{2}a$

  c $(9\sqrt{3} - 4\pi)a^2$

  d 9.07 cm^2 (3 s.f.)

60 a $A:(5a, 0), B:(3a, 0)$

  b $C:\left(4a, \frac{5\pi}{3}\right), D:\left(4a, \frac{\pi}{3}\right)$

  c $A_1 = 2 \times \frac{1}{2}\int_{\frac{\pi}{3}}^{\pi} r^2\,\mathrm{d}\theta = \int_{\frac{\pi}{3}}^{\pi} a^2(3 + 2\cos\theta)^2\,\mathrm{d}\theta$

  $= a^2\int_{\frac{\pi}{3}}^{\pi}(9 + 12\cos\theta + 4\cos^2\theta)\,\mathrm{d}\theta$

  $= a^2\int_{\frac{\pi}{3}}^{\pi}(11 + 12\cos\theta + 2\cos 2\theta)\,\mathrm{d}\theta$

  $= a^2[11\theta + 12\sin\theta + \sin 2\theta]_{\frac{\pi}{3}}^{\pi} = a^2\left(\frac{22\pi}{3} - \frac{13\sqrt{3}}{2}\right)$

  $A_2 = 2 \times \frac{1}{2}\int_{0}^{\frac{\pi}{3}} a^2(5 - 2\cos\theta)^2\,\mathrm{d}\theta$

  $= a^2\int_{0}^{\frac{\pi}{3}}(25 - 20\cos\theta + 4\cos^2\theta)\,\mathrm{d}\theta$

  $= a^2\int_{0}^{\frac{\pi}{3}}(27 - 20\cos\theta + 2\cos 2\theta)\,\mathrm{d}\theta$

  $= a^2\left[27\theta - 20\sin\theta + \sin 2\theta\right]_{0}^{\frac{\pi}{3}} = a^2\left(\frac{27\pi}{3} - \frac{19\sqrt{3}}{2}\right)$

  $A_1 + A_2 = a^2\left(\frac{22\pi}{3} - \frac{13\sqrt{3}}{2}\right) + a^2\left(\frac{27\pi}{3} - \frac{19\sqrt{3}}{2}\right)$

  $= \frac{a^2}{3}(49\pi - 48\sqrt{3})$

Challenge

1 $x = r\cos\theta \Rightarrow \dfrac{\mathrm{d}x}{\mathrm{d}\theta} = -r\sin\theta + \dfrac{\mathrm{d}r}{\mathrm{d}\theta}\cos\theta$

  $y = r\sin\theta \Rightarrow \dfrac{\mathrm{d}y}{\mathrm{d}\theta} = r\cos\theta + \dfrac{\mathrm{d}r}{\mathrm{d}\theta}\sin\theta$

  So l has gradient $\dfrac{r\cos\theta + \dfrac{\mathrm{d}r}{\mathrm{d}\theta}\sin\theta}{-r\sin\theta + \dfrac{\mathrm{d}r}{\mathrm{d}\theta}\cos\theta} = \tan(\alpha + \theta)$

  Thus $\dfrac{\tan\alpha + \tan\theta}{1 - \tan\alpha\tan\theta} = \dfrac{r\cos\theta + \dfrac{\mathrm{d}r}{\mathrm{d}\theta}\sin\theta}{-r\sin\theta + \dfrac{\mathrm{d}r}{\mathrm{d}\theta}\cos\theta}$

  Rearrange and cancel to get

  $-r\sin^2\theta + \dfrac{\mathrm{d}r}{\mathrm{d}\theta}\cos^2\theta\tan\alpha = r\cos^2\theta - \dfrac{\mathrm{d}r}{\mathrm{d}\theta}\tan\alpha\sin^2\theta$

  $\Rightarrow \dfrac{\mathrm{d}r}{\mathrm{d}\theta}\tan\alpha = r \Rightarrow \tan\alpha = \dfrac{r}{\dfrac{\mathrm{d}r}{\mathrm{d}\theta}}$

Exam Practice

1 $x > \sqrt{3}, -\sqrt{3} < x < -1, x < -3$

2 $p = 7, q = 25$

  Using partial fractions,

  $\dfrac{1}{(r + 2)(r + 4)} = \dfrac{1}{2(r + 2)} - \dfrac{1}{2(r + 4)}$

  Using the method of differences,

  $\displaystyle\sum_{r=1}^{n}\dfrac{1}{(r + 2)(r + 4)} = \sum_{r=1}^{n}\dfrac{1}{2(r + 2)} - \dfrac{1}{2(r + 4)}$

  $= \dfrac{1}{6} + \dfrac{1}{8} - \dfrac{1}{2(n + 3)} - \dfrac{1}{2(n + 4)} = \dfrac{n(7n + 25)}{24(n + 3)(n + 4)}$

3 a $z = \cos\theta + \mathrm{i}\sin\theta$

  $z^n = (\cos\theta + \mathrm{i}\sin\theta)^n$

  $z^n = \cos n\theta + \mathrm{i}\sin n\theta$

  $\dfrac{1}{z^n} = \cos n\theta - \mathrm{i}\sin n\theta$

  $z^n - \dfrac{1}{z^n} = 2\mathrm{i}\sin n\theta$

  b $8\sin^4\theta = \dfrac{1}{2}(2\mathrm{i}\sin\theta)^4 = \dfrac{1}{2}\left(z - \dfrac{1}{z}\right)^4$

  $= \dfrac{1}{2}\left(z^4 - 4z^2 + 6 - \dfrac{4}{z^2} + \dfrac{1}{z^4}\right)$

  $= \dfrac{1}{2}(2\cos 4\theta - 8\cos 2\theta + 6)$

  $= \cos 4\theta - 4\cos 2\theta + 3$

4 a $(x + 12)^2 + (y + 5)^2 = 169$

  $(r\cos\theta + 12)^2 + (r\sin\theta + 5)^2 = 169$

  $r^2\cos^2\theta + 24r\cos\theta + 144 + r^2\sin^2\theta + 10r\sin\theta + 25 = 169$

  $r^2 = -24r\cos\theta - 10r\sin\theta$

  $r = -2(12\cos\theta + 5\sin\theta)$

  b

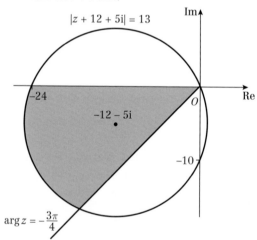

$|z + 12 + 5\mathrm{i}| = 13$

$\arg z = -\dfrac{3\pi}{4}$

  c 252

5 a $y = \cos x(\sin x + A)$

  b $y = \cos x(\sin x + 3)$

6 a $\dfrac{\mathrm{d}y}{\mathrm{d}x} = \dfrac{\mathrm{d}y}{\mathrm{d}t} \times \dfrac{\mathrm{d}t}{\mathrm{d}x}$

$\dfrac{\mathrm{d}y}{\mathrm{d}x} = \dfrac{\mathrm{d}y}{\mathrm{d}t} \times \dfrac{1}{e^t}\left(= \dfrac{1}{x}\dfrac{\mathrm{d}y}{\mathrm{d}t}\right)$

$\dfrac{\mathrm{d}^2 y}{\mathrm{d}x^2} = \dfrac{-1}{x^2}\dfrac{\mathrm{d}y}{\mathrm{d}t} + \dfrac{1}{x^2}\dfrac{\mathrm{d}^2 y}{\mathrm{d}t^2}$

substituting into

$x^2 \dfrac{\mathrm{d}^2 y}{\mathrm{d}x^2} + 8x\dfrac{\mathrm{d}y}{\mathrm{d}x} + 12y = 0$

gives

$x^2 \cdot \dfrac{1}{x^2}\left(\dfrac{\mathrm{d}^2 y}{\mathrm{d}t^2} - \dfrac{\mathrm{d}y}{\mathrm{d}t}\right) + 8x \cdot \dfrac{1}{x}\dfrac{\mathrm{d}y}{\mathrm{d}t} + 12y = 0$

$\dfrac{\mathrm{d}^2 y}{\mathrm{d}t^2} + 7\dfrac{\mathrm{d}y}{\mathrm{d}t} + 12y = 0$

b $y = \dfrac{A}{x^3} + \dfrac{B}{x^4}$

7 $y = 1 + x - \dfrac{3x^2}{2} + \dfrac{2x^2}{3}$

8 a $(x + 4)^2 + (y - 2)^2 = 34$

b, c

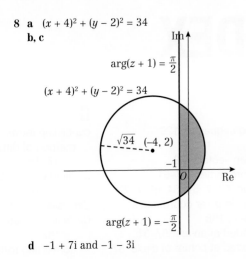

d $-1 + 7\mathrm{i}$ and $-1 - 3\mathrm{i}$

INDEX

A

alternating sequence 129
angles
  between vectors 38
  circle properties 57–61
  half-line 51–2, 57, 64, 65–7, 72
  half-line in polar coordinates 153–4, 158
  subtended at an arc 57–61
  subtended at centre of circle 57, 60
  see also argument; polar coordinates
answers to questions 183–229
arbitrary constants 91, 95, 106–7, 115–17
arc of a circle 57–61
areas
  enclosed by polar curves 158–61
  regions on Argand diagrams 63–9
Argand diagrams 46–82, 86–8
  distances in constant ratio 55–6
  geometric property of argument 51–2, 56–63
  loci on 47–63, 157
  modulus and argument 24, 31, 39, 40
  multiplying complex numbers 27
  polar curves 157
  regions given by complex numbers 63–5
  regions given by inequalities 65–9
  roots of unity 37–8
  transformations of complex plane 70–8
argument 8, 24, 31, 37–40
  loci in terms of 51–2, 56–61
  maximum value 48–9
  principal argument 66
asymptotes 6
auxiliary equation 106–8, 119, 140
  finding complementary functions 112–14, 115, 116

B

binomial expansion 32–3, 34–5, 128, 131
boundary conditions 91, 106, 115–18

C

cancelling terms 3, 4
  method of differences 15, 16, 17, 18
cardioids 155, 158, 162
  concave/convex 156, 164
Cartesian coordinates 81, 150–3
Cartesian equations 47–53, 59–60, 162
  converting to/from polar 151–3
  locus in w-plane 72–3
chain rule 119, 126
circles
  angle subtended at an arc 57–61
  angle subtended at centre 57, 60
  on Argand diagram 47, 48–9, 52, 55–6, 157
  Cartesian equation 47, 48–9, 52, 55
  circle properties 49, 57–61
  polar equation 153–4
  regions on Argand diagrams 63–4, 66–8
  transformations 70–1, 72, 74–5
complementary function 110, 112–14, 115–17
complex conjugate 75
complex conjugate roots 107, 108
complex numbers 22–45, 85–6
  de Moivre's theorem 29–42
  exponential form 23–9, 30, 34, 40
  modulus-argument form 23–5, 26, 29–30, 31, 37, 39
  multiplying and dividing 26–9
  nth roots 37–42
  powers of 29–31
  regions on Argand diagrams 63–5
  trigonometric identities 32–6
  see also Argand diagrams
compound functions 132–6
compound transformations 71–2
concave polar curves 156, 158, 162, 164
constant of integration 92
constant ratio 55
convergent series 129, 130, 132, 137
convex polar curves 156, 159–60, 164
critical values 2–4, 5–6, 8–9, 10

D

de Moivre's theorem 29–32
  deriving trigonometric identities 32–6
  nth roots of a complex number 37–42
derivatives 106, 126–7
  see also differential equations
differences, method of 15–21
differential equations 90–124, 168–71
  boundary conditions 115–18
  complementary function 110, 112–14, 115–17
  family of solution curves 91–4
  first order 90–104
  general solution see general solution
  integrating factor 95–7
  particular integral 110–14, 116–17
  particular solution 91, 93–4, 106, 115–18
  reducible 98–102, 118–21
  second order 105–24
  second order homogeneous 106–10, 112
  second order non-homogeneous 110–15
  separating the variables 91–4, 99, 100
  series solutions 140–4
  solve by auxiliary equation 106–10, 140
  substitution 98–102, 118–21
'dimple' shaped curves 156, 158, 162, 164
distance
  between two points 47, 56
  in constant ratio 55–6
  from origin to a point 49, 50, 150
  see also polar coordinates
division, complex numbers 26, 27–9

E

'egg' shaped curves 156, 159–60
endpoints 57–61
enlargements 70–1, 72
equation of a circle 60, 74–5
  Cartesian form 47, 48–9, 52, 55
  polar form 153–4
equation of a half-line 51–2, 153–4
equation of a line 50, 163–4

Euler's identity 23
Euler's relation 23, 29
exam practice 178–9
exponential form 23–9, 30, 34, 40
exponential function 23, 112
    Maclaurin series 132, 133–4
    Taylor series 137

F

family of solution curves 91–4
finite series, sum of 15–21
first order differential equations *see*
    differential equations
fractions
    in inequalities 2–8
    sum of a series 16–18
functions
    compound functions 132–6
    and differential equations 95–8,
        110–15
    higher derivatives 126–7
    Maclaurin series expansion
        128–36
    polynomial approximations to 125
    Taylor series expansions 136–9
    see also exponential function;
        trigonometric functions

G

general solution 91–8, 106, 110,
    112–15
    family of curves 91–4
    and roots of auxiliary equation
        107–10
    using substitutions 99–102,
        119–21
geometrical reasoning 27
glossary 180–2
graphs *see* sketching graphs

H

half-line 51–2, 57, 59, 71–2
    polar equation of 153–4
    regions formed by 64, 65–7, 158
higher derivatives 126–7
homogeneous second order
    differential equations 106–10,
    112
horizontal asymptotes 6

I

imaginary axis 48, 81
imaginary numbers 23
imaginary roots 107, 108
inequalities 1–13, 83–4, 89
    modulus inequalities 8–11
    regions on Argand diagrams
        65–9

solving algebraically 2–5
    solving graphically 5–10
infinite series 23, 129–30, 137
initial line 150, 157, 158
    tangents parallel to 162–3
    tangents perpendicular to 156,
        162, 163–4
integrating factor 95–7, 99–100
integration
    constant of 92
    finding areas 158, 159, 160
    polar equations 158–61
intersection points 5–9, 159
intersections 64, 67–8, 159–60
intervals 2–4

J

Julia set 46

L

lines 50, 71–4, 75–6
locus of points
    on Argand diagrams 47–63, 157
    from fixed points in constant
        ratio 55
    represented by polar curves 157
    transformations 70–8
logarithmic functions 129–30, 132,
    133, 136
loops 155, 159
Lorentz factor 136

M

Maclaurin polynomials 129–30
Maclaurin series 128–37, 144–8,
    171–3
    compound functions 132–6
    limitations 136–7
    simple functions 128–32
major arc 58–60
maximum value of argument 48–9
method of differences 15–21
minor arc 58–9
modulus 70–1, 73, 74, 75
    minimum/maximum values 49–50
modulus inequalities 8–11
modulus-argument form 26, 29–30,
    31, 37, 39
    and exponential form 23–5
modulus-argument rules 26–7
multiplication, complex numbers
    26–9

N

non-homogeneous second order
    differential equations 110–15
nth roots 37–42
nth roots of unity 38

P

parabolas 73, 94
parametric equations 73, 162
particular integral 110–14, 116–17
perpendicular bisector 47, 50, 64, 74
points
    distance between two 47, 55–6
    distance from origin to 49, 50
    of intersection 5–9, 159
    loci on Argand diagram 47–63, 157
polar coordinates 149–67, 173–7
    converting to/from Cartesian
        150–3
    intersections of polar curves 159
    tangents to polar curves 162–5
polar curves 151–65, 173–7
    area enclosed by 158–61
    intersections 159–60
    loci on Argand diagram 157
    sketching 153–8, 159–61, 164
    tangents to 162–5
polar equations 151–3, 158–61
polynomials 113, 125, 129–30,
    136–8
population growth model 90
positive integer exponents 29–30
power series 23
    see also Maclaurin series; Taylor
        series
powers of complex numbers 29–31
principal argument 66
principle of superposition 110
product rule 95, 99, 119, 126
proof by induction 15, 19, 29–30
Pythagoras' theorem 150–1

R

range of validity 129, 130, 136
ratio test 132
real axis 48, 82
real roots 107
reducible differential equations
    98–102, 118–21
repeated root 107, 108
review questions 83–9, 168–77
    Argand diagrams 78–81, 86–8
    complex numbers 42–4, 85–6
    differential equations 102–4,
        121–3, 168–71
    inequalities 11–13, 83–4, 89
    Maclaurin and Taylor series
        144–8, 171–3
    polar coordinates 165–7, 173–7
    series 20–1, 84–5, 89, 144–8,
        171–3
roots 10, 107–8, 113, 119
    nth roots 37–42
rotation 65, 66, 72

S

second derivatives 106
second order differential equations 105–24
    homogeneous 106–10, 112
    non-homogeneous 110–15
semicircle 57, 58, 61
separating the variables 91–4, 99, 100
sequence, alternating 129
series 14–21, 84–5, 89
    binomial expansion 32–3, 34–5, 128, 131
    convergent 129, 130, 132, 137
    infinite 23, 129–30, 137
    see also Maclaurin series; Taylor series
series expansions 23, 128–9
    binomial 32–3, 34–5, 128, 131
    see also Maclaurin series; Taylor series
series solutions 140–4
set notation 3–4, 10, 64, 67
simultaneous equations 111, 112, 116

sketching graphs
    identifying intervals 2–4
    modulus graphs 8–11
    polar coordinates 150–1, 162
    polar curves 153–8, 159–61, 164
    solution curves 91–4
    to solve inequalities 5–8
    see also Argand diagrams
solution curves 91–4
solution sets 2–4, 6
spiral 153–4
substitution 98–102, 118–21
subtended angles 57–9, 60
sum of a finite series 15–21
symmetric curves 73, 155, 158

T

tangents 49, 156, 162–5
Taylor series 125, 136–9, 145–8, 171–3
    differential equations solutions 140–4
transformations of the complex plane 70–8
translations 70–2

trigonometric functions
    complex numbers 23–5, 26, 27, 29–39
    differential equations 95, 97, 111, 112, 116–17
    polar coordinates 150–3, 155–7, 158–64
    series expansions 23, 130–5, 137–9
trigonometric identities 32–6, 158, 159, 160
trigonometry 49, 150–1

U

unity, nth roots of 38

V

variables
    multiplying inequalities by 2
    separating 91–4, 99, 100
vectors 38, 70, 71, 72, 81
vertical asymptotes 6
vertices of regular n-gon 38
video games 1